MTP International Review of Science

Physiology
Series One

Consultant Editors
**A. C. Guyton and
D. Horrobin**

Publisher's Note

The MTP International Review of Science is an important new venture in scientific publishing, which is presented by Butterworths in association with MTP Medical and Technical Publishing Co. Ltd. and University Park Press, Baltimore. The basic concept of the Review is to provide regular authoritative reviews of entire disciplines. Chemistry was taken first as the problems of literature survey are probably more acute in this subject than in any other. Physiology and Biochemistry followed naturally. As a matter of policy, the authorship of the MTP Review of Science is international and distinguished, the subject coverage is extensive, systematic and critical, and most important of all, it is intended that new issues of the Review will be published at regular intervals.

In the MTP Review of Chemistry (Series One), Inorganic, Physical and Organic Chemistry are comprehensively reviewed in 33 text volumes and 3 index volumes. Physiology (Series One) consists of 8 volumes and Biochemistry (Series One) 12 volumes, each volume individually indexed. Details follow. In general, the Chemistry (Series One) reviews cover the period 1967 to 1971, and Physiology and Biochemistry (Series One) reviews up to 1972. It is planned to start in 1974 the MTP International Review of Science (Series Two), consisting of a similar set of volumes covering developments in a two year period.

The MTP International Review of Science has been conceived within a carefully organised editorial framework. The overall plan was drawn up, and the volume editors appointed, by seven consultant editors. In turn, each volume editor planned the coverage of his field and appointed authors to write on subjects which were within the area of their own research experience. No geographical restriction was imposed. Hence the 500 or so contributions to the MTP Review of Science come from many countries of the world and provide an authoritative account of progress.

Butterworth & Co. (Publishers) Ltd.

INORGANIC CHEMISTRY SERIES ONE

Consultant Editor
H. J. Emeléus, F.R.S.
*Department of Chemistry
University of Cambridge*

Volume titles and Editors

1 MAIN GROUP ELEMENTS—HYDROGEN AND GROUPS I-IV
Professor M. F. Lappert,
University of Sussex

2 MAIN GROUP ELEMENTS—GROUPS V AND VI
Professor C. C. Addison,
F.R.S. and Dr. D. B.
Sowerby, *University of Nottingham*

3 MAIN GROUP ELEMENTS—GROUP VII AND NOBLE GASES
Professor Viktor Gutmann,
Technical University of Vienna

4 ORGANOMETALLIC DERIVATIVES OF THE MAIN GROUP ELEMENTS
Dr. B. J. Aylett, *Westfield College, University of London*

5 TRANSITION METALS— PART 1
Professor D. W. A. Sharp,
University of Glasgow

6 TRANSITION METALS— PART 2
Dr. M. J. Mays, *University of Cambridge*

7 LANTHANIDES AND ACTINIDES
Professor K. W. Bagnall,
University of Manchester

8 RADIOCHEMISTRY
Dr. A. G. Maddock,
University of Cambridge

9 REACTION MECHANISMS IN INORGANIC CHEMISTRY
Professor M. L. Tobe,
*University College,
University of London*

10 SOLID STATE CHEMISTRY
Dr. L. E. J. Roberts, *Atomic Energy Research Establishment, Harwell*

INDEX VOLUME

PHYSICAL CHEMISTRY SERIES ONE

Consultant Editor
A. D. Buckingham
*Department of Chemistry
University of Cambridge*

Volume titles and Editors

1 THEORETICAL CHEMISTRY
Professor W. Byers Brown,
University of Manchester

2 MOLECULAR STRUCTURE AND PROPERTIES
Professor G. Allen,
University of Manchester

3 SPECTROSCOPY
Dr. D. A. Ramsay, F.R.S.C.,
National Research Council of Canada

4 MAGNETIC RESONANCE
Professor C. A. McDowell,
F.R.S.C., *University of British Columbia*

5 MASS SPECTROMETRY
Professor A. Maccoll,
*University College,
University of London*

6 ELECTROCHEMISTRY
Professor J. O'M Bockris,
University of Pennsylvania

7 SURFACE CHEMISTRY AND COLLOIDS
Professor M. Kerker,
Clarkson College of Technology, New York

8 MACROMOLECULAR SCIENCE
Professor C. E. H. Bawn,
F.R.S., *University of Liverpool*

9 CHEMICAL KINETICS
Professor J. C. Polanyi, F.R.S.,
University of Toronto

10 THERMOCHEMISTRY AND THERMO-DYNAMICS
Dr. H. A. Skinner, *University of Manchester*

11 CHEMICAL CRYSTALLOGRAPHY
Professor J. Monteath
Robertson, F.R.S., *University of Glasgow*

12 ANALYTICAL CHEMISTRY —PART 1
Professor T. S. West,
Imperial College, University of London

13 ANALYTICAL CHEMISTRY —PART 2
Professor T. S. West,
Imperial College, University of London

INDEX VOLUME

ORGANIC CHEMISTRY SERIES ONE

Consultant Editor
D. H. Hey, F.R.S.,
*Department of Chemistry
King's College, University of London*

Volume titles and Editors

1 STRUCTURE DETERMINATION IN ORGANIC CHEMISTRY
Professor W. D. Ollis, F.R.S.,
University of Sheffield

2 ALIPHATIC COMPOUNDS
Professor N. B. Chapman,
Hull University

3 AROMATIC COMPOUNDS
Professor H. Zollinger, *Swiss Federal Institute of Technology*

4 HETEROCYCLIC COMPOUNDS
Dr. K. Schofield, *University of Exeter*

5 ALICYCLIC COMPOUNDS
Professor W. Parker,
University of Stirling

6 AMINO ACIDS, PEPTIDES AND RELATED COMPOUNDS
Professor D. H. Hey, F.R.S.,
and Dr. D. I. John, *King's College, University of London*

7 CARBOHYDRATES
Professor G. O. Aspinall,
Trent University, Ontario

8 STEROIDS
Dr. W. F. Johns, *G. D. Searle & Co., Chicago*

9 ALKALOIDS
Professor K. Wiesner, F.R.S.,
University of New Brunswick

10 FREE RADICAL REACTIONS
Professor W. A. Waters,
F.R.S., *University of Oxford*

INDEX VOLUME

MTP International Review of Science

Physiology
Series One

Volume 7
Environmental Physiology

Edited by **D. Robertshaw**
University of Nairobi

Butterworths · London
University Park Press · Baltimore

THE BUTTERWORTH GROUP

ENGLAND
Butterworth & Co (Publishers) Ltd
London: 88 Kingsway, WC2B 6AB

AUSTRALIA
Butterworths Pty Ltd
Sydney: 586 Pacific Highway 2067
Melbourne: 343 Little Collins Street, 3000
Brisbane: 240 Queen Street, 4000

NEW ZEALAND
Butterworths of New Zealand Ltd
Wellington: 26–28 Waring Taylor Street, 1

SOUTH AFRICA
Butterworth & Co (South Africa) (Pty) Ltd
Durban: 152–154 Gale Street

ISBN 0 408 70487 X

UNIVERSITY PARK PRESS

U.S.A. and CANADA
University Park Press
Chamber of Commerce Building
Baltimore, Maryland, 21202

Library of Congress Cataloging in Publication Data

Robertshaw, D
   Environmental physiology.

   (Physiology, series one, v. 7)
    1. Body temperature—Regulation. 2. Temperature
—Physiological effect. 3. Altitude, Influence of.
I. Title. II. Series. [DNLM: 1. Adaptation,
Physiological. 2. Body temperature regulation.
3. Environment. 4. Mammals—Physiology.
QT165 E61 1974]
QP1.P62 vol. 7 [QP135] 599′.01′08s [599′.01′91]
ISBN 0–8391–1056–1   73–16055

First Published 1974 and © 1974
MTP MEDICAL AND TECHNICAL PUBLISHING CO LTD
St Leonard's House
St Leonardgate
Lancaster, Lancs
and
BUTTERWORTH & CO (PUBLISHERS) LTD

Typeset and printed in Great Britain by
REDWOOD BURN LIMITED
Trowbridge & Esher
and bound by R. J. Acford Ltd, Chichester, Sussex

Consultant Editor's Note

The International Review of Physiology, a review with a new format, is hopefully also new in concept. But before discussing the new concept, those of us who are joined in making this review a success must admit that we asked ourselves at the outset: Why should we promote a new review of physiology? Not that there is a paucity of reviews already, and not that the present reviews fail to fill important roles, because they do. Therefore, what could be the role of an additional review?

The International Review of Physiology has the same goals as all other reviews for accuracy, timeliness, and completeness, but it has new policies that we hope and believe will engender still other important qualities that are often elusive in reviews, the qualities of critical evaluation and instructiveness. The first decision toward achieving these goals was to design the new format, one that will allow publication of approximately 2500 pages per edition, divided into eight different sub-speciality volumes, each organised by experts in their respective fields. It is clear that this extensiveness of coverage will allow consideration of each subject in far greater depth than has been possible in the past. To make this review as timely as possible, a new edition of all eight volumes will be published every two years giving a cycle time that will keep the articles current. And in addition to the short cycle time, the publishers have arranged to produce each volume within only a few months after the articles themselves have been completed, thus further enhancing the immediate value of each author's contribution.

Yet, perhaps the greatest hope that this new review will achieve its goals of critical evaluation and instructiveness lies in its editorial policies. A simple but firm request has been made to each author that he utilise his expertise and his judgement to sift from the mass of biennial publications those new facts and concepts that are important to the progress of physiology; that he make a conscientious effort not to write a review consisting of annotated lists of references; and that the important material he does choose be presented in thoughtful and logical exposition, complete enough to convey full understanding and also woven into context with previously established physiological principles. Hopefully, these processes will bring to the reader each two years a treatise that he will use not merely as a reference in his own personal field but also as an exercise in refreshing and modernising his whole body of physiological knowledge.

Mississippi
Nairobi

A. C. Guyton
D. Horrobin

Preface

Life is found in nearly every part of the world with its wide variety of habitats. Environmental physiology which studies both the responses and adaptations that allow life to exist in these habitats has been described as the 'study of the impossible'. This, of course, is man's concept and is purely a personal assessment of what is, and what is not 'possible'.

Although the subject of environmental physiology should embrace all varieties of species, there is probably most interest in the study of mammals and birds (i.e. homeotherms or using Bligh and Johnson's terminology, animals which show tachymetabolism) which can exist in a variety of extremes of climates and yet maintain a constant body temperature. It largely, therefore, becomes a study of temperature regulation, and the subjects chosen for this review are primarily concerned with thermoregulation. The physics of heat exchange in biology has long been of interest to physicists but the complexity of biological systems tend to defeat them. A few, however, have accepted the challenge and have made a great contribution to the field. Recent developments in technology has assisted them and various physical equations are now being tested biologically. The physical approach as opposed to the purely biological approach thus has its place in a review of this kind.

Comparative thermoregulation is now stimulating interest. The study of thermoregulation used to be largely dominated by studies on man; the need to transport men to different environments in times of war obviously demanded this sort of information. Chapters, therefore, have been included which cover both responses and adaptations to low and high temperatures. The desert environment presents problems not only of extreme temperature variation, but also low water availability, and yet it supports a wide variety of species. Here, therefore, the review embraces non-mammalian species.

The ability of animals to maintain a constant body temperature depends very much on their behavioural response to the environment. An authority in this field has, therefore, reviewed present knowledge on the subject.

Inability to dissipate the heat of exercise can limit the performance of long distance runners as well as that of prey and predator; the study of the comparative thermoregulation of exercise is a fairly recent development in environmental physiology and a chapter on this is, therefore, included.

Finally, the physiological effects of altitude are now being studied on a broad basis varying from an examination of the control of respiratory ventilation to subcellular responses to hypoxia.

The authors selected to contribute to this volume tend to be young research workers who are already in the forefront of their discipline. They have given an appraisal of major recent developments which should benefit not only the research worker, particularly the new graduate, but also the teacher. It is nowadays an enormous task for the teacher in physiology to keep abreast of the subject. Since the reviews are not exhaustive but somewhat selective, the non-specialist should find them more instructive than the conventional review article.

Nairobi   D. Robertshaw

Contents

1
Physical Basis of Thermoregulation

DUNCAN MITCHELL
Chamber of Mines of South Africa, Johannesburg

1.1 INTRODUCTION

In the physiology of thermoregulation, and indeed in all physiology, physics plays the dual role of master and servant. No physiological phenomenon can contravene the laws of physics. Physics, the master, is uncompromising. Physics, the servant, on the other hand, is willing but often inadequate. The duties of physics, the servant, are to provide the simple models on which to base an understanding of physiological mechanisms. Here physics is sometimes defeated not by the abtruseness of physiological phenomena but by their complexity.

This paper is an attempt to identify and elaborate some physical laws and concepts which form the basis of thermoregulation, with particular reference to the last decade. It is a view rather than a review. References to the literature are intended to provide a reader, unfamiliar with a particular topic, with entrée to the field, rather than a synopsis of it. Therefore, the publications referred to are often the latest in a series, or reviews.

Much more is known of the physical basis of human thermoregulation than of that of any other animal. Very little is known about thermoregulation in invertebrates. Some of the concepts presented will hopefully be applicable to all animals, but there are undoubtedly many species whose thermoregulatory properties are neglected completely.

It often happens in physiological research that the attention given to a phenomenon is related to the ease of measurement of that phenomenon and not to its importance in animal function. There are many aspects of thermoregulatory function which are neglected simply because the necessary measurements are difficult to make. It is one of the aims of this paper to point where physics, the inadequate servant, is the cause of the neglect.

1.2 FIRST LAW OF THERMODYNAMICS: THE FUNDAMENTAL LAW

1.2.1 The First Law

'In any transformation taking place in a closed system the increase in internal energy is equal to the work done on the system added to the heat absorbed by it'.

Spanner[1]

Of all the physical laws which act as both masters and servants in thermal physiology, probably the most fundamental is the First Law of Thermodynamics. The principle which the law encompasses is that of conservation of energy and, in the context of thermal physiology, it implies simply that, for any animal at any time:

$$\text{Net rate of energy gain} = \text{rate of energy storage} \qquad (1.1)$$

In this simple form, the First Law of Thermodynamics appears to be a truism. It is not. It is actually an experimental finding. However, there are few experiments in thermal physiology which do not assume the inviolability of the First Law, explicitly or implicitly.

How do animals gain energy? It is generally accepted that they can do so in three ways: chemically, by the processes of metabolism; mechanically, by the action of physical forces on their bodies; and thermally, by heat exchange with their surroundings. The rate of chemical energy gain is the metabolic rate (M)*. The rate of energy gain from the action of physical forces is the work rate (W), which has a negative sign in the usual case of the animal doing work against external forces. The total rate of heat release within the body is therefore $M + W$. The rate of heat gain from the surroundings is made up of four components: the rate of radiant heat gain (R), the rate of convective heat gain (C), the rate of conductive heat gain (K) and the rate of evaporative heat gain (E). The energy budget equation for the body of the animal therefore becomes

$$M + W + K + R + C + E = S \qquad (1.2)$$

Equation (1.2) applies at any instant in time and, in general, the value of S, the rate of heat storage within the body, is not zero. At a particular instant, an animal is likely to be storing or losing heat. However, if an animal maintains a fixed work rate in a fixed environment, the net rate of storage (S) will tend to zero. The animal will attain thermal equilibrium with its environment, and, in thermal equilibrium

$$M + W + K + R + C + E = 0 \qquad (1.3)$$

The ability to attain thermal equilibrium in diverse environments is not a property unique to living things, or even unique to homeotherms. Any object, living or not, generating heat at a fixed rate, and placed in a fixed environment, will eventually attain thermal equilibrium within that environment. If the object is wet, its energy budget at thermal equilibrium will satisfy equation (1.3). Homeotherms operate under additional constraints, which will be discussed later (Section 1.4).

The state called 'thermal equilibrium' above, that is, the condition $S = 0$, would be more accurately designated by 'caloric equilibrium'. It is the condition in which the net rate of *heat* storage is zero. Caloric equilibrium is neither a necessary nor a sufficient condition for *temperature* equilibrium (*contra* Kerslake[3]). It is clear that it is not a sufficient condition for even when there is no net heat storage in the body of the animal, the temperature at any site

---

* A list of symbols appears in the appendix. In general, they are those recommended[2] for use in thermal physiology. Energy flows towards the body of the animal are called positive.

will be stable only if there is an equilibrium of heat transfer at that site. Caloric equilibrium is a necessary condition for temperature equilibrium only in the case of a closed system, that is, a system with constant mass. Animals losing water through evaporative cooling do not have constant mass. While losing mass, they may have constant temperature and yet not satisfy the condition $S = 0$.

In general, over periods of a few hours animals, even when exposed to heat, do not lose sufficient water to alter their masses more than a few per cent. If a state of temperature equilibrium can be demonstrated, then caloric equilibrium can be assumed. In fact, in most experiments in thermal physiology the stability of the body temperature is used as the sole criterion of thermal equilibrium.

1.2.2 Other terms in the energy budget

Equation (1.2) is used throughout thermal physiology to describe the energy budget of animals. It is derived from the First Law of Thermodynamics but it does not have the rigour of the First Law, because of the assumptions made about the way in which animals are capable of gaining and storing heat. The variety of situations in which equation (1.2) has been applied successfully suggests that it is generally adequate. However, it is certainly not universally applicable.

A simple example easily demonstrates the lack of rigour in equation (1.2). Elephants apparently employ a method of heat exchange with the environment for which equation (1.2) cannot account: they excrete copious quantities of urine and faeces at body temperature and replace them with cool drinking water[4]. Another such example arises in sheep. The absorption of atmospheric water by wool is exothermic, and therefore contributes to the heat gain of the animal[5]. Equation (1.2) can be readily modified to take account of other methods of energy exchange when the other methods can be identified.

1.3 ENERGY EXCHANGE: PHYSICAL FULFILMENT OF THE LAW

1.3.1 Energy budgets

Equation (1.2) describes the energy budget of an animal exposed to a particular environment but gives no indication of the magnitude of the various quantities involved. There are good reasons for being able to assign quantitative values to the components of the animal's energy exchanges. The reasons, according to Porter and Gates[6] are:

(a) to establish the relative importance of each parameter;

(b) to assess the allowable errors in measurement of these parameters;

(c) to predict the body surface and core temperatures for any animal in specified environments;

(d) to predict the limits of climatic habitat tolerable to any animal.

The best way of obtaining quantitative values for the various components is to measure them directly. Unfortunately, direct measurement is difficult in the laboratory and virtually impossible in the field. Laboratory determinations of all the components in an energy budget have been attempted for a few animals, but it is really only for man that sufficient measurements are available for the values to be reliable. Even then measurements have been made only in a limited number of environments.

In the absence of direct measurements, is there a reasonable alternative method of expressing the energy budget equation quantitatively? Physics, in its role of master, makes it necessary for the laws of energy exchange to be the same for animals as for any other bodies. In its role of servant, physics allows each of the parameters in equation (1.2) to be described, at least approximately, in terms of quantities more easily measurable than the parameters themselves.

1.3.2 Surface area

In the energy budget equation, the units of all the rates of energy transfer are watts per square metre ($W\ m^{-2}$) of body surface. To express the metabolic rate, work rate and storage rate in these units, it is necessary to know body surface area. The error in an estimate of any of the rates of energy transfer is at least as large as the error in the estimate of surface area. It is therefore surprising to find that, in general, the approach to measuring animal surface area for the purpose of thermal physiology is extremely crude.

Measuring the area of a body with a shape as irregular as that of most animals is difficult. The problem is compounded by the fact that the area relevant to one avenue of energy transfer, particularly radiation, is not necessarily the same as that relevant to other avenues. Calculating the area exposed to the sun introduces further complications[7-10]. Finally, if an animal does not have a smooth integument it is difficult even to define what 'surface area' means.

There are three basic approaches to the assessment of surface area. The first is calculation from body dimensions, such as height and mass[11,12], and the second is a geometrical method based on hypothetically dividing the animal into regular shapes[6,13]. The third method is direct measurement[14-17]. Among the direct measurement techniques, the photometric technique[16] is potentially the most useful. It has been used to measure both total and radiating area in humans[17-19], but has not been exploited for other animals.

1.3.3 Metabolic rate

Thermoregulatory physiologists are primarily interested in one aspect of metabolic physiology, namely the quantitative assessment of the rate of metabolic energy production (metabolic rate) at any instant in time. It is important to assess metabolic rate accurately, because animals rarely suffer as great a heat load from other sources as they do from the metabolic heat released during exercise. For example, an exercising man can maintain a metabolic rate of 1 kW[20], which is enough, in the absence of heat dissipation to raise the average temperature of his body tissues 15 °C per hour. In spite of the necessity to measure metabolic rate accurately, there has been little research aimed at validating the traditional measuring techniques in the last 10 years, or even in the last half century.

The traditional techniques[21] of measuring metabolic rate consist of measuring the turnover rate of metabolites involved in the energy-yielding processes and multiplying the turnover rate by the calorific value of that metabolite in animal combustion. The accuracy of the measurement of metabolic rate therefore depends on the accuracy of measurement firstly of the metabolite turnover rate and secondly of the calorific value. The metabolites are chosen for convenience of measurement. In the case of aerobic work, oxygen is the usual metabolite. The classical determinations of its calorific value need to be checked, especially during exercise, using the accurate and rapid calorimeters now available. In the case of anaerobic work, there is, as yet, no satisfactory method for calculating anaerobic metabolic rate during the actual performance of work.

1.3.4 Physical work rate

From the physical point of view, animals work very little during their entire lives. The paradox has a semantic origin: the physical definition and the colloquial meaning of 'work' are not the same. In the energy budget equation (equation 1.2) the term W is the work rate in its strict physical sense. It accounts for energy entering and leaving the body in a form which is neither chemical nor thermal. It is the rate at which physical forces external to the body provide energy to the body. When energy from the body is used to overcome external forces, then the work rate is negative and non-zero. However, when energy from the body is used only to overcome forces within the body, the external physical work rate is zero, because the body is not delivering any power other than heat to its surroundings.

If animals could convert all the chemical energy released by the metabolic processes into physical work done against external forces, then, in equation (1.2), the terms M and W would be equal in magnitude and opposite in sign. Metabolic processes would then impose no heat load on the body, and metabolism would be of minor interest in thermoregulation. However, muscles can convert at most *ca.* 30% of metabolic energy into a form useful for physical work[22], so that at least 70% of metabolic energy is released as heat. In a great many animal activities requiring energy, virtually all the energy is converted to heat. Amongst these activities are level walking and running.

1.3.4.1 Concentric or 'negative' work

In the energy budget equation, the physical work-rate term can have either sign. According to the sign convention employed in this paper, it has a negative sign when the animal does work against external forces. Some of the metabolic energy (M) is converted to physical work and the remainder ($M + W$, W having a negative value) is released as heat. When, on the other hand, work is done on an animal by external forces, for example when the animal moves downhill, then W has a positive sign and constitutes an energy flow towards the animal. It is the latter type of work which is known in physiological parlance as 'negative' work. The use of the word 'negative' tends to produce misconceptions about the energetics of the process, and several authors, particularly the Scandinavians, have recommended the terms 'concentric' to describe work in which the physical energy flow is towards the body, and 'eccentric' for the opposite direction.

Concentric work is important in studies of thermoregulation because, according to the principle of conservation of energy, we must be able to account for the fate of the energy released in the body. It would clearly be advantageous for an animal to be able to convert the energy derived from concentric work into a form other than heat and thus to store useful energy. The metabolic rate during concentric work is indeed well below that displayed during eccentric work of the same intensity[23].

There is some evidence for energy storage within one cycle of exercise[24], but over extended periods of concentric work little energy is stored. Bodil Nielsen[25] demonstrated that a man subjected to W watt of work reacted thermally so as to dissipate ($M + W$) watt of metabolic heat, whether W was positive or negative. More recently, Smiles and Robinson[26] found a correlation coefficient of 0.939 between evaporative cooling and metabolic heat production ($M + W$) for men walking both uphill and downhill in a fixed environment. The energy of extended concentric work has a predominantly but perhaps not entirely[27] thermal fate.

1.3.5 Conductive heat transfer

Conductive heat transfer is the transfer of heat down a temperature gradient by the exchange of kinetic energy from one particle to adjacent particles without appreciable change in the mean position of the particles. It occurs in solids, liquids and gases but, in the fluids, where the particles are free to move, it is generally subordinate to convective heat transfer (Section 1.3.6). Conduction is the only avenue of heat transfer available in opaque solids.

The basic equation governing conductive heat transfer is straightforward. It is simply the diffusion equation[28, 29]. Application of the equation to the case of steady-state conductive heat transfer through a homogeneous slab, the face temperatures of which are known, is also straightforward. It is usually this case only which is treated in texts on physiological heat transfer. The case is relevant to the transfer of heat through a protective cover (Section 1.3.9) but, in the overall context of thermal physiology, it is of minor importance.

When physiological conductive heat transfer does take place, it is generally in inhomogeneous materials. The face temperatures are not known. The materials can contain heat sources and sinks. Steady states are seldom attained. Such cases of conductive heat transfer can sometimes be analysed[30], but physics, the servant, is severely taxed. The analysis is usually so specific to a particular situation, that any attempt to derive a general physical treatment and apply it to physiological heat transfer would be futile.

Let us consider a particular example where conductive heat transfer is important as a channel of energy exchange between an animal and its environment. It is a prerequisite that the animal should have an appreciable contact area with a solid surface, because the rate of conductive heat transfer between two solids is directly proportional to the contact area. Snakes seem to qualify for this category. Figure 1.1 shows, in schematic form, a cross-section through a snake lying on the ground. The rate of conductive heat transfer between the ground and the snake depends primarily on the temperature profile just below the ground surface, the temperature profile just inside the snake and the nature of the interface between the snake and the ground. The dominant factor limiting conductive heat transfer is likely to be in the interface which consists, on the particle level, of two rough

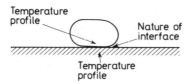

Figure 1.1 Schematic cross-section through a snake, showing some factors influencing conductive heat transfer

surfaces occasionally in contact and otherwise separated by a layer of air of varying thickness. There is no physical means of predicting the 'contact coefficient[31]', or effective conductance, of the interface. The temperature profile in the snake will depend primarily on the cutaneous circulation. The profile in the ground will depend on the nature of the ground and the thermal history (particularly its exposure to the sun). As the snake moves, it will constantly be encountering new ground temperature profiles. A case of conductive heat transfer of this complexity is intractable by physical analysis.

Our inability to write equations for conductive heat transfer between the snake and the ground does not mean that conductive heat transfer is unimportant for the snake. The behaviour of snakes resident in hot areas leaves no doubt about the importance of conductive heat transfer. When the authors of texts on physiological heat transfer dismiss conduction as trivial or irrelevant, they are simply looking the other way. The problem exists but it remains to be solved.

The snake considered above was a hypothetical example of an animal for which conductive heat transfer with the environment might be important. There are reports in the literature of animals which use behavioural means to reduce[32] or enhance[33-35] conductive heat transfer with the environment.

For man under normal conditions of living and working, and for other animals with feet, conductive heat transfer plays a very small role in heat transfer with the environment. Only a small fraction of the body area is in contact with solid surfaces. In the heat balance equation of man, the conduction term K (equation (1.2)) can usually be neglected.

1.3.6 Convective heat transfer

Convective heat transfer is the transfer of heat by the bulk movement of congregations of particles at different temperatures. The movement may be the result of induced flow in the fluid (forced convection) or simply the result of density differences (free convection). Convection processes are qualitatively the same but quantitatively different in gases and liquids.

A great deal of experimental work has been carried out on convective heat transfer because of its importance in engineering. The knowledge gained has been applied with considerable success to the convective heat transfer between animals, particularly man, and their environments.

The coefficient of convective heat transfer (h_c) between a fluid of temperature T_f and a body of mean surface temperature $\bar{T}_s$ is defined by the equation:

$$C = h_c \, (T_f - \bar{T}_s) \, A_c / A_b \qquad (1.4)$$

The area participating in convective heat transfer (A_c) is usually the total body area, so that A_c / A_b is usually equal to unity.

The value of the coefficient h_c depends on the size and shape of the body and on certain properties of the fluid. Its dependence on these variables can be extracted from the interrelationships of four dimensionless groups. The groups are:

Reynolds Number $Re = \rho V L / \mu$
Nusselt Number $Nu = h_c L / k$
Grashof Number $Gr = \rho^2 G \beta \Delta T L^3 / \mu^2$

(where ΔT is the temperature difference between a surface and a fluid in contact with it)

Prandtl Number $Pr = \mu c_p / k$

1.3.6.1 Free convection in air

When a fluid contains temperature gradients, it develops areas of relatively high temperature and low density and others of low temperature and high density. The regions of different density move under the influence of gravity and a net flow of heat occurs. The process is known as free, natural or buoyancy convection. Fluids are rarely isothermal, so that free convection in fluids takes place virtually all the time. It is a fundamental property of free convection that the rate of heat transfer does not depend on the ambient wind speed.

The free convection relevant to physiological heat transfer occurs because the surface temperatures of animals are generally not equal to that of the air surrounding them. The air closer to the animal's surface becomes either hotter or cooler than the air slightly further away and therefore rises or sinks. The presence of free convective air flow over men has been demonstrated elegantly using schlieren photography[36, 37].

The coefficient of free convective heat transfer can be derived from a relationship between three of the groups mentioned above:

$$Nu = f(Gr, Pr) \qquad (1.5)$$

The exact form of the relationship and therefore the value of the coefficient h_c incorporated in the Nusselt Number, varies with the nature of the body and the fluid and can be derived only by experiment.

When free convective heat transfer occurs between a terrestrial animal and its air environment, it takes place from surfaces which may be approximated by large vertical surfaces (plates or cylinders) or horizontal cylinders. Birkebak[13] has presented simplified forms of equation (1.5) which apply to the specific cases of large vertical surfaces and horizontal cylinders in air at sea level.

The accuracy with which free convective coefficients based on engineering heat-transfer determinations predict the free convective heat-transfer rates of animals cannot yet be assessed. There have been no direct measurements of free convective heat transfer from animals. In the case of man, there have been a few indirect measurements[38-40].

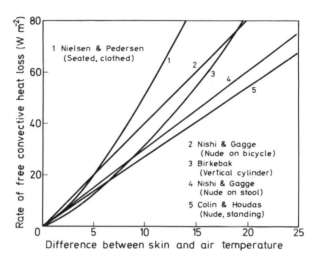

Figure 1.2 Rates of free convective heat transfer for man according to Nielsen and Pedersen[38], Colin and Houdas[39] and Nishi and Gagge[40] compared to the calculated rate for a vertical cylinder[13]

Figure 1.2 shows the various estimates plotted against the difference between skin (or clothing) and air temperatures. Also shown is the estimate based on Birkebak's simplified equation for a large diameter vertical cylinder 2 m high. The agreement between the curves is encouraging.

Free convective heat transfer from animals warrants more attention than it has been given by thermal physiologists. It occurs all the time, and is not of so small a magnitude that it can be summarily dismissed. The free convective heat transfer of animals other than man needs to be measured. Nishi and Gagge's[40] method using naphthalene sublimation awaits exploitation.

1.3.6.2 Forced convection from skin in air

Free convection takes place in air whether or not there is a wind, draught or any induced air movement. However, when there is induced air movement, the importance of free convection is diminished for two reasons. The first is that streaming caused by density differences is disturbed by the imposed air movement. The second is that the coefficients of forced convective heat transfer are considerably higher than those of free convection.

Just as the heat transfer coefficients for free convection can be extracted from a relationship between three dimensionless groups, so can those for forced convection. Analytically

$$Nu = f(Re, Pr) \tag{1.6}$$

and, once more, the detailed form of the relationship can be derived only experimentally. The equations of forced convection from smooth cylinders have been applied successfully to many animals[6, 41, 42] including man[43], and only the smooth cylinder approximation will be dealt with here. Should it be necessary to estimate the forced convection from an animal the shape of which is clearly not cylindrical, there seems to be no reason why the equations for an appropriate alternative shape should not be applied.

For smooth cylinders in transverse air flow, in the range of environments in which animals can live, equation (1.6) can be expressed[44] in the form:

$$h_c \approx c(P_a/1013)^n \, V^n \tag{1.7}$$

where c and n are approximately constant for a particular animal and set of environments.

In the case of forced convection from nude men under head-wind conditions, it has been possible to check the validity of equation (1.7) by direct measurement in a well-controlled wind tunnel using a technique developed by Carroll and Visser[45]. The values of c and n were determined by regression analysis[44, 46], which yielded $c \approx 8.28 \pm 0.06$ (SE) and $n \approx 0.6$. The equation of convective heat exchange becomes

$$C = (8.28 \pm 0.06) \, (P_a/1013)^{0.6} V^{0.6}(T_a - \bar{T}_s) \tag{1.8}$$

and is shown in graphical form in Figure 1.3, for various atmospheric pressures.

In the literature there are reported numerous indirect estimates of the values of c and n for man under transverse air flow[47, 48]. Kuehn[48] has re-analysed much of the original data and shown the measurements generally to be consistent with a value for the exponent n of 0.6. This value is also in good agreement with the value obtained for smooth cylinders of a size approximating that of man[49].

There seems to be no reason why equation (1.8) should not be applied to any animal in transverse air flow, provided the animal has a shape that is approximately cylindrical. The numerical constants are best fitted by experiment but, in the absence of experiment, may be estimated from the values appropriate for cylinders of similar size[49].

Equation (1.8) refers specifically to transverse air flow, that is, flow perpendicular to the animal's major axis. In natural environments, the flow is parallel to the major axis as often as it is perpendicular to it. Although the theoretical justification for using an equation of the same form for axial flow is tenuous, studies using indirect calorimetry on man suggests that such an equation may indeed be suitable[47]. Recently, Colin and Houdas[39] obtained the following equation for nude men reclining on a net under conditions of axial flow:

$$C = 8.7 \, (P_a/1013)^{0.67} V^{0.67}(T_a - \bar{T}_s) \tag{1.9}$$

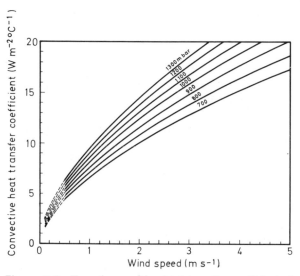

Figure 1.3 Forced convective heat transfer coefficient at various atmospheric pressures for nude men sitting in a transverse wind

The discussion thus far has assumed tacitly that the air movement responsible for the forced convective heat transfer arises from a source external to the animal. This restriction on the source of the air movement is not necessary. The wind speed V throughout is the rate of air movement relative to the animal and may be the result of movement of the animal itself. Nishi and Gagge[40] have recently measured the forced convection during some human activities. Humans move slowly relative to many other animals. Flying birds[50], for example, have air speeds over them equal to their flying speeds, which may be 30 m s⁻¹. Convective heat transfer in flying birds seems to have aroused little interest, however. A recent review of thermoregulation in birds[51] makes only passing reference to it (see Chapter 5).

1.3.6.3 Mixed convection from skin in air

When there is no induced air movement over an animal's surface, there is no forced convective heat transfer but only free convective heat transfer.

When there is appreciable induced air movement, free convection is of minor, if not negligible, importance. How, then, does one calculate convective heat transfer in the zone of transition between free and forced convection? The solution to that problem is known to neither physiologists, physicists, nor engineers.

For man, free convection ceases to be important once the ambient wind speed reaches c. 0.2 m s^{-1} [40,52]. Environments with wind speeds of 0.1–0.2 m s^{-1} could be considered to lie in the transition zone, a zone where mixed free and forced convection occur. To calculate the rate of convection in this zone, Fanger[53] suggests calculating both the free and the forced coefficients and using the larger.

1.3.6.4 Convective heat transfer in the respiratory tract

Terrestrial animals transfer heat by convection not only at the external surfaces of the bodies but also in their respiratory tracts. Because the air must enter and leave the tract through well-defined orifices, respiratory convection rates can be calculated by measuring the rate of air flow through the tract (the ventilation) and the change of air temperature between inspiration and expiration.

Order-of-magnitude calculations of the respiratory convection in animals in which the necessary parameters have been measured prove respiratory convection to be a minor avenue of heat exchange. Respiratory heat exchange occurs predominantly through evaporation and not convection.

1.3.6.5 Convective heat transfer in water

Convective heat exchange takes place by basically the same process in any fluid, whether liquid or gas. The equations $Nu = f(Gr, Pr)$ for free convection and $Nu = f(Re, Pr)$ for forced convection apply in both liquids and gases but the convective heat transfer coefficients in water are two or three orders of magnitude larger than those in air. Therefore, for the same temperature difference between the surface of the animal and the surrounding fluid, convection takes place at a rate in water which is two or three orders of magnitude faster in water than in air. Without some compensatory adjustment, it would be impossible for animals to survive in cold water.

The compensatory adjustment which allows aquatic life is a reduction in the temperature difference between skin and surroundings. Most fishes have body temperatures almost equal to that of the water in which they live[54]. Aquatic mammals, and those fishes which do have selected tissues at temperatures higher than that of the water, have deposits of insulating tissue and specialised circulatory systems which allow them to maintain a low skin temperature in spite of a higher tissue temperature elsewhere[54,55]. Convective heat exchange is low simply because the temperature difference driving it is small.

Man is not equipped thermally to spend extended periods in water, especially cold water. There is as yet, no agreement on the actual value of the heat transfer coefficients[56-59] nor has a satisfactory relationship between theoretical calculations and experimental measurements been demonstrated[56].

1.3.7 Radiant heat transfer

Radiant heat transfer is the transfer of heat by the exchange of electromagnetic energy. The difference between radiant heat and other electromagnetic radiation, for example, x-rays, light or microwaves, is purely quantitative: the wavelength is different. Radiant heat, like other electromagnetic energy, is capable of travelling through a vacuum.

The radiant heat which participates in the energy budget of animals covers a wavelength range of $c.$ 0.2–80 μm. It is customary in physiology to divide the spectrum into a short-wave region (wavelength $<$ 2–3 μm) and a long-wave region (wavelength $>$ 2–3 μm). The division is based purely on a difference in the optical properties of animal coats in the two regions.

The wavelength of infrared radiation depends primarily on the temperature of the source from which it emanates (the Wien Displacement Law[60]). Radiation emanating from the animal itself falls entirely into the long-wave region, as does the radiation from the ground, vegetation or indoor enclosures. No environment is ever devoid of long-wave radiant heat exchange. Certain environments have short-wave radiation exchange as well, the most common source of short-wave radiant heat being the sun.

1.3.7.1 Long-wave radiant heat exchange

The rate of radiant heat exchange between two surfaces of areas A_1 and A_2, temperatures T_1 and T_2, and emittances ε_1 and ε_2 respectively is given by[61]

$$J_r = \sigma F A_1 (1/\varepsilon_1 + 1/\varepsilon_2 - 1)^{-1}[(T_2 + 273.2)^4 - (T_1 + 273.2)^4] \quad (1.10)$$

where F is a configuration factor depending on the view the surfaces have of one another. The configuration factor is extremely difficult to calculate except for the simplest geometries. Fanger[62] and Ibamoto and Nishi[63] have calculated factors for a few configurations relevent to human heat exchange. The configuration factor, and indeed equation (1.10) itself, can be simplified considerably in the case of an animal within a solid enclosure. It becomes[61]:

$$J = \sigma A_1 [1/\varepsilon_1 + (1/\varepsilon_2 - 1)A_1/A_2]^{-1}[(T_2 + 273.2)^4 - (T_1 + 273.2)^4] \quad (1.11)$$

where the subscript '2' refers to the radiant environment and '1' to the animal. In the case of an animal in an enclosure much larger than itself ($A_1 \ll A_2$), equation (1.11) reduces further to

$$R = \sigma \varepsilon_s (A_r/A_b) [(\bar{T}_r + 273.2)^4 - (\bar{T}_s + 273.2)^4] \quad (1.12)$$

in the symbols recommended for thermal physiology[2] (see Appendix).

Equation (1.12) is inconvenient to handle because it incorporates the fourth powers of absolute temperatures. Provided that the temperature difference

$(\bar{T}_r - \bar{T}_s)$ is much smaller than the sum $(\bar{T}_r + \bar{T}_s + 546.4)$, the equation can be reduced to an approximate linear form:

$$R \approx h_r(A_r/A_b)\,(\bar{T}_r - \bar{T}_s) \qquad (1.13)$$

where
$$h_r \approx \tfrac{1}{2}\,\sigma\varepsilon_s(\bar{T}_r + \bar{T}_s + 546.4)^3$$

The linear radiant heat transfer coefficient (h_r) will be approximately constant over a range of environments and can be calculated by taking mean values for skin temperature $(\bar{T}_s)$ and mean radiant temperature $(\bar{T}_r)$.

The only factors in equations (1.12) and (1.13) which are specific to particular animals are the surface emittance (ε_s) and the ratio of radiating area to total area (A_r/A_b). Methods are now available for measuring the area ratio directly[16]. The emittance in the long-wave region has theoretical limits of 0 and 1, but is probably between 0.9 and 1 for all animals[65, 82]. The calculation of the long-wave radiant heat exchange between an animal and its environment therefore presents no problem apart from the calculation of the configuration factor.

1.3.7.2 Mixed long- and short-wave radiant heat exchange

The Stefan–Boltzmann law of radiant heat transfer, on which equation (1.10) is based, holds only for radiation with an energy distribution spectrum corresponding to Planck's law[60]. In particular, the radiation spectrum must be complete, that is, have no bands of absent wavelengths and the emittance of the surfaces involved must not be a function of wavelength. The conditions are met in the case of long-wave radiant heat transfer, but not in the case of short-wave radiation. In the short-wave spectrum, the emittance of animal skins is a strong and complicated function of wavelength (which is why animals have different colours) and the atmosphere absorbs radiation of particular wavelengths. The Stefan–Boltzmann approach cannot be employed and, in fact, no general theory of the short-wave radiant heat exchange of animals can be developed.

Gates[6, 66] has suggested an approach which is a compromise between empiricism and theoretical analysis. His approach consists of dividing the total heat exchange into its components and then calculating each component by a combination of measurement and estimation. The rate of radiant heat emanation from the animal is calculated by assuming it to be radiating to free space. The possible origins of radiant heat falling on the animal are given in Figure 1.4.

Gates' approach has been applied to several animals[6, 42]. Perhaps its most successful application has been the analysis by Virginia Finch[64, 67] of the energy budget of African antelope at Nairobi. Miss Finch measured the components of radiation over a summer day (Figure 1.5), determined emittances by spectrophotometer and estimated the areas exposed to the various components. She demonstrated, inter alia, the surprising result that for antelope exposed to the direct sun, long-wave radiation imposes a greater heat load than short-wave radiation does.

1.3.8   Evaporative heat transfer

In the past decade more research effort has been directed towards evaporative heat transfer than towards any other term in the energy budget equation. The mechanisms of evaporative heat exchange have been elucidated qualitatively and quantitatively in many animals[68, 69]. Three aspects of this wealth of work are relevant to the topic of this chapter, the value of the latent heat of sweat, the relationship between evaporation and convection, and evaporation in the respiratory tract.

1.3.8.1   Latent heat of sweat

Evaporative and condensative heat transfer is the transfer of heat associated with the transition between the liquid and gaseous phases. Evaporation is endothermic and condensation exothermic. In animals the heat transfer usually takes the form of evaporative cooling as a result of the conversion of body water to water vapour. The water may originate from diffusion across the skin, from the sweat glands or from the membranes of the respiratory tract. The origin of the water is unimportant from the energetic point

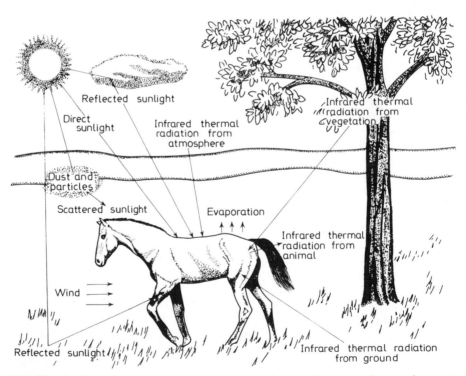

Figure 1.4 Channels of heat transfer for an animal exposed to an outdoor environment (from Porter and Gates[6] by permission of the Duke University Press)

of view. Each gram of water which evaporates accounts for the same amount of heat, whether the evaporation takes place on the skin or in the respiratory tract.

The ratio of the heat absorbed during evaporation to the mass of liquid changing phase is the latent heat of evaporation (λ). There is no theoretical reason why the latent heat of evaporation of body water should be any different from the latent heat of pure water, in spite of the dissolved salts in body water[70,71]. However, many thermoregulatory physiologists have held the belief that the heat of evaporation of sweat, particularly, is higher than that of pure water. In fact, Hardy[72] constructed a theoretical equation which predicted a high heat of evaporation of sweat, but his equation is not acceptable[71,73,74], basically because he assumed erroneously that the evaporation and subsequent dispersion of sweat is a reversible thermodynamic process.

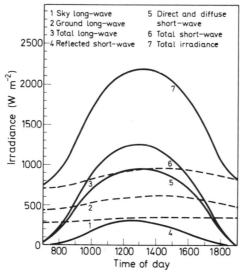

Figure 1.5 Irradiance due to various sources on a horizontal surface near Nairobi (redrawn from Finch[64] by permission of the Zoological Society of London)

The fact remains, however, that some recent experiments on human evaporative heat transfer yielded an anomalously high heat of evaporation of sweat. The results of a calorimetric study of men exposed to various environments in a wind tunnel[75] suggested, but did not prove with statistical validity, that the heat of evaporation of sweat was some 7% higher than the latent heat of water at the same temperature. A subsequent, more careful, study in a human calorimeter, conducted with the express aim of measuring the heat of evaporation of sweat[73], yielded a value of 2600 ± 40 J g^{-1}, indeed 7% higher than that expected for water.

Some objections have been raised to the latter study[70,71,74], suggesting that the anomalous value is simply a spurious measurement. The subject clearly requires further investigation.

1.3.8.2 Evaporation and convection

Once the law of convective heat transfer between an animal and its environment has been established, the law of evaporative heat transfer can be deduced theoretically. The fixed relationship between convective and evaporative heat transfer is the result of an analogy between heat and mass flow across a boundary layer, frequent use of which is made in engineering practice. The analogy was demonstrated by Lewis in 1922, and its relevance to human heat transfer was accepted by Murlin[76] in 1939. However, the analogy does not seem to have been recognised by other physiologists until it was re-discovered experimentally[77] in 1958, and the theory was couched in physiological terms[78]. That the so-called 'modified Lewis relation' must apply to physiological heat transfer has been emphasised recently by several authors[40,79] but one still finds theoretically incompatible equations published in new physiology textbooks[80].

The analogy between heat and mass transfer across a boundary layer is based on the similarity between the physical processes of molecular transport of heat energy and molecular diffusion of one gas through another. The analogy has been expressed mathematically in different ways. The form used in modern engineering practice was derived by Colburn, who demonstrated that if the driving forces were expressed correctly, the ratio of heat transfer rate to its driving force must be the same as the ratio of the mass transfer rate to its driving force. The driving force for heat transfer is, of course, a temperature difference. That for mass transfer is really the mass concentration gradient[81], but is more conveniently expressed as a vapour pressure difference.

The evaporative heat transfer coefficient (h_e) is defined, by analogy with the convective coefficient (equation (1.4)), as the proportionality coefficient between the rate of evaporative heat transfer and the vapour pressure difference:

$$E_{max} = h_e(A_e/A_b)\,(\varphi P_{wa} - P_{ws}) \tag{1.14}$$

The subscript 'max' is necessary because evaporative heat transfer can be predicted from purely environmental parameters only in the case of a fully wet skin. When the skin is not fully wet

$$E = wE_{max} \tag{1.15}$$

where the skin wettedness (w) depends primarily on the amount of evaporation required to bring the energy balance equation into equilibrium (equation 1.3).

According to the Colburn analogy[83], in normal environments:

$$P_a h_e/h_c = (0.622\lambda/c_p)\,(Pr/Sc)^{2/3}[P_a/(P_a - \varphi P_{wa})]^2 \tag{1.16}$$

The Schmidt Number Sc is the dimensionless group in mass transfer analogous to the Prandtl Number in heat transfer. Substituting reasonable average values for the terms on the right-hand-side of equation (1.16) gives

$$P_a h_e/h_c \approx 0.700\lambda\,°C \tag{1.17}$$

Therefore, from equations (1.14) and (1.17),

$$E_{max} \approx (0.700\lambda h_c/P_a)(A_e/A_b)(\varphi P_{wa} - P_{ws}) \tag{1.18}$$

so that, if the convective heat transfer coefficient (h_c) can be established, maximum evaporative heat transfer can be predicted.

The forced convective coefficient has been established for nude men (equation 1.8). Assuming the area ratio A_e/A_b to be unity, and the latent heat λ to be 2600 J g^{-1}, equation (1.18) becomes, for nude men in the realm of forced transverse convection:

$$E_{max} \approx (15\ 100/P_a)(P_a/1013)^{0.6}V^{0.6}(\varphi P_{wa} - P_{ws}) \tag{1.19}$$

Equation (1.19) has two features that need to be emphasised. The first is that the exponent n of wind speed, here 0.6, must necessarily be the same for convective and evaporative heat transfer. The second is that evaporative

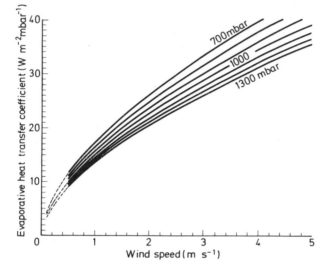

Figure 1.6 Evaporative heat transfer coefficient at various atmospheric pressures for nude men sitting in a transverse wind

heat transfer is proportional to $1/P_a^{0.4}$, and therefore, contrary to the prediction of Taylor and Buettner[84], increases with altitude. Values for the evaporative heat transfer coefficient are shown in Figure 1.6.

1.3.8.3 Evaporation in the respiratory tract

The rate of evaporative heat loss from the respiratory tract is proportional to the rate of water loss which, in turn, depends on the ventilation and the humidity of inspired and expired air. The rate of respiratory heat exchange can be calculated from measurements of the ventilation and the humidity of respired air simply by using a psychrometric chart[85]. For man, a simple equation[86, 87] suffices over a wide range of environments.

Many animals use the evaporation of water from the mucosa of the respiratory tract as the major, if not the only, source of evaporative cooling[88]. For these panting animals, a high rate of respiratory water loss is desirable. However, as Schmidt–Nielsen has pointed out[89,90], a more universal function of the respiratory mucosa is the conditioning of air before it reaches the lungs. The water required may then severely tax the body fluid balance in animals with limited access to drinking water.

Several animals for which excessive respiratory water loss would constitute a fluid balance problem have respiratory tracts adapted to conserve water[89]. The technique they use is known in engineering parlance as recuperative or regenerative heat exchange. Inspired air is warmed to deep body temperature and saturated with water before reaching the lungs but in these animals the structure of the nasal passages is such that the air is cooled during expiration to well below the dew-point reached in the lungs. Much of the water condensed out is available to condition subsequent inspirations.

Some degree of recuperation is inevitable whenever inspired and expired air travels along the same pathway. Under heat stress the dog, which relies entirely on panting for evaporative cooling, circumvents recuperation by inhaling through the nose and exhaling through the mouth[91].

1.3.9 Protective covers

The foregoing discussion of heat transfer between animals and their environments has assumed tacitly that the interface between the animal and the environment is naked and smooth, which, of course, is seldom the case. Man wears clothing and other animals have fur or leathers. These protective covers influence heat exchange with the environment considerably. The influence of clothing has been dealt with in two recent texts[92,93].

It does seem worthwhile, however, to emphasise the degree of simplification which enters into the treatment of protective covers in thermal physiology. The usual approach is to consider the protective cover to add a resistive term to the equations of sensible heat transfer (that is, combined radiation and convection) and evaporative heat transfer. Equations (1.4), (1.13) and (1.14) become

$$R + C = (A_o/A_b) (1/h_o + I_{rc})^{-1} (T_o - \bar{T}_s) \tag{1.20}$$

$$E_{max} = (A_e/A_b) (1/h_e + I_e)^{-1} (\varphi P_{wa} - P_{ws}) \tag{1.21}$$

where I_{rc} and I_e are the resistances to sensible and evaporative heat transfer respectively. The subscript 's' refers to skin under the cover and the subscript 'o' refers to the operative condition[94]; h_o is the combined sensible heat transfer coefficient[95,96].

Implicit in the form of equations (1.20) and (1.21) are the assumptions that sensible and evaporative heat transfer through the protective cover are single and separate processes through a porous layer of well-defined boundaries. The processes are not single, are not necessarily separate and the protective layer seldom has well-defined boundaries.

What is assumed to be a single process is in fact three heat transfer processes in series: the transfer from skin into the layer, the transfer through the layer and the transfer from the layer to the environment. Each is a function of different variables. Evaporation and sensible heat transfer are not necessarily separate, because it is quite possible to have sensible heat transfer between the skin and the layer, evaporative transfer through the layer with recondensation within the layer, and sensible transfer between layer and environment. Finally, animal coats do not have well-defined and fixed interfaces with the environment either in the case of convection[97] (and therefore evaporation) or in the case of radiation[98,99,144].

1.4 REGULATION: PHYSIOLOGICAL IMPLEMENTATION OF THE LAW

The First Law of Thermodynamics, the physical law fundamental to thermoregulation, is obeyed by any body, living or not. Any body also eventually reaches thermal equilibrium with its environment. The uniqueness of the animals which are considered 'temperature regulators' is, therefore, not related to their ability to attain thermal equilibrium but to their ability to attain equilibrium in different environments with only a small change in their own temperatures.

Inert bodies cannot satisfy the joint constraints of thermal equilibrium and small temperature deviation when exposed to diverse environments. Their responses to environmental changes are passive in nature. The responses of temperature regulating animals, on the other hand, are active.

1.4.1 What is controlled?

The active adjustments of rates of energy exchange to produce a state of equilibrium without large excursions in body temperature suggest that the animals concerned are attempting to control their temperatures. A constant body temperature is considered to be an advantage in terms of Claude Bernard's concept of a *milieu intérieur*, but there is no conclusive evidence of what particular temperature in the body is being controlled.

Many texts on thermoregulation state or imply that deep body temperature is the controlled temperature, because it is generally more stable than other temperatures. The argument is not valid. The anatomy of animals is such that the deep body temperature will be the most stable whatever temperature is controlled[100]. There are indeed indications that thermoregulation is not directed towards the control of deep body temperature. Several animals with well developed mechanisms for thermoregulation have deep body temperatures which are quite labile. The camel[101] and the eland[102,103] are examples. The oryx, an antelope and undoubtedly a temperature regulator, allows its deep body temperature to remain at 45 °C for several hours of the day[104].

It is the thermoregulatory behaviour of the oryx which provides a clue as to what organ indeed requires temperature control. The oryx has a carotid rete, as do many other animals[105]. The carotid rete serves to keep the brain below the temperature of the rest of the body during exposure to heat. It may be that the electrochemical activity of the central nervous system, and particularly the brain, requires a constant temperature (see Chapter 5).

Man has no carotid rete. Recent evidence[46, 100, 106-108] has indicated that the temperature which appears to be controlled in man is simply the mean body temperature, or average temperature of all the tissues of the body. It may be the case that man achieves control of brain temperature by controlling mean body temperature.

1.4.2 The control system

The application of negative feed-back control theory to thermoregulation[109, 110] is probably the single most outstanding contribution to thermal physiology of the research of the last decade. The temperature regulating animals, when confronted with a thermal disturbance which tends to destroy their energy balance and therefore to change their temperature, initiate deliberate control actions in a way such as to oppose the effect of the disturbance. The response is characteristic of a negative feed-back control system, a generalised form of which is shown in Figure 1.7.

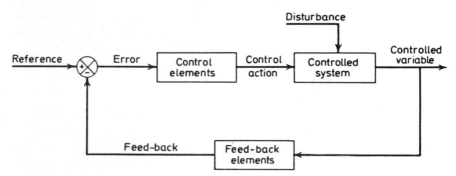

Figure 1.7 Basic negative feed-back control system (from Mitchell, Snellen and Atkins[130] by permission of Springer-Verlag)

The block diagram in Figure 1.7 consists of a controlled system, which, in the case of thermoregulation, is the body of the animal. The controlled system is subject to disturbances, which may be environmental heat or cold or metabolic heat. As a result some controlled variable changes. The controlled variable has not been positively identified (see Section 1.4.1 above) but is presumably a body temperature or combination of temperatures. Some sensory system detects the change in the controlled variable and transduces it into a neural signal, the feed-back. The neural information enters the central nervous system and is focused in the hypothalamus[111]. The feed-back information is compared against some reference information, the difference being the error signal, which in turn actuates control elements, presumably networks of neurones. An efferent neural signal emerges, which initiates appropriate control actions, behavioural or autonomic, to oppose the effect of the disturbance.

Our understanding of the structure and function of the biological analogues of the different components of the negative feed-back system is very varied. For example, far more is known about the control actions than any other component of the system. Current knowledge of the various components is reviewed in detail in other parts of this book. Only brief comments arising from viewing the control system 'through physical spectacles[112]' will be made here.

1.4.2.1 Feed-back elements

Neurones specifically sensitive to temperature have been found in a variety of temperature-regulating animals ranging from lizards to man. Thermosensitivity has been detected not only at sites in the central nervous system and the skin[113] but also in the body core[114, 115], in or near the respiratory tract[116, 117], in the heart or great blood vessels[118] and some veins[119]. It seems likely that temperature regulating animals have temperature detectors distributed widely in their bodies.

Although it has never been proved that the temperature-sensitive neurones are actually involved in the animal's temperature regulation, they seem to have all the desirable properties. They provide neural information which is a sensitive and unambiguous measure of the local temperature.

1.4.2.2 Control elements

By comparison with what is known about the rest of the thermoregulatory control system, very little is known about the control elements. Yet, by comparison with what is known about other neural control systems, a great deal is known about the control elements in thermoregulation. It is probably in the field of the function of these control elements that thermoregulatory research will make significant advances over the next few years, and perhaps it is in this field that thermoregulatory physiology will make its biggest contribution to physiology as a whole.

Research into the locality and function of the control elements has advanced along four fronts:

(a) study of the input/output relationships of the control elements as a black box[100].

(b) study of the effects of making lesions, and of local heating and cooling at the postulated sites of the control elements[110, 120].

(c) study of the behaviour of single neurones at the postulated localities of the control elements[121].

(d) study of the action of putative transmitter substances in the hypothalamus[122, 123].

It remains for the advances along these four fronts to be integrated successfully.

1.4.2.3 Control actions

By virtue of the ease with which they can be measured, a great deal is known
about the control actions of thermoregulation. Until recently, attention was
devoted almost entirely to the autonomic actions such as sweating, panting,
shivering, circulatory adjustment and piloerection. Behavioural actions
(see Heath[143], Cabanac[124] and Chapter 7) are now given full recognition as
well-controlled and effective thermoregulatory control actions.

Although control actions are generally well understood, additional research
is clearly called for into the role of circulatory adjustments in thermoregulation. A hiatus exists between what is known about the properties of the
circulatory system and what its role in thermoregulation is. For example,
it is far from clear what the function is of the thermosensitivity of veins[125].
It is not yet possible to predict with any accuracy peripheral temperature
distributions and heat flows from the state of the peripheral circulation.
Finally, circulatory countercurrent heat exchange is often invoked to account
for thermoregulatory phenomena, yet a careful biophysical analysis[126] has
shown that no significant countercurrent exchange is possible in man or
even in the flukes of porpoises.

1.4.2.4 'Set-point'

In engineering control systems the desired operating level of the controlled
variable is set by comparing the feed-back with some reference information,
as depicted in Figure 1.7. When the feed-back information is steady and
equal to the reference information, no control actions are operative. The
concept of a 'set-point' established by reference information is widely
accepted in thermoregulatory physiology as the means by which temperature-
regulating animals maintain body temperature at a fixed level[110, 127].

Whereas such a mechanism could indeed be applicable in thermoregulation,
it is not the only possibility. A fixed operating temperature can be achieved
equally well by the dynamic balance of two opposing feed-back signals[128-130].
The dynamic balance mechanism would require two categories of temperature
sensor: one sensitive at high and the other at low temperatures. It does appear
that the temperature-sensitive neurones fall into two such distinct populations[130, 131].

1.4.3 Modulation and local control

The control system displayed in Figure 1.7 is, of course, a gross oversimplification[100]. It is incomplete and naïve in many ways. As long as its shortcomings
are borne in mind, as a model it is nevertheless very useful. There is an
unfortunate tendency to believe in models, which are, after all, only 'descriptions that work'[132]. It seems worthwhile to point out one particular misconception that the block diagram in Figure 1.7 might produce, namely
that all thermoregulatory control loops pass through the central nervous

system. At least two types of thermoregulatory control loops have been demonstrated outside the central nervous system.

The first type is pure open-loop local control, that is, implementation of a control action by a direct effect of the thermal environment on an effector organ. One example is the local control of peripheral vasomotor tone by local temperature, an action so strong that it is able to override any influence of nervous drives to peripheral vascular muscles[133]. Another example is the apparent direct effect of solar radiation on the sweat glands[134, 135] and peripheral blood vessels[136] of some animals.

The second type is external to the central nervous system but not independent of it. It is modulation: the modification of the response of a thermoregulatory effector organ to a central drive by the local thermal conditions prevailing at the organ. The influence in man of local skin temperature on local sweat rate is a modulatory effect[137, 138]. Local temperature affects the response of the sweat gland to an arriving nerve impulse[139, 140]. An analogous effect occurs in the peripheral blood vessels. The tone developed in the vascular smooth muscle as a result of sympathetic activity is modified by the local temperature prevailing at the vessel[125, 141].

1.5 CONCLUSION

There is no doubt that physical principles and concepts can be discovered throughout the physiology of thermoregulation. The First Law of Thermodynamics is fundamental to the energy budgets of animals. The physical laws which describe the processes of energy transfer in inert bodies also apply to the bodies of animals. Thermoregulation is achieved by the active adjustment of the rates of heat transfer, the mechanism conforming largely to the concepts of negative feed-back control.

Can one claim, however, that the role of physics is that of master and servant? Physics, the servant, is after all, unable to cope with the complexity of the living process. It would be more comfortable for physiologists if physics, the master, did not have to be obeyed. Is the role of physics not that of intruder? In answer, one can call to witness Claude Bernard[142]:

'unless we deny the possibility of biological science, the principles of science are everywhere the same'.

Acknowledgements

For their help in the preparation of this paper, I am grateful to A. R. Atkins, G. D. Brown, Virginia Finch, D. M. Gates, D. Rabe, D. Robertshaw, K. Schmidt–Nielsen, N. B. Strydom, C. R. Taylor and C. H. Wyndham.

APPENDIX: List of symbols

A	area	(m^2)
C	rate of convective heat gain, per unit of total body area	$(W\ m^{-2})$
E	rate of evaporative heat gain, per unit of total body area	$(W\ m^{12})$
F	configuration factor	
G	gravitational constant	$(m\ s^{-2})$
I	insulation	$(m^2C\ W^{-1})$
J	rate of energy flow	(W)
K	rate of conductive heat gain per unit of total body area	$(W\ m^{-2})$
L	characteristic dimension	(m)
M	rate of metabolic energy consumption per unit of total body area	$(W\ m^{-2})$
P	pressure	$(mbar)$
R	rate of radiant heat gain per unit of total body area	$(W\ m^{-2})$
S	rate of heat accumulation in the body, per unit of total body area	$(W\ m^{-2})$
T	temperature	$(°C)$
V	wind speed	$(m\ s^{-1})$
W	power generated by external forces, per unit of total body area	$(W\ m^{-2})$
c	constant	
c	specific heat	$(J\ kg^{-1}C^{-1})$
h	heat transfer coefficient	$(W\ m^{-2}C^{-1})$ or $(W\ m^{-2}mbar^{-1})$
k	thermal conductivity	$(W\ m^{-1}C^{-1})$
n	exponent	
w	fractional wetted area	
β	volume expansion coefficient	$(1/K)$
ε	emittance	
λ	latent heat	$(J\ kg^{-1})$
μ	dynamic viscosity	$(kg\ s^{-1}m^{-1})$
ρ	density	$(kg\ m^{-3})$
σ	Stefan–Boltzmann constant	$(W\ m^{-2}K^{-4})$
φ	relative humidity (as fraction)	
Gr	Grashof Number	
Nu	Nusselt Number	
Pr	Prandtl Number	
Re	Reynolds Number	
Sc	Schmidt Number	
a	air, ambient, atmosphere	
b	body	
c	convective	
e	evaporative	
f	fluid	
max	maximum	

o	standard, operative
p	pressure
r	radiant
s	skin
wa	water vapour, saturated at T_a
ws	water vapour, saturated at T_s

References

1. Spanner, D. C. (1964). *Introduction to Thermodynamics*, 19 (London: Academic Press)
2. Gagge, A. P., Hardy, J. D. and Rapp, G. M. (1969). Proposed standard system of symbols for thermal physiology. *J. Appl. Physiol.*, **27**, 439
3. Kerslake, D. McK. (1972). *The Stress of Hot Environments*, 14 (Cambridge: University Press)
4. Young, E. (1972). The elephant's temperature-control mechanisms. *Custos*, **1**, 32
5. Thwaites, C. J. (1967). Fleece length and the reactions of sheep to elevated humidity and radiant heating at high temperatures. *Res. Vet. Sci.*, **8**, 463
6. Porter, W. P. and Gates, D. M. (1969). Thermodynamic equilibria of animals with environment. *Ecol. Monographs*, **39**, 227
7. Fanger, P. O., Angelius, O. and Kjerulf-Jensen, P. (1970). Radiation data for the human body. *ASHRAE Trans.*, **76 (II)**, 338
8. Kelly, C. F., Bond, T. E. and Heitman, H. (1954). The role of thermal radiation in animal ecology. *Ecology*, **35**, 562
9. Ward, E. J. and Underwood, C. R. (1967). The effect of posture on the solar radiation area of man. *Ergonomics*, **10**, 399
10. Clapperton, J. L., Joyce, J. P. and Blaxter, K. L. (1965). Estimates of the contribution of solar radiation to the thermal exchanges of sheep at a latitude of 55° north *J. Agr. Sci.*, **64**, 37
11. Kleiber, M. (1961). *The Fire of Life*, 181 (New York: Wiley)
12. Du Bois, D. and Du Bois, E. F. (1916). A formula to estimate the approximate surface area if height and weight be known. *Arch. Internal. Med.*, **17**, 863
13. Birkebak, R. C. (1966). Heat transfer in biological systems. *Intern. Rev. Gen. Exptl. Zool.*, **2**, 269
14. Stitt, J. T., Hardy, J. D. and Nadel, E. R. (1971). Surface area of squirrel monkey in relation to body weight. *J. Appl. Physiol.*, **31**, 140
15. Hori, T., Tokura, H. and Tadaki, E. (1972). Surface area in the Japanese monkey, *Macaca fuscata. J. Appl. Physiol*, **32**, 409
16. Halliday, E. C. and Hugo, T. J. (1963). The photodermoplanimeter. *J. Appl. Physiol.*, **18**, 1285
17. Van Graan, C. H. (1969). The determination of body surface area. *S. African Med. J.*, **43**, 952
18. Mitchell, D., Strydom, N. B., Van Graan, C. H. and Van der Walt, W. H. (1971). Human surface area: comparison of the Du Bois formula with direct photometric measurement. *Pflügers Archiv. Europ. J. Physiol.*, **325**, 188
19. Frei, D. H. (1971). The influence of clothing and posture on radiant heat transfer in men. *Thesis*, University of the Witwatersrand, Johannesburg, South Africa.
20. Astrand, P-O. and Rodahl, K. (1970). *Textbook of Work Physiology*, 431 (New York: McGraw-Hill)
21. Astrand, P-O. and Rodahl, K. (1970). *Textbook of Work Physiology*, 277 (New York: McGraw-Hill)
22. Whipp, B. J. and Wasserman, K. (1969). Efficiency of muscular work. *J. Appl. Physiol.*, **26**, 644
23. Asmussen, E. (1965). Muscular exercise. *Handbook of Physiology Section 3 Respiration*, Vol. II, 939 (W. O. Fenn and H. Rahn editors) (Washington: American Physiological Society)
24. Thys, H., Faraggiana, T. and Margaria, R. (1972). Utilization of muscle elasticity in exercise. *J. Appl. Physiol.*, **32**, 491

25. Nielsen, B. (1966). Regulation of body temperature and heat dissipation at different levels of energy- and heat production in man. *Acta Physiol. Scand.*, **72, 25**
26. Smiles, K. A. and Robinson, S. (1971). Regulation of sweat secretion during positive and negative work. *J. Appl. Physiol.*, **30,** 409
27. Knuttgen, H. G. and Klausen, K. (1971). Oxygen debt in short-term exercise with concentric and eccentric muscle contractions. *J. Appl. Physiol.*, **30,** 632
28. McAdams, W. H. (1954). *Heat Transmission*, 7 (New York: McGraw-Hill)
29. Jakob, M. and Hawkins, G. A. (1957). *Elements of Heat Transfer*, 26 (New York: Wiley)
30. Carslaw, H. S. and Jaeger, J. C. (1959). *Conduction of Heat in Solids* (Oxford: Clarendon)
31. McAdams, W. H. (1954). *Heat Transmission*, 17 (New York: McGraw-Hill)
32. Schmidt-Nielsen, K., Taylor, C. R. and Shkolnik, A. (1971). Desert snails: problems of heat, water and food. *J. Exptl. Biol.*, **55,** 385
33. Herreid, C. F. (1963). Temperature regulation of Mexican free-tailed bats in cave habitats. *J. Mammal.*, **44,** 560
34. Herreid, C. F. and Schmidt-Nielsen, K. (1966). Oxygen consumption, temperature, and water loss in bats from different environments. *Amer. J. Physiol.*, **211,** 1108
35. Mount, L. E. (1968). *The Climatic Physiology of the Pig*, 183 (London: Arnold)
36. Lewis, H. E., Foster, A. R., Mullan, B. J., Cox, R. N. and Clark, R. P. (1969). Aerodynamics of the human microenvironment. *Lancet*, **1969(I),** 1273
37. Lewis, H. E. (1971). How man survives the cold. *Science J.*, **7,** 29
38. Nielsen, M. and Pedersen, L. (1952). Studies on the heat loss by radiation and convection from the clothed human body. *Acta Physiol. Scand.*, **27,** 272
39. Colin, J. and Houdas, Y. (1967). Experimental determination of coefficient of heat exchanges by convection of human body. *J. Appl. Physiol.*, **22,** 31
40. Nishi, Y. and Gagge, A. P. (1970). Direct evaluation of convective heat transfer coefficient by naphthalene sublimation. *J. Appl. Physiol.*, **29,** 830
41. Mount, L. E. (1968). *The Climatic Physiology of the Pig*, 167 (London: Arnold)
42. Bartlett, P. N. and Gates, D. M. (1967). The energy budget of a lizard on a tree trunk. *Ecology*, **48,** 315
43. Kerslake, D. McK. (1972). *The Stress of Hot Environments*, 31 (Cambridge: University Press)
44. Mitchell, D., Wyndham, C. H., Vermeulen, A. J., Hodgson, T., Atkins, A. R. and Hofmeyr, H. S. (1969). Radiant and convective heat transfer of nude men in dry air. *J. Appl. Physiol.*, **26,** 111
45. Carroll, D. P. and Visser, J. (1966). Direct measurement of convective heat loss from human subject. *Rev. Sci. Instr.*, **37,** 1174
46. Mitchell, D. (1972). Human surface temperature: its measurement and its significance in thermoregulation. *Thesis*, University of the Witwatersrand, Johannesburg, South Africa.
47. Kerslake, D. McK. (1972). *The Stress of Hot Environments*, 33 (Cambridge: University Press)
48. Kuehn, L. A., Stubbs, R. A. and Weaver, R. S. (1970). Theory of the globe thermometer. *J. Appl. Physiol.*, **29,** 750
49. McAdams, W. H. (1954). *Heat Transmission*, 258 (New York: McGraw-Hill)
50. Schmidt-Nielsen, K. (1972). *How Animals Work*, 51 (Cambridge: University Press)
51. Dawson, W. R. and Hudson, J. W. (1970). Birds. *Comparative Physiology of Thermoregulation*, Vol. I, 223 (G. C. Whittow, editor) (New York: Academic Press)
52. Whillier, A. and Mitchell, D. (1968). Prediction of the cooling rate of the human body. *J. S. African Inst. Mining Met.*, **68,** 10
53. Fanger, P. O. (1967). Calculation of thermal comfort: introduction of a basic comfort equation. *ASHRAE Trans.*, **73(II),** 103
54. Schmidt-Nielsen, K. (1972). *How Animals Work*, 71 (Cambridge: University Press)
55. Fry, F. E. J. and Hochachka, P. W. (1970). Fish. *Comparative Physiology of Thermoregulation*, Vol. I, 79 (G. C. Whittow editor) (New York: Academic Press)
56. Witherspoon, J. M., Goldman, R. F. and Breckenridge, J. R. (1971). Heat transfer coefficients of humans in cold water. *J. Physiol. (Paris)*, **63,** 459
57. Boutelier, C., Colin, J. and Timbal, J. (1971). Détermination du coefficient d'échange thermique dans l'eau en écoulement turbulent. *J. Physiol. (Paris)*, **63,** 207

58. Bullard, R. W. and Rapp, G. M. (1970). Problems of body heat loss in water immersion. *Aerospace Med.*, **41**, 1269
59. Rapp, G. M. (1971). Convection coefficients of man in a forensic area of thermal physiology: heat transfer in underwater exercise. *J. Physiol. (Paris)*, **63**, 392
60. Hottel, H. C. (1954). Radiant-heat transmission. *Heat Transmission*, 55 (W. H. McAdams, editor) (New York: McGraw-Hill)
61. Kerslake, D. McK. (1972). *The Stress of Hot Environments*, 47 (Cambridge: University Press)
62. Fanger, P. O. (1970). *Thermal Comfort*, 175 (Copenhagen: Danish Technical Press)
63. Ibamoto, K. and Nishi, Y. (1968). Thermal sensation analysis and its application to air-conditioning. *Bull. Fac. Eng. Hokkaido Univ.*, **46**, 73
64. Finch, V. A. (In press). Energy exchanges with the environment of two East African antelopes, the eland and the hartebeest. *Symp. Zool. Soc. London* No. 31
65. Mitchell, D., Wyndham, C. H. and Hodgson, T. (1967). Emissivity and transmittance of excised human skin in its thermal emission waveband. *J. Appl. Physiol.*, **23**, 390
66. Gates, D. M. (1968). Energy exchange between organisms and environment. *Aust. J. Sci.*, **31**, 67
67. Finch, V. A. (1972). The effects of solar radiation on temperature regulation and heat balance in two East African antelopes, the eland and the hartebeest. *Amer. J. Physiol.* **222**, 1374
68. Whittow, G. C. (1970). *Comparative Physiology of Thermoregulation Vol. 1 Invertebrates and Nonmammalian Vertebrates.* (New York: Academic Press)
69. Whittow, G. C. (1971). *Comparative Physiology of Thermoregulation Vol. 2 Mammals.* (New York: Academic Press)
70. Kerslake, D. McK. (1972). *The Stress of Hot Environments*, 29 (Cambridge: University Press)
71. Wenger, C. B. (1972). Heat of evaporation of sweat: thermodynamic considerations. *J. Appl. Physiol.*, **32**, 456
72. Hardy, J. D. (1949). Heat transfer. *Physiology of Heat Regulation and the Science of Clothing*, 78 (L. H. Newburgh editor) (Philadelphia: Saunders)
73. Snellen, J. W., Mitchell, D. and Wyndham, C. H. (1970). Heat of evaporation of sweat. *J. Appl. Physiol.*, **29**, 40
74. Monteith, J. L. (1972). Latent heat of vaporization in thermal physiology. *Nature, New Biology*, **236**, 96
75. Mitchell, D., Wyndham, C. H., Atkins, A. R., Vermeulen, A. J., Hofmeyr, H. S., Strydom, N. B. and Hodgson, T. (1968). Direct measurement of the thermal responses of nude resting men in dry environments. *Archiv. Ges. Physiol.*, **303**, 324
76. Murlin, J. R. (1939). Skin temperature, its measurement and significance for energy metabolism. *Ergeb. Physiol. Biol. Chem. Exptl. Pharmakol.*, **42**, 153
77. Brebner, D. F., Kerslake, D. McK. and Waddell, J. L. (1958). The relation between the coefficients for heat exchange by convection and by evaporation in man. *J. Physiol. (London)*, **141**, 164
78. Woodcock, A. H. and Breckenridge, J. R. (1965). A model description of thermal exchange for the nude man in hot environments. *Ergonomics*, **8**, 223
79. Rapp, G. M. (1970). Convective mass transfer and the coefficient of evaporative heat loss from human skin. *Physiological and Behavioral Temperature Regulation*, 55 (J. D. Hardy, A. P. Gagge and J. A. J. Stolwijk, editors) (Springfield: Thomas)
80. Carlson, L. D. and Hsieh, A. C. L. (1970). *Control of Energy Exchange*, 45 (New York: MacMillan)
81. Sibbons, J. L. H. (1966). Assessment of thermal stress from energy balance considerations. *J. Appl. Physiol.*, **21**, 1207
82. Veghte, J. H. (1972). Infrared radiography and related studies—annotated bibliography. *Report AMRL-TR-71-127*, United States Aerospace Medical Research Laboratory, Wright-Patterson Air Force Base, Ohio. (Copies available from National Technical Information Service, 5285 Port Royal Road, Springfield, Virginia 22151, United States).
83. Whillier, A. (1967). The calculation of heat exchange between air and wet surfaces. *J. S. African Inst. Mining Met.*, **67**, 396
84. Taylor, C. L. and Buettner, K. (1953). Influence of evaporative forces upon skin temperature dependency of human perspiration. *J. Appl. Physiol.*, **6**, 113

85. Chambers, A. B. (1970). A psychrometric chart for physiological research. *J. Appl. Physiol.*, **29**, 406
86. Fanger, P. O. (1970). *Thermal Comfort*, 28 (Copenhagen: Danish Technical Press)
87. Mitchell, J. W., Nadel, E. R. and Stolwijk, J. A. J. (1972), Respiratory weight losses during exercise. *J. Appl. Physiol.*, **32**, 474
88. Richards, S. A. (1970). The biology and comparative physiology of thermal panting. *Biol. Rev.*, **45**, 223
89. Schmidt-Nielsen, K., Hainsworth, F. R. and Murrish, D. E. (1970). Counter-current heat exchange in the respiratory passages: effect on water and heat balance. *Resp. Physiol.*, **9**, 263
90. Schmidt-Nielsen, K. (1972). *How Animals Work*, 1 (Cambridge University Press)
91. Schmidt-Nielsen, K., Bretz, W. L. and Taylor, C. R. (1970). Panting in dogs: unidirectional air flow over evaporative surfaces. *Science*, **169**, 1102
92. Fourt, L. and Hollies, N. R. S. (1970). *Clothing: Comfort and Function* (New York: Marcel Dekker)
93. Kerslake, D. McK. (1972). *The Stress of Hot Environments*, 95 (Cambridge: University Press)
94. Gagge, A. P. (1940). Standard operative temperature, a generalized temperature scale, applicable to direct and partitional calorimetry. *Amer. J. Physiol.*, **120**, 277
95. Colin, J. M , Timbal, J., Guieu, J. D., Boutelier, C. and Houdas, Y. (1970). Combined effect of radiation and convection. *Physiological and Behavioral Temperature Regulation*, 81 (J. D. Hardy, A. P. Gagge and J. A. J. Stolwijk, editors) (Springfield: Thomas)
96. Gagge, A. P. and Hardy, J. D. (1967). Thermal radiation exchange of the human by partitional calorimetry. *J. Appl. Physiol.*, **23**, 248
97. Tregear, R. T. (1965). Hair density, wind speed and heat loss in mammals. *J. Appl. Physiol.*, **20**, 796
98. Kovarik, M. (1964). Flow of heat in an irradiated protective cover. *Nature (London)*, **201**, 1085
99. Hutchinson, J. C. D. and Brown, G. D. (1969). Penetrance of cattle coats by radiation. *J. Appl. Physiol.*, **26**, 454
100. Mitchell, D., Atkins, A. R. and Wyndham, C. H. (1972). Mathematical and physical models of thermoregulation. *Essays on Temperature Regulation*, 37 (J. Bligh and R. E. Moore editors) (Amsterdam: North-Holland)
101. Schmidt-Nielsen, K. (1962). Comparative physiology of desert mammals. Brody Memorial Lecture 11, Special report 21, Agricultural Experimental Station, University of Missouri, United States.
102. Bligh, J. and Harthoorn, A. M. (1965). Continuous radiotelemetric records of the deep body temperature of some unrestrained African mammals under near-natural conditions. *J. Physiol. (London)*, **176**, 145
103. Taylor, C. R. (1970). Strategies of temperature regulation: effect on evaporation in East African ungulates. *Amer. J. Physiol.*, **219**, 1131
104. Taylor, C. R. (1969). The eland and the oryx. *Sci. Amer.*, **220** (1), 88
105. Schmidt-Nielsen, K. (1972). *How Animals Work*, 68 (Cambridge: University Press)
106. Snellen, J. W. (1966). Mean body temperature and the control of thermal sweating. *Acta Physiol. Pharmacol. Neerl.*, **14**, 99
107. Colin, J. and Houdas, Y. (1966). La notion de température moyenne du corps dans l'étude du déclenchement de la sudation thermique. *Compt. Rend. Soc. Biol.*, **160**, 2076
108. Saltin, B. and Gagge, A. P. (1971). Internal body temperatures and skin sweating during exhaustive exercise. *Federation Proc.*, **30**, 320 Abs
109. Hardy, J. D. (1965). The 'set-point' concept in physiological temperature regulation. *Physiological Controls and Regulations*. 98 (W. S. Yamamoto and J. R. Brobeck editors) (Philadelphia: Saunders)
110. Hammel, H. T. (1968). Regulation of internal body temperature. *Ann. Rev. Physiol.*, **30**, 641.
111. Bligh, J. (1966). The thermosensitivity of the hypothalamus and thermoregulation in mammals. *Biol. Rev.*, **41**, 317
112. Hill, A. V. (1956). Why biophysics. *Science*, **124**, 1233
113. Bligh, J. and Moore, R. E. (1972). *Essays on Temperature Regulation*, (Amsterdam: North-Holland)

114. Hales, J. R. S., Kao, F. F., Mei, S. S., Wang, C. and Gretenstein, M. (1970). Panting in heated cross-circulated dogs. *Amer. J. Physiol.*, **218**, 1389

115. Rawson, R. O. and Quick, K. P. (1970). Evidence of deep-body thermoreceptor responses to intra-abdominal heating of the ewe. *J. Appl. Physiol*, **28**, 813

116. Beakley, W. R. and Findlay, J. D. (1955). The effect of environmental temperature and humidity on the respiration rate of Ayrshire calves. *J. Agri. Sci.*, **45**, 452

117. Bligh, J. (1963). The receptors concerned in the respiratory response to humidity in sheep at high ambient temperature. *J. Physiol. (London)*, 168, 747

118. Downey, J. A., Mottram, R. F. and Pickering, G. W. (1964). The location by regional cooling of central temperature receptors in the conscious rabbit. *J. Physiol. (London)*, **170**, 415

119. Thompson, F. J. and Barnes, C. D. (1970). Evidence for thermosensitive elements in the femoral vein. *Life Sci.*, **9** (I), 309

120. Klüssman, F. W. and Pierau, Fr.-K. (1972). Extrahypothalamic deep body thermosensitivity. *Essays on Temperature Regulation*, 87 (J. Bligh and R. E. Moore, editors) (Amsterdam: North Holland)

121. Eisenman, J. S. (1972). Unit activity studies of thermoresponsive neurons. *Essays on Temperature Regulation*, 55 (J. Bligh and R. E. Moore, editors) (Amsterdam: North-Holland)

122. Hellon, R. (1972). Central transmitters and thermoregulation. *Essays on Temperature Regulation*, 71 (J. Bligh and R. E. Moore, editors) (Amsterdam: North-Holland)

123. Bligh, J. (1972). Neuronal models of mammalian temperature regulation. *Essays on Temperature Regulation*, 105 (J. Bligh and R. E. Moore, editors) (Amsterdam: North Holland)

124. Cabanac, M. (1972). Thermoregulatory behaviour. *Essays on Temperature Regulation*, 19 (J. Bligh and R. E. Moore, editors) (Amsterdam: North-Holland)

125. Wyndham, C. H. (In press). The physiology of exercise under heat stress. *Ann. Rev. Physiol.*

126. Mitchell, J. W. and Myers G. E. (1968). An analytical model of the counter-current heat exchange phenomena. *Biophys. J.*, **8**, 897

127. Stolwijk, J. A. J. and Hardy, J. D. (1966). Temperature regulation in man—a theoretical study. *Archiv. Ges. Physiol.*, **291**, 129

128. Bazett, H. C. (1949). Blood temperature and its control. *Amer. J. Med. Sci.*, **218**, 483

129. Vendrik, A. J. H. (1959). The regulation of body temperature in man. *Ned. Tijdschr. Geneesk.*, **103** (I), 1

130. Mitchell, D., Snellen, J. W. and Atkins, A. R. (1970). Thermoregulation during fever: change of set-point or change of gain. *Archiv. Ges. Physiol.*, **321**, 293

131. Hensel, H. (1970). Temperature receptors in the skin. *Physiological and Behavioral Temperature Regulation*, 442 (J. D. Hardy, A. P. Gagge and J. A. J. Stolwijk, editors) (Springfield: Thomas)

132. Weizenbaum, J. (1972). On the impact of the computer on society. *Science*, **176**, 609

133. Bligh, J., Cottle, W. H. and Maskrey, M. (1971). Influence of ambient temperature on the thermoregulatory responses to 5-hydroxytryptamine, noradrenaline and acetylcholine injected into the lateral cerebral ventricles of sheep, goats and rabbits. *J. Physiol. (London)*, **212**, 377

134. Robertshaw, D. (1971). The evolution of thermoregulatory sweating in man and animals. *Internal. J. Biometeorol.*, **15**, 263

135. Murray, D. M. (1966). A comparison of cutaneous evaporation rates in cattle exposed to heat in a climate laboratory and in the field. *J. Agr. Sci.*, **66**, 175

136. Brown, G. D. (1971). Studies of the responses of sheep and kangaroos to climatic conditions in a natural environment using multichannel telemetry. *Proc. Symp. Pretoria Biotelemetry.* (Council for Scientific and Industrial Research, In press, Pretoria, South Africa)

137. Bullard, R. W., Banerjee, M. R., Chen, F., Elizondo, R. and MacIntyre, B. A. (1970). Skin temperature and thermoregulatory sweating: a control systems approach. *Physiological and Behavioral Temperature Regulation*, 597 (J. D. Hardy, A. P. Gagge and J. A. J. Stolwijk editors) (Springfield: Thomas)

138. Nadel, E. R., Bullard, R. W. and Stolwijk, J. A. J. (1971). Importance of skin temperature in the regulation of sweating. *J. Appl. Physiol.*, **31**, 80

139. MacIntyre, B. A., Bullard, R. W. Banerjee, M. and Elizondo, R. (1968). Mechanism of enhancement of eccrine sweating by localised heating. *J. Appl. Physiol.*, **25,** 255

140. Ogawa, T. (1970). Local effect of skin temperature on threshold concentration of sudorific agents. *J. Appl. Physiol.*, **28,** 18

141. Webb-Peploe, M. M. and Shepherd, J. T. (1968). Peripheral mechanism involved in response of dogs' cutaneous veins to local temperature changes. *Circulation Res.*, **23,** 701

142. Randall, J. E. (1962). *Elements of Biophysics,* opposite title page (Chicago: Year Book Medical Publishers)

143. Heath, J. E. (1970). Behavioural regulation of body temperature in poikilotherms. *Physiologist,* **13,** 399

144. Dawson, T. J. and Brown, G. D. (1970). A comparison of the insulative and reflective properties of the fur of desert kangaroos. *Comp. Biochem. Physiol.*, **37,** 28

2
Physiological Effects of Cold Exposure

A. J. F. WEBSTER
Rowett Research Institute, Aberdeen

2.1 INTRODUCTION

Since each of us sees with his own eyes, it is inevitable that our attitude to
the problem of cold stress is conditioned by the fact that man is a naked,
sweaty animal probably more sensitive to cold than any other homeotherm
of comparable size. Studies on the physiological effects of cold on man and
small animals like the laboratory rat have tended to emphasise the response
to the stress of cold; i.e. those mechanisms designed to maintain homeothermy
in the wide range of environmental circumstances where heat loss exceeds
that which would normally be produced in metabolism.

A most important characteristic of many species of birds and mammals
which have evolved in temperate and cold climates, and this includes many
of the domesticated species of agricultural importance, is their extreme
resistance to excessive heat loss. Conditions which would be intolerably
cold for an unprotected man may not, for example, elicit any measurable
physiological response from a sheep in full fleece. In these cold adapted
species therefore, the more important physiological questions concern the
mechanisms which contrive to minimise the intensity of the stimulus of cold.

The cold tolerance of an animal is therefore determined both by its capacity
to minimise the stimulus of cold and its capacity to respond to that stimulus.
This chapter will consider the interactions between an animal and its thermal
environment which determine the intensity of the stimulus of cold and those
physiological mechanisms which are invoked in response to its effects. The
following chapter then goes on to consider in terms of these basic stimulus/
response mechanisms how cold tolerance and the response to cold may change
in individuals and in species as they adapt to cold environments.

2.2 CRITERIA OF PHYSIOLOGICAL RESPONSE TO COLD

Current concepts concerning the physiological response to cold can only be
considered in terms of the basic and well established principles which govern
the exchange of heat between a homeotherm and its physical environment.
These are presented here briefly and in a form just sufficiently elaborate to
interpret the text that follows. More elegant treatments can be found elsewhere.

Homeothermy requires that in any environment the amount of heat
produced in metabolism (H_P) must ultimately equal the heat lost to the
environment (H_L).
This is expressed by,

$$H_P \pm H_s = H_L = H_N + H_E \qquad (2.1)$$

where H_N is heat lost by convection, conduction and radiation (Newtonian
heat transfer). H_E is heat lost by evaporation of moisture from the skin and
the respiratory tract and H_s is heat storage in the body. Over a long period
of time H_s becomes very small in relation to the other terms in the equation.

The *thermoneutral zone* is that in which H_P is independent of air temperature.
The lower end of the thermoneutral zone is defined as the *critical temperature*. Below the critical temperature H_P exceeds the amount of heat that an

animal would produce as an inevitable consequence of metabolism (the *thermoneutral metabolic rate*). In these circumstances the animal is compelled either to elevate H_P by the processes of cold thermogenesis or to permit body temperature to fall. The effect of cold on H_P therefore has a threshold, the critical temperature, above which it does not elicit a response.

The term H_N may be described most simply by

$$H_N = A.C.(T_B - T_A) \qquad (2.2)$$

where $(T_B - T_A)$ is the gradient of temperature from the body (T_B) to the air (T_A). A is surface area and C is the total thermal conductance of the body. According to the limited definition provided by equation (1.2), H_N is a continuous linear function of $(T_B - T_A)$ and has no threshold. At air temperatures below T_B and above the critical temperature, H_L is regulated to equal H_P, principally by varying H_E. The critical temperature then describes the transition point between the thermal zone in which an animal maintains homeothermy by regulating H_L (physical thermoregulation) and the zone in which homeothermy can only be maintained by regulating H_P (chemical thermoregulation).

The relationships between air temperature and heat exchanges in a homeotherm are illustrated in Figure 2.1. This is a stylised and slightly refined version of the classical temperature metabolism curve[1] and is not intended to relate to any particular species of mammal. It assumes moreover that the animal in question is in thermal equilibrium with its environment (i.e. $H_P = H_L$) and that the only factor determining the effective coldness or *thermal demand* of the environment is air temperature.

In these idealised circumstances the effect of increasing thermal demand on H_P, H_N and H_E in any homeotherm can be described by curves qualitatively similar to those in Figure 2.1. When $T_B = T_A$, sensible heat loss, H_N is zero. The slope relating H_N to T_A at air temperatures below T_B is initially steep, indicating that the thermal conductivity of the animal is high. Dilated blood vessels close to the body surface convect a large proportion of the circulating blood through the superficial tissues from whence the heat may readily be lost to the environment. At lower air temperatures (about 22 °C in Figure 2.1), vasoconstriction occurs and the slope of H_N is reduced as a greater proportion of the cardiac output is retained within the central body core. Vasoconstriction, as a heat conservation mechanism has obvious survival value. There are, however, areas and circumstances where it must be relaxed.

The extremities of the body, for example the ears, feet and fingers in man, have little metabolically active tissue and are thus almost entirely dependent on their blood supply for a source of heat. When vasoconstriction occurs, the surface temperature of the extremities falls to a value close to air temperature and H_N from these areas becomes very small. At air temperatures below 0 °C cold induced vasodilatation in the extremities must occur to increase their blood supply and prevent them from freezing. The effect of cold induced vasodilatation is to increase the slope of H_N (Figure 2.1).

Evaporative heat loss (H_E) is obviously equal to H_P when H_N is zero. The regulation of H_E in the heat is outside the scope of this chapter. As T_A is reduced, thermoregulatory sweating and panting are progressively inhibited and H_E falls to a minimum value which is reached at an air temperature close to the critical temperature. At this point both cutaneous and respiratory moisture losses are minimal. Below the critical temperature cutaneous water loss is unchanged but respiratory evaporative loss must perforce increase slightly as pulmonary ventilation rate is increased to meet the increased metabolic rate (Figure 2.1).

In Figure 2.1 heat production at air temperatures above the critical temperature is shown to be constant. This, the *thermoneutral metabolic rate* is often taken as being synonymous with basal metabolic rate, a misleading assumption that will be discussed later. At air temperatures below the critical, H_P

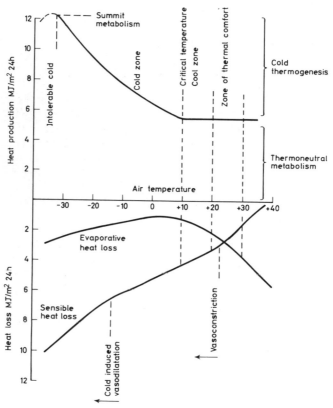

Figure 2.1   Stylised representation of the heat exchanges of a homeotherm at air temperatures from $-40\,°C$ to $+40\,°C$

increases at a rate determined principally by H_N. The increase in H_P above thermoneutral metabolism is called *cold thermogenesis*. The limit to the capacity of an animal to elevate metabolic rate in the cold is called *Summit Metabolism*. If H_N is increased further the intensity of the cold becomes intolerable and body temperature falls.

The progression of an environment from being comfortable to being intolerably cold can therefore be divided into four zones.

1. *Zone of thermal comfort*—a relatively narrow thermal zone in which homeothermy is maintained by small variations in H_E and H_N.

2. *Cool zone*—heat conservation mechanisms approach their limits but H_P is not elevated. Behavioural and postural changes designed to conserve heat are important at this time.

3. *Cold zone*—air temperatures below critical. Homeothermy maintained by cold thermogenesis.

4. *Zone of intolerable cold*—the capacity to maintain homeothermy by cold thermogenesis is exceeded. Body temperature falls. *past critical temp.*

2.3 MEASUREMENT OF ENERGY EXCHANGES

The standard unit of energy is the joule (J). Rate of expenditure of energy may be expressed in watts ($J s^{-1}$). The watt is a convenient expression for the physicist or engineer concerned with the exchanges of energy between an animal and its environment. It is less helpful to the biologist concerned with nutritional and biochemical problems relating to the energy conversions of man and animals in different environmental circumstances. This fraternity have traditionally worked in calories (4.184 J) and usually expressed the rate of heat production of an animal in terms of calories produced over a period of 1 h or 1 day. Nutritionists accustomed to expressing the energy requirements of man and animals in kilocalories (kcal)/24 h have been requested to convert to the use of the joule[2]. Generally this chapter uses the joule as the standard unit of energy and expresses rate of energy expenditure in kJ or megajoules (MJ)/24 h, a compromise between the watt school and the calorie school that ensures that while neither group will be entirely familiar with the units, both will have but one conversion to make.

The problem becomes a little more complex when we consider units of thermal insulation, which have traditionally been expressed as °C.area.time/cal. This is a rather complex unit and when joules are substituted for calories I find that the published data, including my own, becomes unrecognisable. In this case therefore, I have decided to express units of thermal insulation in both ways, thus for example, Tissue insulation = 1.6 (6.7) °C.m².24h/MJ (Mcal). Prediction equations for thermal insulation taken from the literature have been left in their original form.

2.3.1 Direct calorimetry

Direct measurement of heat losses from animals can be made in heat sink or thermal gradient calorimeters. The heat sink principle depends on absorbing the animal's heat loss and measuring it as a rise in temperature in the absorbing medium, which may be the air stream ventilating the chamber[3] or water circulating outside its walls[4]. Evaporative heat loss can be measured as a separate entity by the increase in relative humidity of the ventilating air stream only if there is no condensation of water vapour within the chamber.

A novel variation on the heat sink principle involves the measurement of the heat gain in the fluid circulating through a water-cooled garment worn by men under normal insulative clothing[5].

The thermal gradient principle depends on the measurement of the temperature difference existing across a conducting layer interposed between an animal and a constant temperature source. The first accurate gradient layer calorimeter for man was that of Benzinger and Kitzinger[6]. In this and later gradient layer calorimeters[7] H_N is measured rapidly and precisely from the e.m.f. created as the result of the temperature difference across a thermopile created between the inner walls of the animal chamber and the outer walls in contact with a constant temperature water bath. Evaporative heat loss can be made with equal rapidity and precision by the inclusion of gradient layer thermopiles into the air conditioning system for the chamber.

Direct calorimetry is in principle the most attractive way of measuring and partitioning the exchanges of heat between an animal and its environment and the gradient layer calorimeter represents the most elegant if the most expensive technique. There are practical problems in running direct calorimeters at air temperatures below 5 °C. This is not a severe limitation to their use in the study of responses to cold in man and small mammals. However, most species of agricultural importance and those species of particular interest to environmental physiologists because of their exceptional cold tolerance show little or no metabolic response to cold at air temperature above 0 °C.

Heat loss from animals at selected sites may be measured using heat flow discs which are, in essence, small gradient layer thermopiles which may be attached to the skin surface or implanted just underneath[8] the skin. These instruments provide a useful record of fluctuations in regional heat loss but their absolute precision is low principally because the presence of the heat flow disc interferes with the normal pattern of heat flow.

2.3.2 Indirect calorimetry

The heat production (H_P) of an animal can be estimated from measurements made of its respiratory exchange. The respiratory quotient (ratio of CO_2 produced to O_2 consumed) when a mixture of carbohydrates and fats are totally oxidised is determined by the molar proportions of the two classes of substrates involved. Measurement of O_2 consumption and CO_2 production therefore accurately reflects the heat of combustion of any mixture of carbohydrate and fat[9]. Not all substrates are however, completely oxidised to CO_2 and H_2O. Urea is the principal end product of the incomplete oxidation of proteins in mammals. Anaerobic fermentation of carbohydrate in the rumen or large bowel of herbivores generates copious amounts of methane.

The most widely accepted equation for the estimation of H_P from measurements of chemical exchanges in metabolism is that of Brouwer[10] re-expressed here in kJ.

$$H_P(kJ) = 16.17 \times 1\ O_2 + 5.021 \times 1\ CO_2 - 2.167 \times 1\ CH_4 - 5.987 \times gN$$

$$(2.3)$$

The correction factors for CH_4 production and for urinary N excretion are quite small. If these latter two terms are neglected altogether, the error of estimate will exceed $\pm 2\%$ only in exceptional circumstances. The CH_4 term is of importance only in ruminants and the N correction is meaningless unless measurements are continued for at least 24 h. MacLean[11] has recently shown that when the open circuit method (q.v.) is used for short-term measurements of respiratory exchange, heat production in most normal circumstances can be estimated with comparable precision from the simple equation.

$$H_p(kJ) = 20.46 \times 1\ O_2 \qquad (2.4)$$

Most measurements of respiratory exchange have been made using the open circuit method (Figure 2.2). Expired air is continuously collected into an air stream which can be made to pass through a mouthpiece, a face mask, a hood containing the animal's head, or an air conditioned chamber containing the entire animal. The volume, temperature and relative humidity of the air leaving the animal system per unit time are measured. In most modern methods continuous samples of the ventilating air stream are passed over a paramagnetic analyser to measure O_2 concentration and infrared analysers to measure CO_2 and CH_4 where appropriate. The analysers are calibrated against atmospheric air (zero) and a gas mixture of known concentration (span). The ventilation rate of the entire system is usually regulated so that the concentration of CO_2 is between 0.5 and 1.0%. This concentration produces only small changes in respiratory frequency[9].

The main advantage of the open circuit system is its flexibility. It is not essential to control the environment around the animal and a wide variety of ways to collect expired air can be employed. However, to obtain an accuracy of $\pm 2\%$ in the measurement of, e.g. O_2 consumption, when the concentration of O_2 in the sample differs only 0.5% from atmospheric, requires that O_2 concentration must be measured with an absolute precision of 1 part in 10 000. Chemical analysis of gases by the Haldane method cannot achieve this. A recent gravimetric method for the simultaneous calibration of gas meters and analysers used in open-circuit respiration apparatus is more precise but more time consuming[12]. In any case, all these methods ultimately depend on the lack of precision involved in the assumption that the concentration of O_2 and CO_2 in atmospheric air is constant. For this reason the errors of determination of H_p from respiratory exchange can never be reduced below $\pm 2\%$. Small errors in calibration of gas analysers can induce errors of bizarre proportions.

Short-term measurements on man (the standard basal metabolism test) usually require the subject to expire air through a mouthpiece and valves into a bag or through a meter for immediate or subsequent analysis. The principle of the method is the same. Mouthpieces and valves are unacceptable to animals and not acceptable to man for long periods.

The closed circuit method requires the subject to be confined in a temperature controlled chamber. Air from the chamber is continuously recycled through containers of absorbent for water vapour and CO_2. As these products of respiration and transpiration are removed, pressure inside the circuit tends to fall and this permits pure O_2 to enter (Figure 2.2). The main advantage of this method is that measurement of O_2 consumption and CO_2 production are respectively volumetric and gravimetric and therefore precise. Since the method gives not only H_P but also H_E, evaporative heat loss, from loss of water vapour, H_N can be obtained by difference when the period of measurement is sufficiently long to ensure that H_s is small (equation (2.1)).

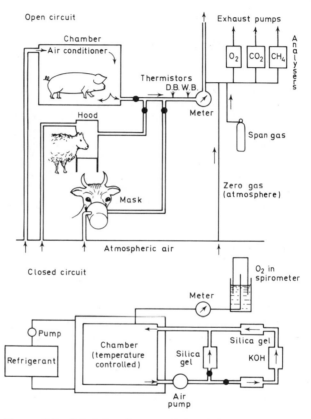

Figure 2.2 Principles of open and closed circuit measurement of respiratory exchange

In fact the technique is unsuitable for measurements of less than 12 h duration, and air temperature in the chamber cannot be altered during the course of the measurement. Nevertheless, much very valuable information concerning the energy exchanges of animals in cold environments has emerged from studies using closed circuit chambers[9]. Recent comprehensive reviews of the principles and relative merits of different techniques of respiration calorimetry are those of Flatt[13] and Blaxter[9,14].

2.3.3 Estimation of the energy expenditure of unrestrained animals

All the methods described above for determining the heat exchanges of man and animals involve some degree of confinement or restraint. The activity of the subject is inevitably limited as is the range of environmental conditions to which he may be exposed. In order to estimate the energy exchanges of individuals behaving normally in a natural environment several attempts have been made to discover a physiological variable that is measurable in the unrestrained individual and which correlates closely with heat production.

The relationship between heart rate and heat production has been explored in several species[15]. The exact nature and the precision of the relationship is different in each individual and varies from time to time. In sheep, heat production can be predicted from heart rate with a precision of better than $\pm 10\%$ in about 50% of cases[16]. Heart rate telemetry transmitters are commercially available. Continuous measurement and integration of cardiac output is more likely, on theoretical grounds, to predict heat production with precision. The most promising technique for the continuous telemetry of cardiac output from unrestrained animals is the Döppler shift ultrasonic method[17].

An entirely different approach involves the continuous infusion of ^{14}C labelled bicarbonate into animals in order to estimate their CO_2 production[18]. Measurements of the specific activity of CO_2 can be obtained at convenient intervals from samples of blood or urine. The method would appear to provide a good measurement of CO_2 production over long periods. Production of CO_2 is however, not by itself, a particularly good predictor of heat production.

2.4 THERMAL INSULATION

Sensible heat loss (H_N) describes the flow of heat down temperature gradients from the sites of metabolic heat production in the animal to the environment by the pathways of convection, conduction and radiation. In all cool and cold environments the principal factor determining the intensity of the stimulus of cold is H_N. The physical laws that determine the transfer of heat between an animal and its environment are, in themselves, quite simple. The multiplicity of sites and rates of heat production in the animal and the multiple pathways of heat loss make a precise mathematical solution of the heat exchanges very complex[19]. For most purposes the empirical but effective scheme proposed by Burton and Edholm[20] is quite adequate. A slightly modified version of their scheme follows.

Sensible heat is lost from the body core (the sites of heat production) to the environment through three layers of insulation in series.

Tissue insulation (I_T) describes the resistance of the skin and the superficial tissues of the body to heat loss by convection and conduction. If core temperature is taken as rectal temperature (T_R) and $\bar{T}_s$ is the mean temperature of the skin surface,

$$I_T = (T_R - \bar{T}_s)/H_N \tag{2.5}$$

In this case, at thermal equilibrium $H_N = H_P$

Coat insulation (I_c) describes the resistance to heat loss conferred on a man or animal by the coat of clothing, hair, wool or fur and the air trapped therein. If $\bar{T}_c$ is the mean temperature of the coat surface,

$$I_c = (\bar{T}_s - \bar{T}_c)/H_N \tag{2.6}$$

At thermal equilibrium $H_N = H_P + H_E$. In cold environments H_E is approximately constant (Figure 2.1) so that at air temperatures below the critical, equation (2.6) may be rewritten as

$$I_c = (\bar{T}_s - \bar{T}_c)/(H_P - k) \tag{2.7}$$

Air insulation (I_A) describes the resistance to heat flow conferred by the boundary layer on the surface of the coat.

$$I_A = (\bar{T}_c - T_A)/H_N \tag{2.8}$$

Since the temperature of the surface of the coat of an animal is very hard to measure or even to define with precision it is often convenient to sum I_c and I_A to obtain a value for total *external insulation* (I_E) which is therefore

$$I_E = (\bar{T}_s - T_A)/H_N \tag{2.9}$$

Heat loss from the surface to the environment proceeds principally by radiation and convection. The exchange of heat by radiation between two surfaces x and y is proportional to $(T_x^4 - T_y^4)$. Equation (2.8) does not take this into account. Burton and Edholm[20] have however described the 'fortunate accident of physics' whereby equation (2.8) does apply at a wide range of air temperatures so long as the effective radiant temperature of the environment does not differ significantly from air temperature (T_A). This occurs indoors only when the mean temperature of the walls is the same as air temperature and outdoors, for the same reason, when the sky is completely overcast. In all other circumstances the effective radiant temperature of the environment (T_E) differs markedly from air temperature[21].

In these circumstances heat loss from the surface may be considered as proceeding through two conductances in parallel, C_R the conductance to radiant heat loss and C_c the conductance to convective heat loss. Then,

$$H_N = C_R(\bar{T}_c - T_E) + C_c(\bar{T}_c - T_A) \tag{2.10}$$

Here C_R is an empirical constant for this particular equation and does not directly describe the true emissivity of the coat surface.

Total thermal insulation provided by the sum of I_T, I_c and I_A determine H_N and thus both the lower limit of the zone of thermoneutrality, the critical temperature, and the rate at which the body must elevate metabolic rate at air temperatures below the critical.

Critical temperature (T_{ac}) may be defined in terms of the equations presented above by the following[22]

$$T_{ac} = (T_R + H_E^*.I_E) - H_P^*(I_T + I_E) \tag{2.11}$$

where H_E^* is a constant describing the minimal loss of heat by evaporation in cold environments and H_P^* is thermoneutral metabolic rate. There is, in reality, no clear cut critical temperature below which the heat production of an animal must inevitably rise. Critical temperature is best considered as the midpoint of a range of air temperatures of about 5 °C through which an animal passes from being cool but comfortable to the point where it begins to shiver or initiate other exergonic processes designed to maintain homeothermy.

2.4.1 Tissue insulation

The factors that determine tissue insulation (I_T) may be divided into the physical, those which are an inevitable consequence of anatomy, and the physiological, those which are capable of regulation. The physical determinants of I_T are principally the thickness of the skin and the subcutaneous fat. The main physiological determinant is the rate of blood flow through the superficial tissues. Carlson and Hsieh[23] expanded the empirical equation (2.5) to take account of these two distinct contributors to I_T.

$$H_N = 1/I_T' (T_R - \bar{T}_s) + F.S(T_{blood} - \bar{T}_s) \qquad (2.12)$$

Here I_T' determines the rate of heat loss by conduction through the tissues and $F.S.\Delta T.$ determines heat loss from blood convected through the cool body shell. F is flow and S the specific heat of blood. In cool and cold environments this latter term becomes both small and constant as blood flow through the body shell is reduced to a minimum. In these circumstances I_T achieves a constant maximal value.

Some values for maximal I_T in man and animals are given in Table 2.1. In Caucasians unaccustomed to cold I_T increased with increasing thickness of subcutaneous fat. Thus women tend, on the whole, to have slightly more I_T than men. Certain primitive tribes, in particular the Kalahari bushman, have I_T values comparable to Caucasians although they are much less fat[24].

Table 2.1   Tissue insulation of man and some domestic animals in cold environments when blood flow to the cutaneous tissues is minimal

Species		Skinfold thickness mm*	Tissue insulation °C m².24h/MJ(Mcal)	Reference
Man	White man, normal weight	9.5	1.08 (4.51)	104
	White woman, normal weight	10.9	1.33 (5.56)	
	White man, obese	18.3	1.63 (6.82)	105
	Kalahari bushman	4.7	1.31 (5.48)	24
	Eskimo	5.8	0.98 (4.10	
Pig	Newborn	—	0.24 (1.00)	25
	Adult	—	1.69 (7.07)	106
Sheep	Adult	—	1.55 (6.48)	29
Cattle	1 month old	—	1.05 (4.39)	107
	1 y old, thin	3.7	1.48 (6.19)	
	1 y old, fat	4.9	2.45 (10.25)	26
	Mature fat	8.6	3.25 (13.60)	

* Measurements of skinfold thickness in men and cattle are not comparable. In man they include subcutaneous fat

This suggests an adaptive mechanism to cold which will be discussed in the next chapter. Eskimos, who clothe themselves most efficiently, appear not to show this adaptive response.

The tissue insulation of the newborn pig which has no subcutaneous fat is very low[25]. The adult fat pig is comparable to a fat man. In cattle I_τ is also correlated with skinfold thickness although this measurement is not comparable to that for man (Table 2.1).

At air temperatures below 0 °C blood flow to the skin of the extremities such as the ears and feet increases to prevent the tissues from freezing (q.v.). The effect of this is to decrease I_τ. In cattle I_τ at air temperatures below 0 °C have been described by the equation[26]

$$I_\tau(\text{units/Mcal}) = 5.50 + 0.018 \text{ W} + 0.099T_a \qquad (2.13)$$

where W is body weight (kg) and T_A air temperature *below* 0 °C. The effect of decreasing temperature is therefore to decrease I_τ. Note the units of I_τ in this equation are °C.m².24 h/Mcal.

2.4.2   External insulation

External insulation (I_E), the sum of I_C and I_A, is a function not only of the shape, posture and pelage of the animal but also of environmental factors such as sunshine, wind and precipitation which influence the rate of H_N from the skin surface to the air. The thermal insulation of wool in still air is 2.2 (9.2) °C.m² 24 h/MJ (Mcal) per cm of thickness[1]. Scholander[27, 28] measured the thermal insulation of the pelts of a wide range of arctic and tropical animals using a hot plate. He found an approximately linear relationship between coat depth and I_E having a slope of about 1.8 (7.6) units per cm thickness (Figure 2.3). Joyce and Blaxter[29] measured the heat production of sheep with different fleece depths (D) in cold, still air conditions. In their experiments,

$$I_E(\text{units/Mcal}) = 4.79 + 4.63D(\text{cm}) \qquad (2.14)$$

The intercept value represents the insulation of still air or I_A when I_C is zero (Figure 2.3). Blaxter[9] quoted a mean value of 1.6 (6.6) for I_A in still air where air temperature and the radiant temperature of the environment were equal Our experiments[26] made with cattle in different combinations of cold and wind yielded the following equation, also in Figure 2.3, where V is wind speed.

$$I_E(\text{units/Mcal}) = 11.78 + 2.40D(\text{cm}) - 0.49V^{0.5} \qquad (2.15)$$

The slopes of the lines relating I_E to mean coat depth in sheep and particularly in cattle are conspicuously less steep than that obtained by Scholander from experiments performed on samples of hide stretched out over a hotplate. The irregular shape of live animals, the disturbance of I_E due to shivering and the contribution of the relatively poorly covered extremities to total heat loss, more especially in cattle than in sheep, all contrive to reduce the effective insulation of the coat below that which would be predicted from Scholander's hot plate experiments.

The effect of increasing wind speed is clearly to decrease I_E. Most authors have related I_E to $V^{0.5}$ which is as tidy a first approximation as any, although $V^{0.6}$ is probably better[30]. The intercept term 11.78 units/Mcal obtained with cattle (equation (2.15)) is undoubtedly too high for the insulation of still air. This partly reflects the fact that the radiant temperature of the walls of the wind tunnel in which these experiments were performed was above air temperature but also probably means that the relationship between I_E and coat depth is not linear.

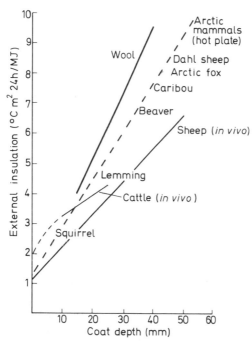

Figure 2.3 Published values for still air external insulation obtained from *in vitro* measurements of heat loss through the hide and coat of different species of cold adapted mammals[1] and from measurements of the respiratory exchange of sheep[29] and cattle[26]

A precise mathematical solution to the problem of partition of radiant and convective heat losses between an animal and its environment is obscured by the difficulty of measuring the effective radiant temperature of the environment[31] and for this reason attempts have been made to find empirical expressions to describe the effects of radiation exchanges on heat losses from animals in cold environments.

Solar radiation adsorbed onto the surface of an animal contributes to its total infrared radiant and convective heat loss and therefore substitutes for heat produced in metabolism in meeting the thermal demand of the environment. This may be quantified empirically by correcting I_A for the effects of sunshine[21].

$$I_A'(\text{in sun}) = I_A(\text{out of sun}) + aR'/H_N I_A \qquad (2.16)$$

where R' is solar radiation ($MJ/m^2.24h$), and a the proportion of solar radiation absorbed. This approach is however of limited relevance to the times and places of most severe cold; the long winter nights in the high latitudes. Swinbank[21] has shown that the effective radiant temperature of the environment on very cold, cloudless nights may be as much as 40°C below T_A. In these circumstances prediction of heat losses from animals out of doors on the basis of air temperature and wind speed alone is likely to be seriously in error.

In order to assess the magnitude of the effects of radiation exchanges on heat losses from cattle in very cold environments I built a model ox 'Moocow'[32] (model ox observing cold outdoor weather) which had the shape, size and I_T of a 250 kg calf. A pumping system circulated a dilute solution of ethylene glycol at 15 l/min from a water bath at 39 °C through a network of copper pipes running under the surface of the trunk and extremities. H_N was assessed from the power consumption necessary to maintain internal temperature at 39 °C. A net radiometer measured the radiant exchange of heat between the upper surface of Moocow and the sky above. Moocow was exposed to air temperatures ranging from +5 to −45°C, wind speeds from 12 to 180 m/min and net radiation (R) values ranging from +7 to −5 $MJ/m^2.24$ h. Several equations to predict H_N from characteristics of the external environment were tested. The simplest and most empirical of these was

$$H_N = (39.0 - T_A)/(I_T + I_A) - \beta R \qquad (2.17)$$

which yielded on solution,

$$H_N \text{ (Mcal)} = (39.0 - T_A)/[7.5 + (13.64 - 0.52V^{0.5})] - 0.25\ R$$

The coefficient of variation attached to the prediction of H_N was $\pm 7.9\%$, an error term which was not improved by the adoption of more mathematically refined equations. The expression describing the effect of wind speed on heat loss from Moocow, $0.52\ V^{0.5}$ was not significantly different from that of $0.49\ V^{0.5}$ obtained from measurements of the respiratory exchange of cattle in a wind tunnel.

The effect of changing patterns of wind and radiation exchanges on H_N in Canadian winter conditions is illustrated in Table 2.2. Net radiation figures represent actual data but temperature and wind speed figures have been rounded off for comparative purposes. The table shows that net radiation could vary from +7.1 $MJ/m^2.24$ h on a sunny day in March at about 0°C to −5.4 in January at −35°C when the nights were long. The final columns in Table 2.2 illustrate the extent to which inclusion of the net radiation term improves the prediction of H_N from livestock out of doors in cold environments. Uncorrected H_N in the examples illustrated, over or underestimated true H_N by as much as 26% and 9% respectively. Only when the sky was completely overcast did the correction for net radiation become insignificant.

The effects of moisture in the form of humidity, precipitation from above or wetness underfoot have not been thoroughly investigated. Wetting the coat of a man or animal reduces I_E as expected. Measurements of the I_E of wet coats are difficult to relate to standard meteorological data because it is

Table 2.2 Predicted values for heat loss from an artificial ox in different cold environments (From Webster[22], by courtesy of J. Appl. Physiol.)

Air temperature (°C)	Wind speed m/min	Net radiation (R) MJ/m².24 h	Description of weather	Predicted heat loss (MJ/m².24 h)	
				corrected for R	uncorrected
0	12	+7.10	10 h Sun, roof cover at night (April)	6.66	8.43
	12	−0.22	Cloudy day, clear night	8.48	8.43
	120	+0.64	Haze	10.42	10.58
	180	−0.26	Completely overcast	11.58	11.51
−15	12	−3.79	5 h Sun, 14 h cloudless night (Feb.)	12.61	11.67
	12	+0.64	8 h Sun, partial cloud at night (Feb.)	11.51	11.67
	60	−0.84	Broken cloud night and day	13.40	13.19
	120	−0.62	Completely overcast	14.80	14.65
−30	12	−5.43	4 h Sun, 16 h cloudless night (Jan.)	16.28	14.92
	12	−2.02	Broken cloud night and day	15.40	14.92
	60	−1.24	Mostly overcast	17.18	16.87

very difficult to predict just how wet the coat will get. Moreover, at air temperatures below 0 °C water tends not to be wet.

In carefully controlled experiments relative humidity was shown to have no significant effect on heat loss and the subjective sensation of cold in naked or lightly clothed man[33, 34]. These disproved the popular belief that 'damp cold' feels colder than 'dry cold'. This misconception can probably be traced to the fact that in maritime environments damp cold days are associated with very low incoming solar radiation. A dry cold day usually means the sun is shining. In a cold continental climate the dry cloudless cold nights are subjectively and actually much colder than the 'damp' cloudy nights because radiant heat loss to the night sky is so much greater.

2.5 ENERGY METABOLISM DURING ACUTE EXPOSURE TO COLD

The critical air temperature, which is the threshold stimulus to the metabolic response to cold, is determined by total insulation and by thermoneutral metabolic rate (TMR) (equation (2.11)). In some textbooks and reviews (which shall be nameless) TMR is considered to be synonymous with basal metabolic rate (BMR). This assumption can be seriously misleading. The BMR of man has been defined as the lowest level of energy expenditure consonant with life. The criteria necessary to satisfy this condition in man are that he is warm, lying down, awake but relaxed and has not eaten for at least 12 h. Clinical measurements of BMR usually involve collection of expired air for two periods of 6 min. It goes without saying that the average TMR over a period of 24 h will be higher than that. It is not generally realised however why and how much TMR can differ from BMR. The factors that conspire to elevate TMR above BMR are level of activity and level of food intake. Comprehensive studies have been made of the energy expenditure of men during brief periods of controlled physical activity[35] but continuous measurements of the heat production of men made over periods of 24 h or longer are very few. Consequently the effects of activity on heat production in man are well understood but not the effects of food intake. This latter effect is usually called specific dynamic action and for want of any better information a figure of 10% is usually added to BMR to account for the effect of food intake irrespective of the quantity and the quality of the food eaten[36].

Calorimetric experiments with domestic animals have, for practical reasons, tended to be concerned more with the evaluation of the efficiency of utilisation of foods than with the energy costs of physical activity. These experiments demonstrate clearly two important points (which could be predicted on thermodynamic grounds).

1. The metabolisable energy of foods cannot be used with the same efficiency as the energy reserves of the body for the biological oxidations essential to the maintenance of life.

2. Metabolisable energy consumed in excess of that required for the maintenance of essential body functions (at any level of activity) cannot be stored in the body as protein or as fat with an efficiency of 100%. The energy to drive all synthetic processes has to come from oxidative processes,

usually through the intercession of the high energy phosphate bond ATP. The extent to which the efficiency of various linked synthesis/oxidation reactions falls below 100% depends on the nature of the synthesis involved and the difference between total synthesis and net retention of synthesised product[37].

It is inevitable therefore that the more any animal or man eats the greater will be its heat production, the actual amount depending on the substrates made available by digestion and the nature of the anabolic and catabolic reactions taking place. The effect of this on TMR is shown in Table 2.3.

Table 2.3   Basal metabolic rates and thermoneutral metabolic rates of a man, a pig and a sheep, all of the same size but having different levels of activity and food intake

		Body weight kg	Basal metabolism* MJ/24 h	Gross energy intake MJ/24 h	Thermoneutral heat production MJ/24 h
Man	Sedentary	75	7.4	11.5	9.2
	Active			18.8	10.8
Pig	Confined, fed to maintenance	75	7.4	11.5	9.2
	Confined, fed *ad lib*			40.0	16.7
Sheep	Confined, fed hay to maintenance	75	7.4	18.2	10.0
	Free range, grazing to maintenance			21.6	13.0
	Confined, fed barley and hay *ad lib*			46.0	23.0

* Calculated from the interspecies mean of 290 kJ/kg.24 h

The gross energy intakes of active and sedentary men are those recommended for athletes and office workers. The values for TMR in this table are elevated above BMR simply as a consequence of the amount of food eaten. Thus the athlete has a higher TMR than the office worker even if they both spend the entire day in bed. The values for the pig and sedentary man eating just enough to maintain body weight are the same. The impresssive appetite of the pig offered food *ad lib* has the effect of elevating TMR about 80% above BMR.

Values for the sheep illustrate the effects both of activity and of the quantity and quality of the food on TMR. High cellulose foods such as hay are metabolised with a relatively low efficiency compared with the typical diets of a monogastric animal. However, the elevation in TMR associated with the metabolism of these foods conspicuously enhances the cold tolerance of ruminant species. Table 2.3 shows that TMR in sheep eating *ad lib* may be three times BMR. The effect of such an elevation in TMR on critical temperature may be deduced by reference to equation (2.11).

2.5.1   Stimulus to cold thermogenesis

Cold thermogenesis is triggered when the incoming sensation of cold reaches an intensity perceived by the integrating centres in the hypothalamus as threshold. The physiology of temperature regulation will be discussed elsewhere in this volume, here it is necessary only to say that sensory receptors sensitive to cold are sited throughout the skin[38,39], and also have been demonstrated in the hypothalamus[38,40] the spinal cord[41] and the abdominal viscera[42] (see Chapter 4). Undoubtedly other thermally sensitive areas exist. Cold receptors are sensitive both to absolute temperature and to rate of change of temperature[43]. Information received from these cold sensors is integrated in the hypothalamus and motor impulses are transmitted to the effector organs involved in cold thermogenesis to bring about the appropriate response[38]. Models of this control system are legion[38,40,44]. Hardy's concept of a continuous proportional control mechanism and a rate control mechanism governing the metabolic response to cold is not new but has a vintage quality.

His model is described by the following equation[44],

$$M - M_o = -am(T - T_o) - \gamma m \frac{dT}{dt} \qquad (2.18)$$

Here $M - M_o$ indicates the increase in metabolic rate from the thermoneutral rate M_o, $(T - T_o)$ the change in regulated temperature from its set point T_o and DT/dt the rate of change of temperature of the thermoreceptors, am and γm are respectively, constants for continuous proportional control and rate control of metabolic rate.

(increase in H_p) $= -$(fall in regulated temperature)
$\qquad \qquad \qquad -$(rate of change of temperature sensors)

This model provides for rapid response to rapid changes taking place in the temperature of receptors, particularly, in natural circumstances in the skin, without any alteration necessarily taking place in the regulated body temperature, T_o. It is not necessary to attribute any specific anatomical site or sites to this regulated body temperature. The hypothalamus may be the most exquisitely thermally sensitive area but it is equally true that all body temperatures are regulated to a greater or lesser extent.

2.5.2 Effector mechanisms of cold thermogenesis

The metabolic response to the stimulus of cold involves practically all the systems in the body. The striated muscles shiver, cardiac muscle beats faster, respiration becomes deeper, urine flow is increased and the sympathetic and pituitary controlled endocrine systems are activated to elevate biological oxidations in all tissues.

Cold thermogenesis will be considered here under three headings:

1. Somatic nervous control—response in striated muscles.

2. Autonomic nervous control—the sympathoadrenal system.

3. Neuroendocrine control—regulation via the anterior pituitary.

These headings differ from the fashionable partition of cold thermogenesis into *shivering* and *non-shivering thermogenesis*. The mechanisms responsible for cold thermogenesis in mammals differ markedly between species and also within certain species according to their previous thermal history. Whereas shivering is a fairly clearly defined response which is common to all homeotherms, the term non-shivering thermogenesis (NST) has come to mean different things to different people. At face value NST should mean all sources of heat produced in metabolism by means other than shivering, a Pooh Bah definition which would include all the contributors to thermoneutral metabolic rate. What is usually meant by NST is regulatory non-shivering cold thermogenesis, i.e. a mechanism for producing heat by means other than shivering whose sole function is to maintain homeothermy in a cold environment. Most references to NST[45] are even more specific, describing catecholamine induced regulatory non-shivering thermogenesis. This last phrase is something of a mouthful but it has a much more specific meaning than that implied by NST alone. The physiological basis of catecholamine regulated NST which has received considerable attention in the last 15 y is discussed below in the section on autonomic nervous control. It is important however to place it in perspective at the outset. It only exists in those species that have significant amounts of brown adipose tissue. Species which have brown adipose tissue as adults are nearly all under 2 kg in weight[46]. The possibility that other forms of regulatory non-shivering cold thermogenesis can exist in man and adult large mammals will be discussed below and in the following chapter. The term NST will be avoided where possible because of its ambiguity.

2.5.2.1 *Somatic nervous control—response in striated muscles*

When man and animals are exposed to acute cold they shiver. Shivering has been described as a tremor or a rhythmic involuntary movement consisting of an oscillation about a mid point in one or several muscles[47]. The effect of this tremor is to elevate heat production in the shivering muscles. Although the tremor is involuntary and can occur in animals without a cerebral cortex it can be inhibited by voluntary effort. The muscular response of shivering therefore is defined by visual inspection. The absence of a recognisable tremor does not necessarily mean that striated muscles are not responding to the stress of cold by an increase in tone or by purposeful activity. For this reason shivering, like NST, is a term better avoided when discussing the metabolic response to cold. This section deals therefore with thermogenesis resulting from contractions of striated muscle in response to an increased rate of discharge of efferent nerves in the somatic nervous system. The fact that the magnitude of the thermogenic response in muscle may be closely related to the intensity of shivering or to the magnitude of an integrated myographic trace is coincidental.

The contribution of striated muscle to cold thermogenesis may be assessed from preparations in which the efferent pathways to muscle have been broken. Cottle and Carlson[48] measured cold thermogenesis in rats paralysed with the neuromuscular junction blocking agent d-tubocurarine. In warm adapted rats muscular thermogenesis was the dominant but not the sole contributor to total thermogenesis. In cold adapted rats an alternative mechanism had emerged. The residual elevation in heat production observed in curarised rats was comparable to that which could be invoked by injection of noradrenaline[49]. These experiments demonstrated the importance of noradrenaline regulated non-shivering cold thermogenesis to the total metabolic response of warm and cold adapted rats to an acute cold stress.

Paralysed men and large animals probably cannot increase heat production on exposure to cold. This point has not been confirmed beyond doubt mainly because experiments using curare on conscious man and animals during exposure to cold are ethically unacceptable and anaesthetised preparations are of limited value since their thermoregulatory mechanisms are disturbed. The capacity of men who have received spinal lesions as a result of accidents, to elevate heat production appears to be related to the amount of muscle remaining under central control[50]. Chatonnet[51] demonstrated that cold thermogenesis in dogs was inhibited by section of motor tracts in the spinal cord, the degree of inhibition depending on the degree of spinal paralysis induced. In animals without brown adipose tissue therefore the integrity of the somatic nervous system seems to be essential to the entire metabolic response to cold.

Hemingway[47] has investigated the motor pathways involved in the control of muscular thermogenesis. He considers the primary motor area to exist in the dorsomedial caudal hypothalamus near the wall of the third ventricle and just ventral to the caudal border of the massa intermedia of the thalamus. Efferent pathways from this centre travel caudally through the midbrain and the pons close to the rubrospinal tracts. In the medulla oblongata and the spinal cord the motor pathways lie close to the ventrolateral surfaces. Subsidiary controlling centres in the brain feed into this final common pathway via the primary motor centre. The rhythm of shivering is undoubtedly regulated via the muscle spindle proprioceptors feeding back impulses in the dorsal roots and through the cerebellum.

The extent to which man and large animals can elevate heat production in muscle in response to cold varies with individuals and with species. *Summit metabolism*, the maximum rate at which cold thermogenesis can be sustained, has been reported for man to be about five times BMR[52]. In dogs values up to ten times BMR have been reported[51] and in sheep about six times BMR[22,53]. These increases are comparable to those which can be sustained during prolonged exercise and the metabolic transformations taking place during the two activities are essentially the same (see Chapter 5).

Cold thermogenesis in striated muscle ultimately derives entirely from the increased rate of hydrolysis of ATP and creatine phosphate releasing energy for muscle contraction, the energy all being dispersed as heat. Conversion of ATP to ADP during shivering acts as a stimulus to the process of oxidative phosphorylation in mitochondria which itself accelerates all catabolic processes. In physiological conditions where the availability of oxygen and oxidisable substrates is not limiting the availability of phosphate acceptor (which usually means the rate of production of ADP) is the principle factor determining the rate of heat production in muscle[54].

Combustion of, for example, 1 mol glucose in muscle generates heat in the following ways.

The free energy of glucose is 2875 kJ mol^{-1}. Complete biological oxidation of glucose to CO_2 and H_2O yields in most circumstances 38 mol ATP. One mole of ATP is used initially in the phosphorylation of the activation process which increases the free energy of the molecule to the point where subsequent reactions will, in the right circumstances, proceed spontaneously. Anaerobic glycolysis of glucose to lactate in the cytoplasm gives a net yield of only 2 mol ATP. Conversion of ADP to ATP occurs predominantly by oxidative phosphorylation in the mitochondria. The free energy contained in the terminal phosphate bond of ATP is usually taken as being about 48 (11.5) kJ (kcal) mol^{-1}[9], although there are several dissenting voices, among them Prusiner and Poe[55] who consider 19.7 (4.7) kJ (kcal) mol^{-1} a better estimate. On the basis of the more popular estimate of 48 kJ mol^{-1}, the heat produced from hydrolysis of the 38 mol ATP produced by oxidation of 1 mol glucose is 1824 kJ, about 63% of the free energy of the original substrate, that produced during the oxidative reactions leading to the phosphorylation of ADP to ATP, 1051 kJ or 37%.

While striated muscle has the mass and the physiological capacity to produce sufficient heat during exercise or during cold stress to elevate whole body metabolic rate from five- to ten-fold for sustained periods, it does not have a copious reserve of domestic fuel. Sustained cold thermogenesis requires that the supply of oxygen and oxidisable substrates to muscle be increased to meet the increased demand. The supply of oxygen is increased by increased cardiorespiratory activity in the same way as during exercise. The physiology of this response is well known. The mobilisation of the oxidisable substrates required to sustain thermogenesis is considered in some detail in the next section.

2.5.2.2 Autonomic nervous control—the sympathoadrenal system

Cold stress is a potent stimulus to the sympathoadrenal system. The magnitude of the response is best assessed by measuring the increase in the urinary excretion of catecholamines since the life of catecholamines released into the blood stream is very short. The mechanisms of synthesis, release, re-uptake and metabolism of the catecholamines has recently been reviewed by Iversen[56].

The effects of the sympathoadrenal system on metabolism have been studied intensively over the last 20 years largely due to the discovery of a range of drugs which modify these effects in a more or less specific fashion. A comprehensible coverage of this work may be obtained from Himms-Hagen's superb review[57] and from the proceedings of a recent symposium 'Adrenergic receptors mediating metabolic responses'[58]. Ahlquist[59] originated the concept of a- and β- adrenergic receptors to resolve the conflict concerning the vasomoter effects of the catecholamines. This concept has been less successful in explaining the multiple effects of the catecholamines on metabolism but it is by no means without value[57, 60].

Let us consider only some of the effects of the sympathetic system on metabolism, those which would be likely to be involved directly or indirectly with cold thermogenesis.

1. In white adipose tissue, which is common to all homeotherms, catecholamines stimulate lipolysis. The sequence of events is probably as follows. Catecholamines activate adenyl cyclase to increase the intracellular concentration of cyclic AMP. This activates triglyceride lipase to begin the hydrolytic

reactions by which fatty acids are removed from the triglyceride[60]. This mechanism is inhibited by the β- receptor blocking agent propranolol and may therefore be classified loosely as a β response. The main consequence of this is an elevation in plasma free fatty acids (FFA) which may be used for oxidative phosphorylation elsewhere, especially in muscle. There is a small increase in heat production in the white fat associated with the resynthesis of ATP from cyclic AMP and ADP produced during hydrolysis of triglycerides and the subsequent phosphorylation of FFA. This increase is however negligible compared with the very large increase in heat production that occurs in brown adipose tissue in response to catecholamines (q.v.).

2. Catecholamines induce hyperglycaemia. The reasons for this are complex[58]. In the liver, catecholamines stimulate glycogenolysis through the action of cyclic AMP. Gluconeogenesis in the liver is also potentiated, principally by increased catabolism of glucogenic amino acids. Both these effects are of the β- receptor type. Catecholamines may also reduce glucose uptake in muscle by inhibiting insulin secretion. This appears to be an a response[61].

3. Catecholamines increase the permeability of the membranes of many cells to cations[58]. This is an a response in, for example the smooth muscle of arterioles but a β response in cardiac muscle. In both cases catecholamines induce sufficient depolarisation of the smooth muscle membranes to enhance the intrinsic tone and rhythm of the tissues. This in itself has a direct calorigenic effect, although not one whose sole function is the generation of heat for the maintenance of homeothermy. Depolarisation of a cell membrane leading to an increase in the permeability of the membrane to the cations Na and K will tend to speed up the Na/K pump responsible for the active transport of Na ions out and K ions into cells against concentration gradients[62]. Moreover, catecholamines have been linked directly with the activity of membrane bound Na^+K^+ linked ATPase which appears to be the regulator of the Na/K pump. Regulation by catecholamines of the rate of pumping of cations across a leaky membrane in order to maintain the *status quo;* i.e. the normal concentration gradients of cations, provides in theory an excellent mechanism for the control of thermogenesis. The possible significance of this mechanism will be discussed later.

4. The known direct thermogenic effect of catecholamines is a phenomenon that varies markedly between species and within species according to their previous thermal history. Injection of noradrenaline undoubtedly has a direct thermogenic effect in most adult small hibernators, for example, bats[63] and ground squirrels[64] and a few adult small non-hibernators, in particular the laboratory rat[46, 49, 65]. In other species noradrenaline only has a significant effect in the first few days of life. These species include rabbits[66], lambs[67] and babies[45]. In all the cases cited above significant amounts of brown adipose tissue (BAT) were present. Although some workers have claimed a small direct action of noradrenaline on heat production in man and larger mammals which do not possess BAT, there is now general agreement that noradrenaline does not directly elevate the metabolic rate of conscious animals unless BAT is present.

Noradrenaline induced regulatory NST described earlier refers then exclusively to the direct thermogenic effect of noradrenaline released in

Table 2.4 Effector pathways involved in cold thermogenesis in man and large* animals

Control system	Relays	Transmitting agent	Target organ	Response	Contribution to cold thermogenesis
1. Somatic nervous system(–caudal hypothalamus and proprioreceptor system)	Somatic motor nerves	Acetylcholine	Striated muscle	Shivering increased tone	$ATP \rightarrow ADP$ + heat during contraction and active transport of ions. Substrate + $ADP \rightarrow ATP$ + heat, e.g. glycolysis, substrate phosphorylation (TCA cycle), oxidative phosphorylation
2. Autonomic nervous system (hypothalamus)	Sympathetic nerves –post ganglionic fibres –adrenal medulla	Noradrenaline Adrenaline	White adipose tissue* (β- receptors)	Lipolysis β oxidation increased turnover	Mobilises substrates for oxidative phosphorylation ATP hydrolysis in cyclic AMP production and activation
			Liver and muscle (β- receptors)	Glycogenolysis and protein catabolism gluconeogenesis inhibits insulin	Mobilises substrates
			Striated muscle (α- receptors ?) Cardiac and smooth muscle (α- and β- receptors)	Potentiates shivering Increased tone and rhythm	Depolarisation of muscle membrane (increased active transport)
3. Neuroendocrine system (hypothalamus anterior pituitary)	Adrenal cortex	Cortisol corticosterone	White adipose tissue, muscle, liver	Potentiate α- β- receptors to catecholamines? increase net protein catabolism	Normal function of both essential to proper action of catecholamines
	Thyroid	Thyroxine triiodothyronine	General	Potentiate action of catecholamines, increase synthesis of adenylcyclase	

* Species over 2 kg which have no brown fat except in infancy response to a cold stimulus and exerting its effects directly or indirectly through BAT. It is a phenomenon therefore of rather limited distribution in the animal kingdom. The significance of this mechanism in adaptation to cold in hibernating and non-hibernating small mammals will be discussed in the next chapter. The mechanisms responsible for the direct thermogenic action of the catecholamines will be considered here relatively briefly since they have been comprehensively covered in several recent books and reviews[45, 46, 57].

The thermogenic response to noradrenaline, which is a β- receptor response since it is blocked by propranolol[57, 66, 68] can be of an impressive magnitude. The bat (*Myotis lucifugus*) for example can elevate heat production from 0.25 to 2.69 J/g body weight per min during infusion of noradrenaline[63]. BAT itself has a considerable capacity to produce heat *in situ* since its temperature and O_2 consumption increase markedly during noradrenaline infusion[46, 62]. Brown fat cells are densely populated with mitochondria and have a high potential capacity for oxidation reactions. It might be supposed that since BAT is essential to the direct thermogenic action of noradrenaline the entire elevation in metabolism takes place in this tissue. This assumption has some startling implications. The bat in the example presented above elevated heat production by 2.44 J/g body weight per min. A bat weighing about 10 g would possess at best about 0.35 g of BAT. During noradrenaline infusion therefore the increase in heat production would be about 70 J/g of BAT per min. The same conclusion emerges from studies with rats in which BAT constitutes, at most 0.7% of body weight. Again the thermogenic response to noradrenaline is about 70 J/g BAT per min[46]. This contrasts with a summit metabolic rate in sheep of about 3 J/g muscle tissue per min[22].

These observations provoke two important questions.

1. What are the mechanisms responsible for a rate of heat production in BAT which is, at the very least comparable to the maximum rate which can be sustained aerobically in striated muscle?

2. In animals which possess BAT does heat production increase in response to noradrenaline in tissues other than BAT itself? In other words, might BAT under the influences of catecholamines stimulate thermogenesis in other tissues such as muscle?

It was stated earlier that the driving stimulus to increased metabolism in muscle was the increased rate of production of phosphate acceptor primarily from the hydrolysis of ATP. In BAT, however, there is no obvious work function comparable to shivering which can make use of the free energy contained in ATP. In order to explain its high thermogenic capacity one must assume either an alternative source of work for ATP to perform or that the coupling of oxidation to phosphorylation is loosened thereby enabling oxidation to proceed at a rate not limited by the availability of the phosphate acceptor.

Prusiner and Poe[55] have listed eight theories which seek to explain the thermogenic effect of catecholamines in BAT. Of these, two would seem to be of major significance. In brown fat cells, mobilisation of FFAs in response to catecholamines appears to have two functions, provision of substrates and regulation of energy transfer by loosening the coupling of oxidative phosphorylation[69]. Entry of FFAs into the mitochondria of brown fat cells appears to exert a fine control over the number of ADP to ATP conversions taking place per pair of hydrogen atoms carried through the electron transport chain. The effect of this is to make the metabolic rate in BAT largely independent of the presence of phosphate acceptor.

It has also recently been shown that noradrenaline depolarises brown fat cells and thereby increases their permeability to cations [62,70]. The decrease in membrane potential was associated with an increase in temperature and therefore presumably in thermogenesis in BAT[62]. In BAT, therefore, the theoretical thermogenic mechanism proposed above, namely an increase in the rate of the Na/K pump to maintain the *status quo* across leaky membranes, does appear to make a significant contribution to the total heat production of the tissue by hydrolysing ATP through the intercession of Na/K linked ATPase and increasing the rate of production of phosphate acceptor.

The relative and total contribution of these two mechanisms to noradrenaline induced NST is not known. It is, however, beyond belief that they could achieve a rate of heat production in BAT over 20 times the maximum capacity of muscle for sustained aerobic thermogenesis. One is forced therefore to the conclusion that the direct thermogenic effect of catecholamines in animals which possess BAT operates also in tissues other than BAT itself.

Direct evidence for (or against) the participation of other tissues in noradrenaline induced thermogenesis is scanty. Himms-Hagen[71] showed that surgical removal of the interscapular brown fat pad from cold acclimated rats had no immediate effect on the thermogenic response of the rats to catecholamines, but that the response diminished thereafter progressively over a period of 4 days after surgery. She concluded that the interscapular brown fat is not the major site of noradrenaline induced NST but that it is essential to the response probably as an endocrine gland whose secretory product modifies the ability of other tissues to respond to catecholamines. No such hormone has yet been isolated from brown fat. However, very recently Mejsnar and Jansky[72] demonstrated a direct thermogenic effect of noradrenaline in the perfused gracilis muscle of the cold adapted rat, which has, of course BAT. This supports Himms-Hagen's hypothesis. The next critical experiment (which will doubtless have been done by the time this review is

Table 2.5   Effects of α and β blockade on the response of sheep to an acute cold stress

	Thermoneutrality	Cold exposure (shown at $-30\,°C$)		
		Untreated	a Block	β Block
Heat production MJ/m².24 h	4.8	16.3	14.0	11.7
Intracardiac temperature °C	39.3	39.3	Falls rapidly	Falls slowly
Heart rate/min	75	210	270	120
Glucose mg/100 ml	57	103	132	78
FFA μEq/100 ml	100	250	302	175
Ketones mg/100 ml	2.8	3.6	4.6	2.2

published) will be to see whether noradrenaline still exerts this direct thermogenic effect in isolated muscle one week after removal of the interscapular brown fat pad.

These actions of the catecholamines indicate that the sympathoadrenal system has an important supporting role in cold thermogenesis in all species of homeotherms, that of mobilising oxidisable substrates to sustain an increased metabolic rate in the tissues. The existence of a direct thermogenic role for catecholamines in those species which have BAT is not in doubt. On biochemical grounds catecholamines must have a small thermogenic effect in other species, but it is too small to make a significant direct contribution to the response of these animals to cold.

The above studies which have dealt with effects of administration of catecholamines do not necessarily expose all the ways in which the sympathoadrenal system might participate in the metabolic response to cold. Heitman and I have recently investigated the effects of a and β sympathetic blockade on the metabolic response of sheep to an acute, severe cold stress (Table 2.5.). Untreated sheep elevated heat production to about four times TMR and maintained homeothermy. Catecholamine excretion[73] and the plasma concentration of oxidisable substrates were markedly elevated. Heart rates were over 200 beats/min. β Blockade with propranolol caused a marked reduction in the metabolic response to severe cold although not to moderate cold. Plasma glucose, FFA and ketone concentrations all fell significantly after propranolol. Heart rate also fell to about 120 beats/min, the maximum rate which the sheep can sustain without participation of the sympathetic cardioacceleratory fibres[108]. In the sheep therefore the sympathoadrenal system acting through the β- receptors, is responsible for mobilising carbohydrates and fats and for elevating cardiac output to facilitate their transport. This is as expected and rather similar effects have been observed in baboons made to shiver by hypothalamic cooling[74, 75].

The effects of a blockade with phenoxybenzamine were more equivocal. The most conspicuous effect of a blockade is a massive vasodilatation[59] which reduces I_τ and therefore increases heat loss at any temperature. Rectal temperature fell rapidly in phenoxybenzamine treated sheep partly due to the increased heat loss due to vasodilatation and partly due to a reduction in thermogenesis[73]. In this case the reduction in thermogenesis was associated with an *increase* in plasma glucose, FFA, and ketones (Table 2.5). This implies an inhibition in the utilisation of substrates, perhaps a direct inhibition of thermogenesis in striated muscle. Sheep treated with phenoxybenzamine behaved differently from untreated sheep during exposure to cold. Whereas untreated sheep stood quietly while shivering intensely, treated sheep were very restless. They persistently stamped and shook themselves and for this reason it was not possible to assess whether they exhibited a fine muscle tremor or not. It seems likely that their conscious muscle activity substituted for shivering. Ellaway and Pascoe[76] claimed that phenoxybenzamine, but not phentolamine blocks the transmission of noradrenergic excitatory impulses from the spinal cord to the fusimotor nerves supplying the muscle spindles. Muscle spindle proprioreceptors have been credited with a major role in the regulation of shivering[77]. It is possible, therefore, that the fine control of shivering thermogenesis involves noradrenergic receptors in the spinal cord. Sympathetic ganglion blocking agents have been reported to abolish shivering in goats[78]. This may be another manifestation of the same thing.

2.5.2.3 Neuroendocrine control—regulation via the anterior pituitary

Cold is known to effect activity of both the thyroid and the adrenal cortex. The extent to which these hormones facilitate thermogenesis is incompletely understood. The synergistic effects of the thyroid and sympathetic systems are well known[79, 80]. Hypothyroid animals show a poor response to cold stress and to the effects of catecholamines[80]. Cold thermogenesis in the goat requires a far higher increase in sympathetic activity in thyroidectomised than in intact animals[81]. Obviously normal thyroid activity is essential to a normal response to acute cold stress but even though thyroid secretion rate may increase during acute cold exposure[80] it is unlikely that the effects of the thyroid hormones will be rapid enough to make a significant contribution to the short-term response to cold.

Secretion of the glucocorticoids, principally cortisol and corticosterone rises rapidly following acute exposure to cold[82, 83]. The exact mechanisms whereby thyroid hormones and glucocorticoids interact with the catecholamines to regulate intermediary metabolism during cold exposure or other stimuli to the 'General Adaptation Syndrome'[84] are currently under investigation in several laboratories. To review these interactions now would, I think, be premature. It would, however, be an excellent topic for a future edition of this book.

2.6 VASOMOTOR RESPONSE TO COLD—TEMPERATURE REGULATION IN THE EXTREMITIES

The extremities of the body may be defined as those parts of the head and limbs which have little muscle or visceral tissue capable of producing heat *in situ*. The extremities of man include the head, especially the ears, the hands and the feet. In many mammals the equivalent of the hands and feet, those regions distal to the carpus and tarsus, constitute a relatively larger proportion of total surface area. In ungulates the whole of the limbs ventral to the trunk are extremities by this definition. In cattle, for example, the extremities comprise about 30% of total surface area[85].

The anatomy of these regions is such that they are almost entirely dependent on their blood supply to provide heat. In thermoneutral environments regulation of blood flow through the extremities provide a precise mechanism for the regulation of sensible heat loss to balance the production of heat in metabolism. In cool and cold environments (Figure 2.1) sensible heat loss is minimised by restricting blood flow to the extremities unless their temperature falls so low that freezing or other forms of tissue damage may occur. In such circumstances additional heat must be provided which means inevitably that blood flow must increase. The study of temperature regulation in the extremities is therefore the study of the regulation of blood flow to these regions.

The vascular anatomy of the extremities presents two special characteristics that profoundly influence the way in which variations in blood flow effect their thermal regulation. Limbs being what they are, it is inevitable that blood should enter and leave from the same end. The venous return flows in part in close proximity to the arterial supply. There is an additional complex of veins close to the skin surface which do not have major attendant arteries[86]. In warm and hot conditions much of the arterial supply to the limbs returns through the superficial veins from which heat may readily flow to the air. In colder conditions the supply to these superficial veins is restricted and most of the blood to the limb returns in the deep veins in close proximity to the arteries. In these circumstances the limb cools. Arterial blood entering the limb at core temperature comes into close contact with cooled venous blood. A counter current exchange of heat is established whereby heat is conducted directly across the vessel walls from efferent arterial blood to afferent venous blood. The carpal and tarsal retes contribute significantly to this exchange. The effect of this is to conserve metabolic heat within the body core but also to permit further cooling of the extremities. It has been assumed[1,87] that this counter current cooling mechanism is of prime importance in determining the extreme cold tolerance of Artic birds and mammals accustomed to spending the winter on the polar ice cap. In fact this concept is misleading. The fact that skin temperature in the legs of these animals is maintained close to 0 °C is due not so much to the heat conservation properties of the counter-current mechanism, which is an inevitable consequence of anatomy, as to a precise physiological control of the mechanism of cold induced vasodilatation (CIVD) which regulates blood supply to these areas to a degree that keeps them just above their freezing point.

The other anatomical peculiarity of the extremities is their very high density of arterio-venous anastomoses (AVAs)[88-92], which, when open provide a low resistance direct communication between arterioles and venules thereby short-circuiting the relatively high resistance pathway through the capillary bed. The arteriolar end of the AVAs and the precapillary sphincter, usually just downstream are both rich in sympathetic nerve endings. Blood flow through the AVAs of the superficial tissue of the extremities serves a purely thermoregulatory function independent of the limited requirement of these tissues for a supply of oxygen and metabolites to the capillary bed. While capillary flow in the superficial tissues is maintained both by active vasoconstrictor and vasodilator sympathetic stimuli acting through a- and β- receptors respectively, blood flow through the AVAs in thermoneutral environments has been shown to be regulated via the a- receptors alone[93]. There is no evidence for a direct sympathetic vasodilator effect on the AVAs.

Although the control of blood flow in the peripheral circulation has been a subject for continuous intensive study, that aspect of it which deals with vasomotor response to cold, particularly cold induced vasodilatation is still poorly understood. The critical factor limiting advance in this endeavour is the lack of a really satisfactory method for measuring blood flow in the extremities of conscious animals exposed to cold environments. Venous occlusion plethysmography is perhaps the most direct technique for measuring blood flow in limbs. The arms or hand for example is enclosed in a container of constant volume. A light tourniquet around the limb temporarily occludes venous return. The immediate rise in the volume of the limb, attributable to the inflow of the arterial blood is registered as an increase in pressure in the container[20]. The method is insensitive at the low rates of blood flow that occur in cold environments and is unable to correct for changes in the capacity of the venous bed[94].

Quantitative measurements of blood flow in the extremities have been made using the principle of direct calorimetry[94,95]. Measurements of heat loss as indicators of blood flow must be applied with caution but if the necessary corrections concerning changes in heat content and *in situ* heat production in the extremities are applied the method is probably as accurate as any. More recently, estimates of regional blood flow have been made using the radioactive tracers, e.g. ^{24}Na[88] and the inert gases Krypton[96] and Xenon[97]. Interpretation of these experiments requires a precise knowledge of the distribution and fate of the injected isotopes and the promise of the early studies has not perhaps been fulfilled.

Qualitative estimates of blood flow to the surface of the extremities can be obtained from measurements of skin temperature, thermal conductivity, photoelectric measurements[98] or most directly, by observation, as originally reported by Grant in his classic studies on blood flow to the ear of the rabbit[89].

The fine control of blood flow to the extremities that contributes to the maintenance of homeothermy *in thermoneutral environments* is effected almost entirely by variations in sympathetic tone in the AVAs. Sympathectomy abolishes this precise control as does blockade of the a- receptors. Intense local or general cooling of the body surface produces an intense lasting vasoconstriction, to the extent where blood flow to the extremities is reduced to immeasurably low values (less than 1 ml/min entering the human hand[20,98]). Sympathetic vasoconstriction can therefore effectively halt blood flow to the extremities. This is not, of course, a situation that can be maintained without causing injury. During this time the extremity cools to a temperature very close to air temperature. However, metabolism continues in the tissues, albeit at a reduced rate and potentially toxic metabolites accumulate. Restoration of a flow of blood to the extremities adequate to prevent freezing or other forms of tissue damage must eventually occur.

The pattern of CIVD in man was first described in 1930 by Lewis[99] who showed that when a finger was immersed in a mixture of ice and water skin temperature first fell rapidly to about 1 °C and then fluctuated rapidly between 1 and 8 °C. Skin temperature would increase rapidly and then within 1–2 min begin an exponential descent back to nearly 0 °C whereupon the pattern would repeat itself. This was clearly due to a succession of sudden, transient, massive increases in blood flow, followed by more prolonged periods when blood flow was minimal or absent. Lewis called this response the 'Hunting phenomenon' and he attributed it to an axon reflex in sensory nerves. Later work, particularly the studies of Greenfield and his colleagues[94,98] indicated that this response is a very variable phenomenon. The sudden increases in skin temperature ('hunts') produced in the finger are profoundly affected by the general thermal state of the body, i.e. the warmer the body generally the greater the increase in temperature during CIVD. The hunting response can be demonstrated in sympathectomised subjects and persists in a modified form even after degeneration of all sensory and motor nerves. The intensity and rhythm of hunting is variable in normal subjects. Hunts appear asynchronously in different extremities and are usually preceded by a sensation of pain[20,98]. These observations suggest that the increase in temperature during the hunting response is due to a humoral agent, probably not histamine as was first suggested but some vasoactive polypeptide[100-102] elaborated in the cells during the temporary ischaemia caused by maximal vasoconstriction. Immediately blood flow recommenced it would wash out the vasodilator substance and sympathetic vasoconstriction would resume.

While this mechanism would appear quite feasible it may not be the sole factor contributing to CIVD. In man CIVD can undoubtedly occur without any obvious signs of the temperature fluctuations characteristic of the hunting phenomenon[20,98] which is, as its name implies, an inefficient mechanism for maintaining a physiologically optimal temperature in the tissues. A more precise control of the temperature of the extremities in the cold suggests a more precise mechanism than that described above. Men accustomed to working with their hands in cold water have apparently a fine control of CIVD[20]. Generally, however, man's capacity to control CIVD is very poor compared with other mammals. Frostbite and immersion foot in man are two clinical conditions resulting respectively from freezing or prolonged ischaemia in cold extremities and both result from an inadequate control of CIVD. Obviously neither condition is a serious problem to species of mammals and birds wintering in the Arctic. I have seen frostbite in the ears and feet of pigs put outside into air temperatures below $-40\,°C$, in calves newly born into blizzard conditions and occasionally in the teats of dairy cows. I have never observed it in uninjured extremities of domestic or wild ruminants living outside during the Canadian winter. A man compelled to spend one night barefoot at $-40\,°C$ would inevitably experience frostbite if he survived at all. Clearly the capacity and probably the control of CIVD in animals is superior to that in man.

In sheep two distinct patterns of CIVD have been observed[8,92]. One is identical to the hunting phenomenon, the other presents more of the characteristics of a continuous proportional control mechanism. In this case the temperature of the extremities was regulated just above their freezing point without the sudden rapid temperature changes of the hunting response. We obtained indirect evidence to show that blood flow to the limbs of the sheep was, in these circumstances, regulated so as to maintain the temperature of the skin tissue constant at about $4\,°C$. This observation suggested that a very precise mechanism existed to transduce and regulate skin temperature at this level. It is certain however, that the sheep in these experiments could sense touch on the skin of the shanks at these temperatures.

More recent studies[103] have confirmed that individual sheep either exhibit the hunting reaction in their extremities or maintain a very constant skin temperature. These two mechanisms which are quite distinct appear to be peculiar to individual animals and uninfluenced by previous thermal history.

We have also studied the effects of noradrenaline and sympathectomy on the pattern of CIVD in the ears of sheep exposed to an air temperature of

25 °C. These results are condensed into Figure 2.4. The sheep in Figure 2.4a exhibited hunting which was abolished by the intravenous infusion of noradrenaline. Skin temperature was, however, still maintained effectively above 0 °C. Other vasoconstrictor agents such as angiotensin and vasopressin were without effect on skin temperature in the ears. The sheep in Figure 2.4b

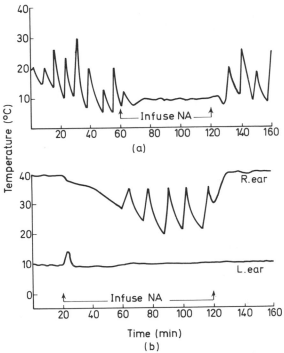

Figure 2.4   Temperature changes on the skin of the ears of sheep at −25 °C.
(a) 'Hunting in the intact ear abolished by infusion of noradrenaline (NA) (1µg/kg.min) for 60 min.
(b) Continuous proportional control in the intact left ear unaffected by noradrenaline; vasoconstriction and then 'hunting' in the sympathectomised right ear during noradrenaline infusion (From Meyer and Webster[103], by courtesy of the *Can. J. Physiol. Pharmacol.*)

was one that habitually exhibited the continuous proportional control type of response. In this animal the right ear had been sympathectomised by section of the right vagosympathetic trunk in the neck. This ear normally remained close to 40 °C even at an air temperature of −25 °C. During infusion of noradrenaline it slowly cooled and then commenced to hunt regularly but at a skin temperature about 15 °C higher than was usual in intact ears.

These observations support the conclusion that CIVD in either of its manifestations is achieved by a balance between sympathetically induced vasoconstrictor tone and opposing vasodilator stimuli which are independent of the nervous systems. Infusion of noradrenaline into a normal ear shifted the balance in favour of greater vasoconstriction. Infusion of noradrenaline into a sympathectomised ear created a small vasoconstrictor stimulus that was easily overwhelmed by opposing vasodilator stimuli.

The exact nature of the vasodilator stimuli, be they intermediary metabolites, vasoactive polypeptides, a noradrenaline inhibitor or any combination of these three remains to be established. However, it now seems likely that the so-called proportional control of CIVD can be attributed to the same opposing stimuli as the hunting reaction. In the sympathectomised ear skin temperature rose with each hunt almost to blood temperature. During normal hunts rises in skin temperature were smaller and more variable, indicating that blood flow through the AVAs in the extremities was considerably below maximum and suggesting therefore than a significant degree of vasoconstrictor tone persisted. The so-called proportional control mechanism may only be an example of an even more precise control of vasoconstrictor tone achieved by the sympathetic nerves to the AVAs firing in relays giving different intensities of tone in different vessels at any time. In this case stimuli to vasodilatation would only overcome vasoconstrictor tone in small numbers of individual vessels at any one time thereby avoiding the large temperature changes characteristic of the hunting response.

2.7 CODA

The magnitude and the rate of increase of scientific information are such that no one person can be aware of all the advances that occur even in his own limited compass of specialisation. The modern research worker may now be accused not only of knowing more and more about less and less, but also of knowing less and less of the more and more that becomes known about less and less. This makes a comprehensive review of any scientific topic physically impossible. While this is basically a humiliating situation it is one that confers some freedom from the responsibility of even making the attempt. With this in mind, I have deliberately biased this review (which has a title almost identical to countless other reviews), towards those topics which, in my opinion, merit particular emphasis at the present time. The reasons for selecting each topic for particular consideration are as varied as the topics themselves.

The methodology of measuring energy exchanges was reviewed in some detail because it is central to so many studies relating to cold, and in some of the published experiments, particularly those involving open circuit respiration apparatus, the precision of the method is suspect or impossible to determine.

The discussion on thermal insulation was intended to bring the pioneering work of Scholander and others up to date and also to stress the problems involved in determining with precision the intensity of the sensation of cold. The next chapter discusses experiments which compare adaptive changes in animals during prolonged exposure to different conditions of cold. These experiments may be confounded unless great care is taken to ensure that the physiological and environmental factors that determine the thermal demand of the environment are known.

The review on the metabolic response of animals to cold is inevitably more superficial than this immensely complicated and intensively studied problem deserves. My principle wish here was to resolve some of the confusion that exists in the current literature concerning the sites and mechanisms of cold thermogenesis. The magnitude of regulatory cold thermogenesis cannot be assessed unless the factors that regulate thermoneutral metabolic rate are taken into account. In considering the role of the sympathoadrenal system it is necessary to distinguish between its indirect role in mobilising and transporting energy rich substrates to sustain increased rates of energy metabolism in muscle, and the direct role of the catecholamines in initiating non-shivering cold thermogenesis, which has been demonstrated only in those species which possess brown fat. While this latter topic has focused a tremendous concentration of effort, the regulation of cold thermogenesis in man and the larger animals of economic importance has been relatively neglected in recent years.

The final section on cold induced vasodilatation includes less hard data than the rest because there are less to be found. The gaps in our knowledge here are clear. How to fill them is less obvious.

Appendix of Abbreviations

H is heat, rate of exchange MJ(or Mcal)/m^2.24 h
H_P is heat production; H_L total heat loss; H_N 'Newtonian' heat loss (convection, conduction, radiation); H_E evaporative heat loss; and H_s body heat storage

T is temperature ($^\circ$C)
T_R is rectal temperature; T_s mean skin temperature; T_A air temperature; T_C mean temperature of the coat surface; and T_E effective radiant temperature of the environment

I is thermal insulation $^\circ$C.m^2.24 h/MJ(or Mcal)
I_T is tissue insulation; I_E external insulation; I_c the insulation of the coat; I_A insulation of the air interface

C is thermal conductance MJ(or Mcal)/$^\circ$C.m^2.24 h
C_R and C_C are conductances to radiant and convective heat exchange

V is wind velocity (m/min)

R is net heat exchange by radiation (MJ/m^2.24 h)

R' is solar radiation (MJ/m^2.24)

References

1. Irving, L. (1964). Terrestrial animals in cold: birds and mammals. *Adaptation to the environment. Handbook of Physiology*, Sec. **4**. 361 (D. B. Dill, editor) (Washington: Amer. Physiol. Soc.)
2. Kleiber, M. (1972). Joules v. calories in nutrition. *J. Nutr.*, **102**, 309
3. Kelly, C. F., Bond, T. E. and Heitman, H. (1963). Direct 'air' calorimetry for livestock *Trans. Am. Soc. Agric. Engrs.*, **6**, 126
4. Mount, L. E., Holmes, C. W., Start, I. B. and Legge, A. J. (1967). A direct calorimeter for the continuous recording of heat loss from groups of growing pigs over long periods. *J. agric. Sci. (Cambridge)*, **68**, 47

5. Webb, P., Annis, J. F. and Troutman, S. J. (1972). Human calorimetry with a water cooled garment. *J. Appl. Physiol.*, **32**, 412
6. Benzinger, T. H. and Kitzinger, C. (1949). Direct calorimetry by means of the gradient principle. *Rev. Sci. Instrum.*, **20**, 849
7. Pullar, J. D. (1969). Methods of calorimetry (A) direct. *Nutrition of Animals of Agricultural Importance*. Part 1, 471 (Oxford: Pergamon Press)
8. Webster, A. J. F. and Blaxter, K. L. (1966). The thermal regulation of 2 breeds of sheep exposed to air temperatures below freezing point. *Res. Vet. Sci.*, **7**, 466
9. Blaxter, K. L. (1962). *The energy metabolism of ruminants*, (London: Hutchinson Ltd).
10. Brouwer, E. (1965). Report of subcommittee on constants and factors. *Energy Metabolism*. E.A.A.P., **11**, 411 (London: Academic Press)
11. McLean, J. A. (1972). On the calculation of heat production from opencircuit calorimetric measurements. *Brit. J. Nutr.*, **27**, 597
12. Brockway, J. M., Boyne, A. W. and Gordon, J. G. (1971). Simultaneous calibration of gas analysers and meters. *J. Appl. Physiol.*, **31**, 296
13. Flatt, W. (1969). Methods of calorimetry (B) indirect. *Nutrition of Animals of Agricultural Importance*, Part 2. 491 (Oxford: Pergamon Press)
14. Blaxter, K. L. (1971). Methods of measuring the energy metabolism of animals and interpretation of the results obtained. *Fed. Proc.*, **30**, 1436
15. Morhardt, J. E. and Morhardt, S. S. (1971). Correlations between heart rate and oxygen consumption in rodents. *Amer. J. Physiol.*, **221**, 1580
16. Webster, A. J. F. (1967). Continuous measurement of heart rate as an indicator of the energy expenditure of sheep. *Brit. J. Nutr.*, **21**, 769
17. Franklin, D. L., Watson, N. W., Pierson, K. E. and Van Citters, R. L. (1966). Technique for radiotelemetry of blood flow from unrestrained animals. *Amer. J. Med. Electron.*, **5**, 24
18. Corbett, J. L., Farrell, D. J., Leng, R. A., McClymont, G. L. and Young, B. A. (1971). Determination of the energy expenditure of penned and grazing sheep from estimates of carbon dioxide entry rate. *Br. J. Nutr.*, **26**, 277
19. Strunk, T. H. (1971). Heat loss from a Newtonian animal. *J. Theoret. Biol.*, **33**, 35
20. Burton, A. C. and Edholm, O. G. (1955). *Man in a cold environment*, (London: Edward Arnold Ltd.)
21. Joyce, J. P., Blaxter, K. L. and Park, C. (1966). The effect of air movement, air temperature and infrared radiation on the energy requirements of sheep. *Res. Vet. Sci.*, **7**, 342
22. Webster, A. J. F., Hicks, A. M. and Hays, F. L. (1969). Cold climate and cold temperature induced changes in the heat production and thermal insulation of sheep. *Can. J. Physiol. Pharmacol.*, **47**, 553
23. Carlson, L. D. and Hsieh, A. C. L. (1965). Cold. *The Physiology of Human Survival*, 15 (O. G. Edholm and A. L. Bacharach editors) (London: Academic Press)
24. Hammel, H. T. (1964). Terrestrial animals in cold: recent studies of primitive man. *Adaptation to the Environment*, Sec. **4**, 413 (D. B. Dill, editor) (Washington: Amer. Physiol. Soc.)
25. Mount, L. E. (1964). The tissue and air components of themal insulation in the new-born pig. *J. Physiol. (London)*, **170**, 286
26. Webster, A. J. F. (1970). Direct effects of cold weather on the energetic efficiency of beef production in different regions of Canada. *Can. J. Anim. Sci.*, **50**, 563
27. Scholander, P. F., Hock, R., Walters, V. and Irving, L. (1950). Adaptation to cold in arctic and tropical mammals and birds in relation to body temperature, insulation and basal metabolic rate. *Biol. Bull.*, **99**, 259
28. Scholander, P. F., Walters, V., Hock, R. and Irving, L. (1950). Body insulation of some arctic and tropical mammals and birds. *Biol. Bull*, **99**, 225
29. Joyce, J. P. and Blaxter, K. L. (1965). The effect of wind on heat losses of sheep. *Energy Metabolism*, E.A.A.P., **11**, 355 (K. L. Blaxter, editor) (London: Academic Press)
30. Mitchell, D., Wyndham, C. H., Vermeulen, A. J., Hodgson, T., Atkins, A. R. and Hofmeyr, H. S., (1969). Radiant and convective heat transfer of nude man in dry air. *J. Appl. Physiol.*, **26**, 111
31. Swinbank, W. C. (1963). Long wave radiation from clear skies. *Quart. J. Roy. Meteorol. Soc.*, **381**, 339

32. Webster, A. J. F. (1971). Prediction of heat losses from cattle exposed to cold outdoor environments. *J. Appl. Physiol.*, **30**, 684.
33. Burton, A. C., Snyder, P. A. and Leach, W. G. (1955). Damp cold versus dry cold. Specific effects of humidity on heat exchange of unclothed man. *J. Appl. Physiol.*, **18**, 269
34. Iampetro, P. F. and Buskirk, E. R. (1960). Effects of high and low humidity on heat exchanges of lightly clothed men. *J. Appl. Physiol.*, **15**, 212
35. Passmore, R. and Durnin, J. V. G. A. (1955). Human energy expenditure. *Physiol. Rev.*, **35**, 801
36. Harper, H. A. (1969). *Review of Physiological Chemistry*, 508 (Los Altos, California: Large Medical Publications)
37. Milligan, L. P. (1971). Energetic efficiency and metabolic transformations. *Fed. Proc.*, **30**, 1454
38. Bligh, J. (1966). The thermosensitivity of the hypothalamus and thermoregulation in mammals. *Biol. Rev.*, **41**, 317
39. Keatinge, W. R. and Nadel, J. R. (1965). Immediate respiratory response to sudden cooling of the skin. *J. Appl. Physiol.*, **20**, 65
40. Hammel, H. T. (1968). Regulation of internal body temperature. *Ann. Rev. Physiol.*, **30**, 641
41. Simon, E., Rautenberg, W. and Jessen, C. (1965). Initiation of shivering in un-anaesthetised dogs by local cooling within the vertebral canal. *Experientia*, **21**, 476
42. Rawson, P. O. and Quick, P. (1970). Evidence of deep-body thermoreceptor response to intraabdominal heating of the ewe. *J. Appl. Physiol.*, **28**, 813
43. Hensel, H. and Zotterman, Y. (1951). The response of the cold receptors to constant cooling. *Acta. Physiol. Scand.*, **22**, 96
44. Hardy, J. D. (1961). Physiology of temperature regulation. *Physiol. Rev.*, **41**, 521
45. Jansky, L. (1970). *Non shivering thermogenesis*, (Swets and N. V. Zeitlinger editor) (Amsterdam)
46. Lindberg, O. (1970). *Brown adipose tissue*, (New York: Elsevier Publishing Co. Inc.)
47. Hemingway, A. (1963). Shivering. *Physiol. Rev.*, **43**, 397
48. Cottle, W. H. and Carlson, L. D. (1954). Adaptive changes in rats exposed to cold. Caloric exchange. *Amer. J. Physiol.*, **178**, 305
49. Hsieh, A. C. L. and Carlson, L. D. (1957). Role of adrenaline and noradrenaline in chemical regulation of heat production. *Amer. J. Physiol.*, **190**, 247
50. Guttman, L., Silver, J. and Wyndham, C. H. (1958). Thermoregulation in spinal man. *J. Physiol. (London)*, **142**, 406
51. Chatonnet, J. (1959). Sur l'origine de la chaleur libérée dans la régulation chimique de la température. *J. Physiol. (Paris)*, **51**, 319
52. Glickman, N., Mitchell, H. H., Keeton, R. W. and Lambert, E. H. (1967). Shivering and heat production in men exposed to intense cold. *J. Appl. Physiol.*, **22**, 1
53. Alexander, G. (1962). Temperature regulation in the new-born lamb. V. Summit metabolism. *Aust. J. agric. Res.*, **13**, 100
54. Lardy, H. and Wellman, H. (1952). Oxidative phosphorylations: Role of inorganic phosphate and acceptor systems in control of metabolic rates. *J. Biol. Chem.*, **195**, 215
55. Prusiner, S. and Poe, M. (1970). Thermodynamic considerations of mammalian heat production. *Brown adipose tissue*, 263 (O. Lindberg, editor) (New York: Amer. Elsevier Publishing Co. Inc.)
56. Iversen, L. L. (1967). *The uptake and storage of noradrenaline in sympathetic nerves*, (London: Cambridge University Press)
57. Himms-Hagen, Jean (1967). Sympathetic regulation of metabolism. *Pharmacol. Rev.*, **19**, 367
58. American Society of Pharmacology and exp. Therapeutics (1970). Adrenergic receptors mediating metabolic responses. *Fed. Proc.*, **29**, 1350
59. Ahlquist, R. P. (1967). Development of the concept of alpha and beta adrenotropic receptors. *Ann. N. Y. Acad. Sci.*, **139**, 549
60. Himms-Hagen, Jean (1970). Adrenergic receptors for metabolic responses in adipose tissue. *Fed. Proc.*, **29**, 1388
61. Hertelendy, F., Takahashi, K., Machlin, L. J. and Kipnis, D. M. (1970). The effect of chronic adrenergic blockade on the inhibition by epinephrine of growth hormone and insulin release in sheep. *Horm. Metabol. Res.*, **2**, 257

62. Horwitz, B. A., Horowitz, J. M. and Smith, R. Em. (1969). Norepinephrine-induced depolarisation of brown fat cells. *Proc. Nat. Acad. Sci.*, **64**, 113
63. Hayward, J. S. (1968). The magnitude of noradrenaline-induced thermogenesis in the bat (*Myotis lucifugus*) and its relation to arousal from hibernation. *Can. J. Physiol. Pharmacol.*, **46**, 713
64. Pohl, H. and Hart, J. S. (1965). Thermoregulation and cold acclimation in a hibernator *Citelus tridecemlineatus. J. Appl. Physiol.*, **20**, 398
65. Jansky, L. and Hart, J. S. (1963). Participation of skeletal muscle and kidney during, non-shivering thermogenesis in cold-acclimated rats. *Can. J. Biochem. Physiol.*, **41**, 953
66. Heim, T. and Hull, D. (1966). The effect of propranolol on the calorigenic response in brown adipose tissue of new-born rabbits to catecholamines, glucagon, cortico-trophin and cold exposure. *J. Physiol. (London)*, **187**, 271
67. Thompson, G. E. and Jenkinson, D. Mc.E (1969). Nonshivering thermogenesis in the newborn lamb. *Can. J. Physiol. Pharmacol.*, **47**, 249
68. Estler, C. J. and Ammon, H. P. (1969). The importance of the adrenergic beta-receptors for thermogenesis and survival of acutely cold-exposed mice. *Can. J. Physiol. Pharmacol.*, **47**, 427
69. Hittelman, K. J. and Lindberg, O. (1970). Fatty acid uncoupling in brown fat mito-chondria. *Brown adipose tissue*, 245 (O. Lindberg, editor) (New York: Amer. Elsevier Publishing Co. Inc.)
70. Girardier, L., Seydoux, J. and Clausen, T. (1968). Membrane potential of brown adipose tissue. A suggested mechanism for the regulation of thermogenesis. *J. Gen. Physiol.*, **52**, 925
71. Himms-Hagen, Jean (1969). The role of brown adipose tissue in the calorigenic effect of adrenaline and noradrenaline in cold acclimated rats. *J. Physiol. (London)*, **205**, 393
72. Mejsnar, J. and Jansky, L. (1971). Means of noradrenaline action during non-shivering thermogenesis in a single muscle. *Int. J. Biometeor.*, **15**, 321
73. Webster, A. J. F., Heitman, J. H., Hays, F. L. and Olynyk, G. P. (1969). Catechol-amines and cold thermogenesis in the sheep. *Can. J. Physiol. Pharmacol.*, **47**, 719
74. Gale, C. C., Jobin, M., Notter, D. and Fox, H. (1970). Endocrine thermoregulatory responses to local hypothalamic cooling in unanaesthetised baboons. *Amer. J. Physiol.*, **219**, 193
75. Gale, C. C., Muramoto, K., Toivola, P. T. K. and Stiner, D. (1972). Sympathetic control of substrates and thermogenesis during central cooling. *Int. J. Biometeorol.*, **15**, 162
76. Ellaway, P. H. and Pascoe, J. E. (1968). Noradrenaline as a transmitter in the spinal cord. *J. Physiol. (London)*, **197**, 8P
77. Maxwell, D. R. and Sumpter, E. A. (1972). Noradrenergic receptors and the control of fusimotor activity. *J. Physiol. (London)*, **222**, 173P
78. Anderson, B., Brook, A. H., Gale, C. C. and Hökfelt, B. (1964). The effect of a ganglionic blocking agent on the thermoregulatory response to preoptic cooling. *Acta. Physiol. Scand.*, **61**, 393
79. Harrison, T. S. (1964). Adrenal medullary and thyroid relationships. *Physiol. Rev.*, **44**, 161
80. Heroux, O. (1969). Catecholamines, corticosteroids and thyroid hormones in non-shivering thermogenesis under different environmental conditions. *Physiology and Pathology of Adaptation Mechanisms*, 347 (E. Bajusz, editor) (London: Pergamon Press)
81. Andersson, B., Ekman, L., Hökfelt, B., Jobin, M., Olsson, K. and Robertshaw, D. (1967). Studies of the importance of the thyroid and the sympathetic system in the defence to cold of the goat. *Acta. Physiol. Scand.*, **69**, 111
82. Boulouard, R. (1963). Effects of cold and starvation on adrenocortical activity of rats. *Fed. Proc.*, **22**, 750
83. Panaretto, B. A. and Vickery, M. R. (1970). The rates of plasma cortisol entry and clearance in sheep before and during their exposure to a cold, wet environment. *J. Endocrinol.*, **47**, 273
84. Selye, H. (1950). Stress. The physiology and pathology of exposure to stress. *Acta. Montreal*

85. Whittow, G. C. (1962). The significance of the extremities of the ox (*Bos taurus*) in thermoregulation. *J. Agric. Sci.*, **58**, 109
86. Bazett, H. C., Mendelson, E. S., Love, L. and Libet, B. (1948). Precooling of blood in the arteries, effective heat capacity and evaporative cooling as factors modifying cooling of the extremities. *J. Appl. Physiol.*, **1**, 169
87. Scholander, P. F. and Scheville, W. F. (1955). Counter current vascular heat exchange. *J. Appl. Physiol.*, **8**. 279
88. Edwards, M. A. (1967). The role of arteriovenous anastomoses in cold induced vasodilatation, rewarming and reactive hyperaemia as determined by [24]Na clearance. *Can. J. Physiol. Pharmacol.*, **45**, 39
89. Grant, R. T. (1930). Observations on direct communication between arteries and veins in the rabbits ear. *Heart*, **15**, 281
90. Grant, R. T. and Bland, E. F. (1931). Observations on arteriovenous anastomoses in human skin and in the birds foot with special reference to the reaction to cold. *Heart*, **15**, 385
91. Lopez-Majano, V., Rhodes, B. A. and Wagner, H. N. (1969). Arterio-venous shunting in extremities. *J. Appl. Physiol.*, **27**, 782
92. Molyneux, G. S. (1965). Observations on the structure, distribution and significance of arteriovenous anastomoses in sheep skin. *Biology of the Skin and Hair Growth*, (A. G. Lyne and B. F. Short, editors) (New York: Amer. Elsevier Publishing Co. Inc.)
93. Spence, R. J., Rhodes, B. A. and Wagner, H. N. (1972). Regulation of arterio-venous anastomotic and capillary blood flow in the dog leg. *Amer. J. Physiol.*, **222**, 326
94. Greenfield, A. D. M. and Shepherd, J. T. (1950). A quantitative study of the response to cold of the circulation through the fingers of normal subjects. *Clin. Sci.*, **9**, 323
95. Edwards, M. and Burton, A. C. (1960). Correlation of heat output and blood flow in the finger, especially in cold induced vasodilatation. *J. Appl. Physiol.*, **15**, 201
96. Sejrsen, P. (1967). Diffusion processes invalidating the intraarterial Krypton-85 beta particle clearance method for measurement of skin blood flow in man. *Circulat. Res.*, **21**, 281
97. Sejrsen, P. (1969). Blood flow in cutaneous tissue in man studied by washout of radioactive Xenon. *Circulat. Res.*, **25**, 215
98. Greenfield, A. D. M. (1963). The circulation through the skin. *Handbook of Physiology*, Sec. 2. *Circulation* **2**, 1325 (W. F. Hamilton, editor) (Washington: Amer. Physiol. Soc.)
99. Lewis, T. (1930). Observations upon the reactions of the vessels of the human skin to cold. *Heart*, **15**, 177
100. Frolich, E. D. (1965). Vascular effects of the Krebs intermediate metabolites. *Amer. J. Physiol.*, **208**, 149
101. Hilton, S. M. (1962). Local mechanisms regulating peripheral blood flow. *Physiol. Rev.*, **42**, 265
102. Lewis, G. P. (1960). Active polypeptides derived from plasma proteins. *Physiol. Rev.*, **40**, 647
103. Meyer, A. A. and Webster, A. J. F. (1971). Cold induced vasodilatation in the sheep. *Can. J. Physiol. Pharmacol.*, **49**, 901
104. Rennie, D. W. (1962). Physical insulation of Korean diving women. *J. Appl. Physiol.*, **17**, 961
105. Wyndham, C. H., Williams, C. G. and Loots, H. (1968). Reactions to cold. *J. Appl. Physiol.*, **24**, 282
106. Irving, L., Peyton, L. J. and Monson, M. (1956). Metabolism and insulation of swine as bare skinned mammals. *J. Appl. Physiol.*, **9**, 421
107. Gonzalez-Jiminez, E. and Blaxter, K. L. (1962). The metabolism and thermal regulation of calves in the first month of life. *Br. J. Nutr.*, **16**, 199
108. Hays, F. L. and Webster, A. J. F. (1971). Effects of cold, eating, efferent nerve stimulation and angiotensin on heart rate in sheep before and after autonomic blockade. *J. Physiol.* (*London*) **216**, 21

3
Adaptation to Cold

A. J. F. WEBSTER
Rowett Research Institute, Aberdeen

3.1 INTRODUCTION

The capacity of the earth to sustain life is governed ultimately by the capacity of plants to fix solar energy. The long, cold and dark winters in the Arctic and Boreal regions of the globe limit severely the overall capacity of the land to sustain plant growth and stop growth altogether for periods of many months. Yet wherever plant life exists there exist animal species to harvest it. The Musk ox, for example, range the Arctic islands of Canada where the temperature only rises high enough to support plant growth for about 2–3 months a year. Even in southern Canada, cattle are raised for pleasure and profit in areas where the annual mean temperature is below 0 °C.

It goes without saying that the species of animals which are indigenous to the cold regions of the world are adapted to their physical environment, otherwise they would not continue to be there. This chapter deals mainly with adaptation of man and mammals to the direct effects of cold. It is important to emphasise however, that the more important effect of cold in limiting animal species is an indirect one: namely the limit it imposes on the food supply. When adequate food is available, the direct effects of winter do not constitute a major threat to the survival of Boreal species. Cold and starvation are however, comparable and additive stresses since the effect of both is to diminish the energy reserves of an animal, the former by increasing energy expenditure and the latter by reducing intake. Birds and mammals during a severe winter are therefore faced by two conflicting demands, the need to increase energy expenditure to maintain homeothermy in conditions where heat loss is excessive and the need to conserve energy until such time as the new growth of plant food begins.

Before considering in detail the physiology of adaptation to cold, it is necessary to introduce a few simple concepts concerning the type of adaptation to cold that best favours the survival and welfare of different species.

Heat loss from animals in cold environments is related to surface area. The capacity of an animal to produce heat and its reserves of heat and chemical energy are related more closely to body mass. The smaller an animal, the greater its surface area to mass ratio[1]. Generally therefore, the smaller the animal the more susceptible it is both to excessive heat loss and to exhaustion of its energy reserves. There are, moreover, obvious physical limits to the extent that small animals can increase their thermal insulation by growing a thicker coat[2]. On the other hand, small animals can create favourable microenvironments for themselves by building nests or burrows to protect themselves from the worst excesses of the winter weather.

Adaptation to cold in small mammals has taken two main forms. Hibernation, which may be defined as regulated hypothermia, has the effect of reducing both heat loss and food energy requirement and thus removes the need to leave a relatively comfortable burrow in search of food. The second characteristic of adaptation in small mammals is an increased capacity for cold thermogenesis. During arousal from hibernation or during a short sojourn out of the burrow in search of food, they must elevate heat production substantially in order to achieve or maintain body temperature high enough to support functional efficiency. During these periods, which must inevitably be brief, the need to maintain homeothermy overrides the need to conserve energy.

Winter presents different problems to larger mammals, which have a relatively larger mass to surface area ratio, a larger reserve of heat and chemical energy and a larger frame on which to hang a thick coat to provide thermal insulation. In species like the large Boreal ruminants, the moose and the caribou, the most severe natural cold stresses demand a relatively small metabolic response. However, these animals, by virtue of their size, are unable to obtain effective shelter from the weather and must expose themselves to the environment and seek food, often in very difficult circumstances throughout the winter. Thus in larger animals we find less evidence for adaptive changes designed to enhance cold thermogenesis and more evidence for insulative and other adaptive changes designed to promote energy conservation during the winter months.

Man is not quite such a special case as he might, at first sight, appear. The response of man to the stress of cold has been essentially cultural; the development of clothes, housing and heating designed to remove the stimuli to physiological adaptation. One might therefore expect to find evidence for physiological adaptation to cold only in certain primitive tribes and in those individuals in a modern community who, for economic or more bizarre reasons subject themselves to intensities of cold that most people are not prepared to tolerate. The most convincing evidence for physiological adaptation to cold in man does emerge from studies of primitive man[3], and, for example, polar explorers[4,5], Korean diving women[6] and North Atlantic fishermen[7]. Yet there are indications too that the domestic microenvironments selected by men are dictated as much by considerations of economics and fashion as by the fundamental laws of heat exchange. Burton and Edholm[8] in 1955 wrote that 'room temperature' for man meant, in the U.S.A. about 24 °C, in Britain about 18 °C and in one Russian paper about 12 °C! These so-called optimal temperatures may well have increased since this report. Within limits then, it seems that thermal comfort in man is determined as much by physiological adaptation to the environment which his culture has evolved, as by cultural adaptation to the heat exchanges determined by his anatomy and metabolism.

These opening generalisations concerning man and animals provoke one last flagrant oversimplification. The thermally comfortable environment for any animal is, within limits, the environment to which it has grown accustomed. The extent to which this statement holds true is a measure of the success achieved by an animal as a result of those physiological and behavioural changes invoked in adapting to its environment.

3.2 DEFINITIONS

So far adaptation has been used as a portmanteau word to include all changes which favourably effect the response of an individual or a species to the stress of cold. This conforms to the general definition of adaptation given by Hafez[9];

Adaptation (biological) refers to the morphological, anatomical, physiological, biochemical and behavioural characteristics of the animal which promote welfare and favour survival in a specific environment.

In an attempt to refine this definition for use in experimental biology, Hart[10] proposed that the term *Acclimatisation* should be used to describe physiological changes induced by 'a complex of factors such as seasonal and climatic changes', and *Acclimation* should describe changes induced by 'a single environmental factor, as in controlled experiments'. This is a helpful distinction which has come into general use. There has also been pressure to define adaptation more specifically as referring only to those heritable animal characteristics which favour survival of a population in a given environment[10-12]. I would personally prefer a different word for this phenomenon. It is not always possible to place a particular biological response categorically into any one of these three compartments. For this reason, I prefer to retain the term adaptation in its broadest sense for use on those occasions when it is impossible to be more specific.

Another important definition is that of *Habituation* which is a gradual quantitative change in response as a result of repeated stimulation. This has the effect of diminishing the physiological response to an incoming stimulus of constant intensity.

Other terms specific to cold physiology were defined in the preceding chapter.

3.3 METABOLIC ACCLIMATION TO CONTROLLED ENVIRONMENTS

In order to study a natural homeostatic mechanism it is often necessary to impose rather unnatural stimuli. Metabolic adaptation to cold has been studied most comprehensively in the laboratory rat by exposing it for a prolonged period of time to a constant air temperature of about 5 °C, which has the effect of keeping heat production permanently elevated above thermoneutral metabolic rate. In these highly artificial circumstances the term metabolic acclimation can be used. The extent to which this compares with acclimatisation to naturally occurring cold winter conditions will be considered later.

The two most obvious indices of acclimation in growing rats kept at 5 °C are that they gradually recover their normal rate of growth, and secondly that they are able to survive for a longer time exposure to an intolerably cold environment (−30 °C). These two criteria do not indicate what combination of mechanisms contributes to this increased cold tolerance. Clearly a recovery in weight gain can be attributed to increased appetite and thermal insulation. Prolonged survival at −30 °C can be attributed to any combination of increased thermoneutral metabolism, increased body weight and thermal insulation and increased summit metabolism.

In order to establish whether metabolic acclimation to cold *per se* has occurred in any animal as a result of prolonged continuous or intermittent exposure to low air temperatures, it is necessary to confirm beyond doubt that the effects of appetite on thermoneutral metabolic rate and the effects of thermal insulation on the response to a standard cold stress (exposure to −30 °C) are either accounted for, or preferably eliminated. In these circumstances metabolic acclimation to cold may be claimed if one or more of the following criteria are established.

(a) The capacity of the animal to elevate and sustain heat production during acute exposure to severe cold is enhanced.

(b) A change takes place in the site or the mechanism of cold thermogenesis or the substrates involved in that mechanism.

(c) The metabolic rate of the animal remains elevated even after the stress of cold is removed.

(d) The secretion and effects of those hormones which influence, directly or indirectly the metabolic response to cold undergo a gradual change.

This last criterion is considered first since one would expect it to influence the other three.

3.3.1 Endocrine changes

About 10 y ago the case for an increased role for the thyroid, and the adrenal cortex and medulla in metabolic acclimation to cold in the laboratory rat appeared to be reasonably well proven[13]. Since that time however, confusion has increased rather than diminished.

Table 3.1 attempts to summarise how things stood in 1964 and in 1972. In 1964 it had been established that when rats were continuously exposed to about 5 °C, urinary excretion of catecholamines initially showed a sharp increase and then a slow decline (excretion still being slightly elevated 100 days after the onset of cold exposure)[14]. An increased thermogenic response to noradrenaline injection developed over about 5 weeks and persisted throughout the duration of cold exposure[15, 16]. The thyroid and adrenal cortex hypertrophied during the first 1–3 weeks but tended to return to more normal weights after 1–2 months[17, 18]. Plasma protein bound iodine levels and thyroid secretion rates were reported to reach peak values within 1–3 weeks and remain high as long as the cold exposure persisted[19-21]. Plasma corticosteroids increased to peak values within 30 min of exposure to cold but returned to normal within about 30 days[21-23].

The most reasonable interpretation of these observations was that the sympathoadrenal system was essential to the metabolic response to cold at all times. During the early 'alarm' phase of cold exposure the adrenal cortex played a major permissive role in the mobilisation of substrates required for cold thermogenesis, but as metabolic acclimation to cold progressed the role of the adrenal cortex diminished as the activity of the thyroid increased. Hyperthyroidism potentiated the thermogenic effects of the catecholamines[24] and increased thermoneutral metabolic rate[13]. Substitution of increased thyroid activity for adrenocortical activity was considered to be a major criterion of acclimation to cold.

Nearly all the experiments quoted above involved young rats continuously exposed to air temperatures about 5 °C and offered standard commercial diets *ad lib*. One problem arising from this apparently reasonable experimental design is that the intensity of cold experienced by the animals steadily decreases. Growing rats, eating food *ad lib* and gaining weight steadily during prolonged exposure to a steady air temperature increase thermoneutral metabolic rate as a result of increased food intake and increase thermal insulation as they fatten and as their mass to surface area ratio increases. Attempts to evaluate long-term changes in hormonal response to the stress of cold are confounded by the fact that the stimulus of cold at the end is much less than it was at the beginning.

Increased secretion of catecholamines is an immediate response to acute cold. The decline in urinary excretion of noradrenaline with prolonged exposure[14] can be attributed to the diminishing intensity of cold. It has not

76

Table 3.1 Endocrine changes reported to occur in laboratory rats during prolonged exposure to continuous cold (0–5 °C)

	Before 1964			1964-1972			
	Elevation	Time to peak	Persistence	Elevation	Time to peak	Persistence	Remarks
Catecholamine excretion secretion synthesis	+++	<1 day	Slow decline[14]	+++ +++ ++	8 h 8 h 8 h	Slow decline[25]	Slow decline in secretion and excretion probably due to diminishing intensity of cold
Thermogenic effect of noradrenaline	+++	3–4 weeks	Throughout[15,16]	+++		Throughout	
Thyroid weight	++		<60 d[17,20]	Inconsistent[31,32]			Changes dominated by dietary intake of iodine[32]
Secretion rate	++	7–21 days	Throughout[17,20]				
Plasma protein bound iodine	++		Throughout				
Plasma TSH				++	6 h	<1 day[33]	
Adrenal cortex weight	++	14 days	ca. 30 days[17,18]	++	7–10 days	ca. 30 days[21]	Increased adrenocortical activity while rat is in negative energy balance[32]
Plasma corticosteroids	++	30 min	10–30 days[22]	++	<3 days	18 days[23]	

been established whether a gradual change would take place in secretion of catecholamines if rats were chronically exposed to cold of constant intensity, i.e. the case for a change in catecholamine release during cold acclimation is not proven. Shum, Johnson and Flattery[25] estimated rates of synthesis, secretion and excretion of catecholamines from urinary excretion of their different metabolites. Secretion and excretion of catecholamines were elevated about six times during the first 6 days of exposure. Catecholamine synthesis, which normally greatly exceeds secretion rate, was elevated about threefold.

The gradual development of an enhanced thermogenic response to noradrenaline, which has been linked to the gradual increase in mass of brown adipose tissue[26, 27], is undoubted evidence for metabolic acclimation to cold but is, of course, restricted to those species which possess brown fat.

Boulouard[22, 23] showed that in rats adrenal cortex secretion rate *in vitro* and plasma corticosteroids *in vivo* were only elevated while the animals were in negative energy balance. If food intake was restricted, so that rats continued to lose weight in the cold plasma corticosteroids remained high. As soon as weight gain resumed they returned to normal values. This confirms other observations that caloric deficiency is a very potent stimulus to increased activity of the adrenal cortex[28, 29]. Gradual changes in adrenocortical function in rats chronically exposed to cold cannot be construed either as evidence of metabolic acclimation to cold *per se*.

The thyroid story is not at all clear at the present time. What can be said with reasonable certainty is that the earlier allegations of an increased turnover of thyroid hormones in rats chronically exposed to cold can be attributed for the most part to their increased intake of commercial rat diets which are very rich in iodine. Rates of thyroxine secretion, excretion and faecal elimination have all been shown to be closely related to iodine intake and the fibre content of the diet[30, 31]. In experiments where low bulk diets containing controlled levels of iodine were fed to rats chronically exposed to cold, changes in thyroid secretion rate have been inconsistent[31, 32]. Plasma levels of thyrotropin apparently are only elevated during the first 6 h of exposure to cold in the rat[33].

Moreover, the two main roles suggested for the thyroid in acclimation to cold now seem to be in dispute. Increased sensitivity to the direct thermogenic effects of the catecholamines develops quite normally in thyroidectomised rats maintained on constant levels of thyroxine[34]. Rats maintained on a low constant iodine intake which show no increase in thyroxine secretion rate still demonstrate some increase in thermoneutral metabolic rate following acclimation to cold although it is probably less than in animals receiving high iodine intake[31]. Normal thyroid status is essential to ensure the proper actions of catecholamines in mediating the metabolic response to acute or chronic cold exposure[35], but the evidence in support of the popular assumption that increased thyroid activity is an integral part of the normal process of adaptation to cold is weak, and the evidence to the contrary is getting stronger.

One may conclude therefore that, with the single and conspicuous exception of increased sensitivity to the thermogenic effect of noradrenaline, there is very little evidence to suggest that metabolic acclimation to cold in the rat involves significant changes in the secretion and effects of those hormones that regulate energy metabolism.

Our knowledge of changes in thyroid and adrenal activity accompanying metabolic acclimation to cold in large mammals like man and, for example, the large ungulates, is not very far beyond that which was known about the rat 10 years ago[36-38]. Catecholamine excretion is undoubtedly elevated during acute and chronic cold exposure[39], but while some workers have claimed a small direct thermogenic effect of noradrenaline[49], there is no indication that the magnitude of this response changes to a physiologically significant extent during cold acclimation[39]. In mammals without brown fat therefore there is, as yet, no good evidence for any gradual change in the secretion or the effectiveness of hormones as a result of metabolic acclimation to cold.

3.3.2 Non-shivering cold thermogenesis

This heading, for reasons of brevity, resurrects a title that I tried to lose in the previous chapter. Here non-shivering cold thermogenesis (NST) refers specifically to what is more correctly called catecholamine mediated, regulatory non-shivering cold thermogenesis, a phrase which is correct but convoluted. The mechanism of NST was discussed in detail in the last chapter. Four important points need to be restated.

(a) The capacity of paralysed rats to increase heat production during cold stress increases following acclimation.

(b) The direct thermogenic effect of noradrenaline increases following cold acclimation.

(c) NST and the thermogenic response to noradrenaline are abolished by adrenergic β blockers such as propranolol.

(d) The magnitude of NST is proportional to the amount of brown adipose tissue (BAT) that is present, although BAT cannot be considered the sole site of NST.

The physiological consequences to the rat of the development of noradrenaline induced NST during cold acclimation are twofold. Firstly, under conditions of severe cold stress, NST is additional to shivering thermogenesis, i.e. summit metabolism is increased. Cold acclimated rats can survive, on average, 200 min at $-40\,°C$; warm acclimated rats have a comparable survival time at $-20\,°C$[41, 42]. This increased tolerance of severe cold cannot be attributed entirely to NST, since, as Leblanc[43] has shown, rats acclimated to intermittent periods of severe cold stress increase survival time without increasing NST. Nevertheless, the enhanced NST of rats acclimated to continuous cold is undoubtedly the major contributor to their improved tolerance to a severe cold stress.

The second consequence of the development of NST is that, in conditions of moderate cold, NST substitutes altogether for shivering thermogenesis[44]. Cold acclimated guinea-pigs have approximately the same critical temperature (25 °C) as warm acclimated animals. At air temperatures below 25 °C heat production is elevated. Shivering, as indicated by electromyography, increases progressively at air temperatures below 25 °C in warm acclimated animals but does not occur until air temperature falls to about 15 °C, 10 °C below critical in cold acclimated animals, by which time in this species, NST is operating to its maximum capacity. Bruck[44] poses therefore the fascinating question, 'How it is possible that NST is elicited to its full extent before the second mechanism of heat production, shivering is evoked ?'. His own solution to this question depends upon his own demonstration that physiologically significant thermoreceptors are situated not only in the skin and hypothalamus but also in the cervical spinal cord. The threshold for NST in the guinea-pig depends on the balance between hypothalamic temperature and skin temperature which can best be described by a hyperbola (Figure 3.1a). Shivering, he contends, depends not so much on the balance between hypothalamic and skin temperature as on that existing between the temperatures in the skin and in the cervical spinal cord (Figure 3.1b). As a result of cold acclimation, the hyperbola describing the threshold for shivering is shifted downwards and to the left so that the stimulus necessary to induce shivering is greater in cold acclimated guinea-pigs. This latter observation suggests to me a habituation response. The more important observation made by Bruck is that the sites of NST in the interscapular and cervical brown fat are ideally suited to the convection of heat direct to the cervical spinal cord. The main reason why NST suppresses and therefore substitutes for shivering is that the blood leaving the brown fat heats the central receptors responsible for initiating the shivering response.

Non-shivering thermogenesis is probably a more efficient mechanism than shivering for increasing heat production in the cold. The muscular tremor of shivering undoubtedly increases convective heat losses from the body surface and may interfere with normal movement. Efferent blood from brown fat pads carries heat not only to the cervical spinal cord but also flows in close proximity to the arteries leaving the heart[45]. Rapid heat exchange may therefore take place between brown fat and the systemic circulation. It must, of course, be remembered that the greater part of NST is almost certainly generated in tissues other than brown fat.

3.3.3 Acclimation in man and large animals

This section again considers only those metabolic changes which might occur as a result of prolonged continuous, or repeated intermittent exposure of man and large animals to cold in the controlled conditions of a climatic laboratory. The multitude of studies on acclimatisation of man to polar and other such robust natural environments will be considered later. When tested against the four criteria listed earlier, the evidence for metabolic acclimation to cold in man becomes tenuous indeed.

Davis[46] exposed men to a moderate cold stress for 8 h/day for 31 days. The increase in heat production was the same during each successive exposure to cold in the group tested in March. However, the intensity of shivering as measured by electromyography diminished considerably, suggesting that a form of non-shivering cold thermogenesis had developed. Men tested in the autumn showed a gradual diminution in the metabolic response to the cold stress, i.e. a habituation response which will be discussed later. Nobody showed any changes in basal metabolic rate (measured at thermoneutrality) during the period of either trial.

Joy[40] investigated whether the same acclimation procedure would effect the response of men to infusion of noradrenaline. He claimed that noradrenaline elevated heat production slightly (10–15%) in cold acclimated individuals

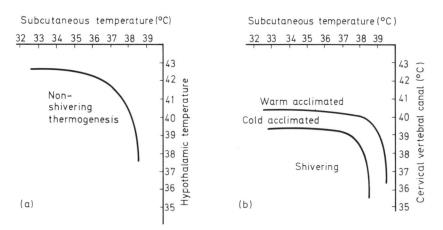

Figure 3.1 Thresholds for shivering and non-shivering thermogenesis in the guinea-pig.
(a) threshold sensation for non-shivering thermogenesis based on receptors in the skin and in the hypothalamus
(b) threshold sensation for shivering in warm and cold acclimated guinea-pigs based on receptors in the skin and in the cervical vertebral canal (from Bruck[44], by courtesy of Elsevier Publications, London)

only. His results, which have not been repeated, suggest that noradrenaline mediated non-shivering cold thermogenesis might develop in man as a result of cold acclimation. Even if this is so, the magnitude of the response was very small, certainly far too small to account for the amount of cold thermogenesis which Davis claimed was produced in acclimated men by a mechanism other than shivering. The diminution in the shivering record during repeaten exposures to cold cannot be taken as firm evidence that a change had taked place in the site or the biochemical reactions involved in cold thermogenesis. Unless firmer evidence appears to the contrary, we can assume that cold thermogenesis in warm and cold acclimated men occurs almost exclusively in muscle in response to stimuli transmitted by the somatic motor nerves.

In sheep, shivering does not diminish during prolonged exposure to cold of constant intensity[47]. Moreover, cold acclimated sheep do not differ from warm acclimated animals in their response to noradrenaline (there is no direct thermogenic effect in either case) or to β- adrenergic blockade with propranolol[39]. The evidence strongly supports the contention that noradrenaline mediated NST does not occur in sheep, except in the young lamb, which contains brown fat in the first few days of life[48] and may retain it for some weeks if exposed to cold continuously[49]. The results with sheep support the general contention that NST cannot occur unless brown fat is present. To an environmental physiologist man is more like a sheep than a rat; comparable in size, comparably dressed and possessing brown fat only at birth. It is less outrageous to deduce that man does not exhibit NST because the sheep does not, than to deduce that he must because it occurs in the rat.

Changes in thermoneutral metabolic rate accompanying acclimation to cold are, of course confounded by changes in food intake. Basal metabolic rate, which excludes the effect of food intake, did not change during cold acclimation in man[46]. Other studies which deal with acclimatisation of men to cold environments will be discussed later. Sykes and Slee[47] obtained indirect evidence to suggest that thermoneutral metabolic rate might increase in sheep on constant food intake following acclimation to cold, and we observed increases in thermoneutral metabolic rate in cold acclimated sheep that could not be accounted for by measured differences in food consumption[50]. On balance the evidence favours a slight increase in thermoneutral metabolic rate in large mammals as a direct consequence of acclimation to cold, although this cannot necessarily, for the reasons given earlier, be linked to increased thyroid activity.

In 1969 we published a preliminary observation that phenoxybenzamine, an a- adrenergic blocking agent, markedly diminished the capacity of warm acclimated sheep to withstand a severe cold stress but had no inhibitory effect on cold thermogenesis in cold acclimated animals[39]. These observations have very recently been confirmed and extended (Heitman, unpublished observations). The effects of phenoxybenzamine on warm acclimated sheep were to induce marked peripheral vasodilatation which increased heat loss, and to reduce heat production so that the treated animals failed to maintain homeothermy at $-30\,°C$ (Figure 3.2). Plasma free fatty acid and glucose concentrations were higher in treated than in untreated animals suggesting that the block was not at the level of substrate mobilisation. In the last chapter I suggested that phenoxybenzamine might inhibit shivering by interfering with the fusimotor nervous control of the muscle spindles.

Cold acclimated sheep exposed to $-30\,°C$ responded exactly the same as warm acclimated animals when phenoxybenzamine was not administered. When exposed to severe cold after receiving 3 mg/kg phenoxybenzamine, they apparently exhibited as much peripheral vasodilatation as the warm acclimated animals (indicated in Figure 3.2 by ear skin temperature), but were able to maintain homeothermy in spite of this increased heat loss by elevating heat production even higher than the untreated animals. Plasma concentrations of glucose and free fatty acids were unaffected by phenoxybenzamine treatment.

If the hypothesis that phenoxybenzamine blocks shivering is correct, then the resistance of cold acclimated sheep to the effects of the drug suggests that they have substituted for shivering some other form of cold thermogenesis. This is perhaps the same form of acclimation as observed in human subjects[36, 46] who shivered progressively less during repeated exposures to cold of constant intensity. Since there is no reason to suppose that the biochemical basis of cold thermogenesis in man or the sheep alters during cold acclimation it is tempting to suppose that changes may take place in the somatic nervous system which replace the involuntary tremor of shivering by an increased

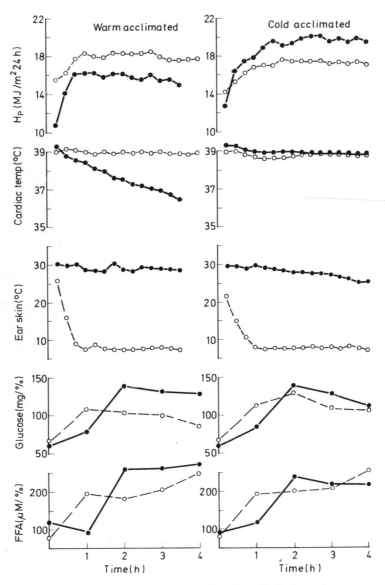

Figure 3.2 Effects of phenoxybenzamine (3 mg/kg i.v.) on the energy metabolism of warm and cold acclimated shorn sheep exposed to an air temperature of −30 °C. ○—○ (control animals) ●—● (treated animals) (Heitman and Webster, unpublished)

tonic contraction that is less dependent on rhythmic barrages of impulses in the fusimotor nerves.

3.4 ACCLIMATISATION TO NATURAL ENVIRONMENTS

So far we have considered the limited and rather academic question, 'Do the metabolic responses of an animal to cold alter during the course of a prolonged period of exposure to controlled low air temperatures in a laboratory?'. This section considers the more general question, 'Do animals acclimatise to naturally occurring winter conditions, and if so how?'. Acclimatisation here refers to any physiological change that improves cold tolerance. For each species under discussion therefore it is necessary to establish first whether its cold tolerance improves as the winter proceeds, and then analyse what metabolic, insulative, vasomotor, or behavioural changes contrive to bring about that acclimatisation.

3.4.1 Acclimatisation in small mammals

Heroux[51] compared patterns of morphological and physiological adjustments in white laboratory rats, exposed individually or in groups to continuous cold (acclimation) with those occurring in white rats wintered outside, or wild rats trapped in midwinter (acclimatisation) (Table 3.2).

Table 3.2 **Morphological and physiological adjustments in rats chronically exposed to cold in the laboratory, or to outdoor winter conditions compared, respectively, with rats kept warm indoors, or outdoors during the summer** (From Heroux[51], by courtesy of *Fed. Proc.*)

	White rats			*Wild rats*
Adjustments	*Constant low temperatures indoors*		*Seasonal variations outdoors*	*Seasonal variations outdoors*
	Isolated at $+6\,°C$	*Grouped at* $-10\,°C$	*Grouped exposure*	*Natural habitat*
Non-specific to the environment				
Survival time at $-38\,°C$	+++	+++	+++	+++
Summit metabolism	+++	+++	+++	+++
Non-shivering thermogenesis	+++	+++	+++	+++
Sensitivity to noradrenaline	+++	+++	+++	+++
Specific to a given environment				
Pelt insulation	0	0	+++	+++
Weights of pituitary, thyroid and adrenal	+++	0	0	0
Cold injuries	+++	0	0	0
Body growth	———	———	———	0
Thyroid secretion rate	+++	?	———	?
Thermoneutral metabolic rate (at $30\,°C$)	+++	+++	0	+++
Adrenal cortex secretion rate	0	0	+++	+++

Symbols: +++ increase (relative to warm groups); —, decrease; 0, no change; ?, not measured

The capacity of all groups to survive a standard cold stress (exposure to −35°C) was enhanced following acclimation or acclimatisation. All groups showed an elevated summit metabolism and an increased capacity for NST as indicated by their response to noradrenaline. The external insulation provided by the pelt increased in outdoor, acclimatised groups only. Cold injuries in the extremities were only observed in individually caged acclimated rats which were also the only group in which the weights of endocrine glands were persistently elevated. Thyroid secretion rate apparently increased only in the isolated, acclimated rats, although, as Heroux points out, this should probably be attributed in part to increased intake and faecal elimination of their high bulk, high iodine diet. Increases in thermoneutral metabolic rate, seen in all groups except the white rats kept outside, were not related to apparent changes in thyroid secretion rate. Adrenal cortex secretion rate was normal in the acclimated groups 30 days after the onset of cold exposure but remained elevated throughout the winter in the acclimatised rats[52].

These results suggest that increased cold tolerance in acclimated rats is accomplished by metabolic acclimation only; increased thermoneutral metabolic rate and NST. Acclimatisation to winter conditions enhances NST, may or may not alter thermoneutral metabolic rate, but also involves insulative and perhaps vasomotor adaptations designed to reduce total heat loss and to prevent cold injury respectively. By these criteria, acclimatised rats were more comprehensively cold tolerant than laboratory acclimated animals, even though they showed a persistent elevation in adrenal cortex secretion rate which might be taken as evidence of continued thermal stress[22, 29].

This distinction drawn by Heroux between the effects of acclimation and acclimatisation is extremely important and most convincing. One minor point of cavil is that it is not possible to say to what extent differences between groups may have been due to the different intensities of cold that each experienced. Although the isolated, acclimated rats were kept at an air temperature 16°C higher than the rats acclimated in groups, their high incidence of cold injuries and their hypertrophied endocrine glands suggest that they were colder in isolation than the rats indoors or out who spent the major part of the experiment huddled together in a slowly shifting heap of warm bodies.

Leblanc has demonstrated that rats[43] and mice[53] can acquire increased cold tolerance, as measured by survival time at −30°C and the incidence of cold injuries, following 15 exposures, of 10 min duration only, to −20°C over a period of 2-days. He called this form of increased tolerance, which is not accompanied by the development of an increased sensitivity to the thermogenic effect of noradrenaline, a habituation response and it seems likely that it may be an important contributor to the increased cold tolerance of rats exposed to the natural, fluctuating and unpredictable stresses of the winter.

Although not much is known about seasonal variations in the mass of brown adipose tissue in mammals such as bats, deer mice, and ground squirrels, which are adapted to areas where the winters are severe, it seems likely that the main period of development of BAT is the autumn[45] (September to November), before the time of most severe weather or the onset of hibernation. The availability of food to promote all forms of fat synthesis is high at this time. Acclimation studies with the white rat suggest that a period of prolonged cold exposure is necessary to stimulate development of BAT, although, as one might expect, a moderate intensity of cold that does not severely restrict normal weight gain is a more effective stimulus than severe cold[27]. The critical temperature of the deer mouse (*Peromyscus sp.*) in isolation is over 20 °C[54]. Species like *Peromyscus* and other small animals in their natural habitat, will therefore be cold nearly all the time, except perhaps in the height of summer, when brown fat development is at its least. By September the stimulus of cold will certainly be continuous and will increase in intensity until the depth of winter or the onset of hibernation. This natural stimulus to the development of BAT and NST is therefore not unlike that applied during acclimation experiments in the laboratory.

3.4.2 Acclimatisation in man

There is little doubt that men who, by choice or necessity, indulge in such rigorous pursuits as polar exploration, or deep sea fishing, can acquire an increased tolerance to cold. It is equally certain that men of certain racial groups who do not make use of clothing or shelter can tolerate cold to a far greater extent than the average citizen from the overdeveloped regions. Proof of acclimatisation to cold in man requires that one or more of the following criteria be satisfied:

(a) Increased thermoneutral metabolic rate, i.e. metabolic acclimatisation.

(b) Reduced heat loss at a given air temperature, i.e. increased tissue insulation.

(c) Decreased susceptibility to pain, numbness or cold injury in the extremities, i.e. vasomotor acclimatisation.

(d) Decreased cutaneous sensory threshold for cold thermogenesis, i.e. habituation.

The evidence for and against each of these criteria of acclimatisation in man is discussed below.

3.4.2.1 Changes in thermoneutral metabolism

The evidence relating to changes in thermoneutral metabolic rate (TMR) induced by exposure to naturally occurring conditions of cold is a mess. For a start, TMR and basal metabolic rate (BMR) are often considered as one and the same thing. The errors in this assumption were discussed in the last chapter. Most authors recognise that changes in the quantity and quality of food intake will alter TMR but the limited control that they are able to exercise over their experimental subjects prevents them from doing much about it. Studies in which food intake and composition were not recorded are worthless in this context. Studies in which a careful record was taken of food consumption, do not reveal any consistent variation in TMR during acclimatisation to cold[36,55]. Measurements of BMR, or true fasting metabolism, should, if made correctly, be independent of food intake. BMR has traditionally been linked with level of thyroid activity, and measurements of BMR of men with a history of exposure to cold have been intended to demonstrate a role for the thyroid in cold acclimatisation[36]. However, the recent careful studies with rats have not only thrown doubt on the hypothesis that thyroid activity perforce increases during acclimatisation to cold but also revealed that changes in thyroid activity and changes in TMR (and probably in BMR) are not necessarily related. At the moment it is not possible to reach any conclusions as to whether or not TMR alters in man as a consequence of acclimatisation. One might say, however, that a small increase in TMR would be of no particular adaptive significance to man in most naturally occurring situations of cold, since even primitive man, unlike the wild rat, is not normally exposed to cold for prolonged periods. An increase in TMR is an energetically wasteful process when cold stress is intermittent but calories are scarce.

3.4.2.2   *The skin and cutaneous circulation*

During acute exposure to cold, vasoconstriction reduces the flow of blood through the cutaneous circulation and thus reduces the convection of heat to the surface. This allows the temperature of the body 'shell' of superficial tissues to cool and increases tissue insulation. However, extreme cooling of the extremities such as the hands and feet brings discomfort, disability and the risk of cold injury. These can only be avoided if vasoconstrictor tone is relaxed. Vasomotor responses to cold are therefore designed to serve two conflicting objectives, the need to minimise heat loss and the need to maintain the integrity of the tissues.

It is known, for example, that deep sea fishermen can work with their hands immersed in water so cold that the hands of most people would, within minutes, be incapacitated by alternating bouts of numbness and pain. Clearly blood flow to the hands of these fishermen must be both more substantial and more regular than in more sheltered individuals; i.e. they must acclimatise to the local sensation of cold in the hands. In this case functional capacity has been enhanced at the expense of additional heat loss.

Some of the experimental evidence relating to local adaptive changes in the circulation to the hands of men with a history of cold exposure is summarised in Table 3.3. The response of different individuals to local cooling has classically been tested by the technique of immersing a finger or the entire hand into very cold water. Acclimatised individuals are better able to tolerate this test when assessed by such criteria as the sensation of pain or numbness, or manual dexterity[56]. This adaptation is apparent both in racial groups accustomed to local cold stress, such as the Eskimos[57,58] and Arctic Indians[59] and in such individuals as Gaspé fishermen[7,60], British fish filleters[61] and polar explorers[62,63]. Krog *et al.*[64] were unable to detect any difference in response to local cooling between Norwegian Lapps and Caucasian fishermen, although, as expected both groups tolerated the standard test better than Caucasian subjects who had no previous history of this type of cold stress. They concluded that tolerance to local cooling was acquired in each individual as a result of acclimatisation and was not an inborn racial characteristic.

Table 3.3 Temperature regulation in the hands of cold adapted racial groups and acclimatised workers compared with unadapted individuals

Subjects	Response to hand immersion in cold water				Response to noradrenaline	
	Hand skin temp	Heat loss/blood flow	'Hunting'	Systolic b.p. rise	Systolic b.p. rise	Skin temperature
Eskimos[57,58]	Higher	Marked increase	Greater fluctuations			
Arctic Indians[59]	Higher	Marked increase				
Lapps[64]	Not significantly higher					
Norwegian fishermen[64]		No change	Earlier onset			
Gaspé fishermen[7,60]	Higher	Increased	Earlier onset	Reduced		
Ama (Korean diving women)[6]	Higher	Reduced	Abolished	No change		
Polar explorers[4,62]				No change	Reduced	No change
US soldiers[40]	Higher				Reduced	No change

The mechanisms that underlie this form of acclimatisation are not known for sure. Most workers (Table 3.3) claimed that the temperature of the hand or finger during immersion in cold water is higher in acclimatised subjects although differences tended to be small. The duration of the initial period of maximum vasoconstriction prior to the onset of the first signs of cold induced vasodilatation (usually the first sharp temperature rise of the hunting response) was shorter in acclimatised subjects. Most studies also indicate that heat loss from the hands, which may be taken as an indicator of blood flow, was greater in acclimatised subjects, an observation which seems at first sight, self evident. However, a very recent study[6] has claimed that in the Ama (Korean diving woman), skin temperature in the hands and arms was maintained higher than in unadapted subjects without increasing total blood flow to the arm, because a relatively larger proportion of the total circulation returned through the veins directly under the skin.

The control of cold induced vasodilatation is still imperfectly understood (see previous chapter). It has been claimed that the development of local tolerance to the effects of cold in the hands and feet might be associated with a reduced sensitivity to the vasoconstrictor effects of noradrenaline[65]. This has been demonstrated in cold acclimated rabbits[66]. There is some evidence that following repeated exposure of men to cold, the rise in systolic blood pressure following the intravenous administration of noradrenaline is reduced[40, 62]. The rise in systolic blood pressure immediately following the shock of immersing a hand in cold water may also be reduced in acclimatised individuals[7, 60], although others have shown no effect[4, 6, 62] (Table 3.3).

Acclimatisation to intense local cooling therefore involves increased blood flow and increased heat loss. The reverse form of adaptation that might occur in the skin and cutaneous circulation, in response to general, moderate cooling is an increase in total tissue insulation brought about by structural changes in the skin, preferential deposition of subcutaneous fat, or by a reduction in total blood flow through the cutaneous circulation. There is no convincing reason to suppose that the structure of the skin of cold acclimatised people is in any way unusual. English channel swimmers carry large amounts of subcutaneous fat[67] but the Ama who doubtless spend at least as much time in the water as potential channel swimmers although eat considerably less, have comparable amounts of subcutaneous fat to domestic Korean women[3]. Changes in subcutaneous fat due to increased food intake again cannot be considered as a specific adaptation to the stress of cold.

It is however, quite reasonable to imagine that total blood flow through the superficial tissues during cold exposure might be reduced in acclimatised individuals, even while blood flow to specialised areas like the hands and feet is increased. Confirmation of this hypothesis is not however quite so straight-forward. Measurements of tissue insulation are only valid at thermal equilibrium, i.e. when all body temperatures have stabilised and heat loss and heat production are equal. Many measurements of tissue insulation based on respiratory calorimetry in man during exposure to a standard cold stress lasting only a few hours are not valid since the subjects were clearly not in thermal equilibrium. This point is discussed in Hammel's review[3]. However, there is good reason to suppose that Australian aborigines and Kalahari

bushmen who customarily go about naked and are mostly very thin by European standards have tissue insulations similar to, or a little higher than most
Europeans (Figure 3.3). Eskimos[68, 69] who are well clothed and well fed,
Arctic Indians rather less well clothed[69, 70], and Alacaluf Indians[70] of Tierra
del Fuego who formerly went about almost naked in a most miserable climate,
all had tissue insulation values comparable to Europeans of comparable
fatness. Tissue insulation in Ama is also no different from that in other Korean
women[3]. The highest tissue insulation values were recorded from very fat
whites[5, 71]. In no case was tissue insulation in a cold adapted race or cold

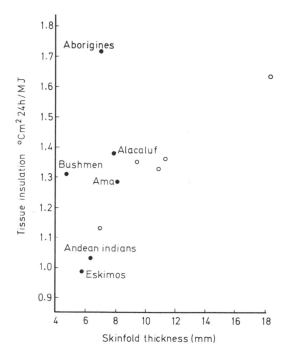

Figure 3.3 Tissue insulation in relation to
skinfold thickness. Open circles refer to Caucasians[3, 5, 68, 69, 70, 71]

acclimatised individual unusually high. In the aborigine and bushman however, tissue insulation appeared to be higher than one would expect from their
extreme lack of subcutaneous fat (Figure 3.3). It is possible that these groups
show a reduced cutaneous circulation as a result of acclimatisation to cold. It
may equally be a consequence of chronic undernutrition.

3.4.2.3 Habituation

When the sensation of cold is repeatedly applied, the physiological response
to that stimulus tends to diminish. The increased flow of blood to the hands
of a fisherman can be called a habituation response, in this case a diminution

in the sympathetic vasoconstrictor response to the sensation of cold in the hands. It cannot be attributed to an enhanced vasodilator response since there are no sympathetic vasodilator receptors in the skin[72].

There is also convincing evidence that the thermogenic response of man may habituate as a result of repeated cold stresses. The Australian aborigine traditionally slept in the open in conditions where heat loss exceeded thermoneutral metabolic rate[73]. Rectal temperature fell steadily and heat production rose slowly as they began to shiver while they slept. When unhabituated whites spent the night in comparable circumstances, they shivered violently, increased heat production and maintained rectal temperature but could not sleep. After some nights white men acquired the ability to sleep and shiver simultaneously, cold thermogenesis was reduced slightly and rectal temperature fell, although not to the same extent as in the aborigine[36, 74].

A gradual reduction in the magnitude and rate of development of the thermogenic response of men to a standard cold stress in the laboratory has been demonstrated following repeated exposures to cold[46] or alternate exposures to cold and to heat[75]. Similar responses have been observed in people accustomed to cold as a result of swimming[8], scuba diving[76], polar exploration[5] or even the less dramatically chilling conditions of a Northern urban winter[55, 77, 78].

In unhabituated men the rapid thermogenic response to a moderately cold sensation at the skin surface is usually sufficient to maintain rectal temperature constant. As habituation proceeds and the immediate thermogenic response to cold diminishes, deep body temperature falls, central cold receptors increasingly reinforce the cutaneous sensation of cold and the total incoming stimuli to cold thermogenesis eventually induce a thermogenic response sufficient to maintain homeothermy. The effect of habituation on the energy exchanges of a man during exposure to moderate cold is illustrated in Figure 3.4 which refers to a man having a body weight of 75 kg, a surface area of 1.62 m^2 and a maximum tissue insulation of $1.25 \degree C.m^2.24 \text{ h/MJ}$. The man is lying naked on a bed at an air temperature of $30 \degree C$. The insulation of the air interface is 1.65, his thermoneutral heat production is 300 kJ/h, his rectal temperature (T_R) $36.5 \degree C$ and his mean body temperature $(\bar{T}_B)$ $35.7 \degree C$ $(0.7 T_R + 0.3 T_s)[8]$. At time zero he is transferred to a room at $20 \degree C$. Heat loss (H_L) initially markedly exceeds heat production (H_P) but falls rapidly as the cutaneous vessels constrict and skin temperature falls. In the unhabituated individual heat production is rapidly elevated, rectal temperature is maintained and thermal equilibrium between heat production and heat loss is re-established within about 3 h, the body having lost about 400 kJ of heat. In the habituated individual heat production rises more slowly and rectal temperature falls $1.0 \degree C$. Thermal equilibrium is not re-established until about 5 h after the onset of cold stress and the drop in body heat content (H_s) is about 640 kJ, an amount equivalent to about 2 h heat production at thermoneutrality. At thermal equilibrium the increased cold tolerance resulting from habituation is quite small, a reduction in critical air temperature of about $2 \degree C$. The real significance of habituation appears in circumstances when the thermal demand of the environment only temporarily exceeds the threshold required to stimulate cold thermogenesis, e.g. during the night. In these circumstances the habituated man is able to conserve energy by relaxing homeothermy and incurring a relatively larger heat debt which can be repaid without the necessity to sustain cold thermogenesis when the sun comes up and the thermal demand of the environment is reduced.

The extreme example of habituation seen in the aborigine may reflect a racial adaptation to intermittent cold superimposed on the capacity of each individual to develop this form of physiological acclimatisation. It may also reflect acclimatisation to the combined stresses of cold and calorie deprivation, a situation similar to that faced by outwintered animals (q.v.). It has been suggested[79, 80] that hypothermia in old, and probably undernourished people might be due to an exaggeration of the normal physiological process of habituation to cold to the stage where it becomes detrimental to welfare; the old people become dangerously hypothermic without ever becoming aware that they are cold. This important possibility requires further investigation.

3.4.2.4 The integrated response

Hammel[3] suggested that acclimatisation to cold in man could take one of two forms. The Australian aborigine and Kalahari bushman, faced by the combined stresses of cold and food shortage show a hypothermic-insulative response; i.e. increased tissue insulation and a delayed thermogenic response to cold which together favour energy conservation at the expense of some loss of functional efficiency and manual dexterity due to central and local

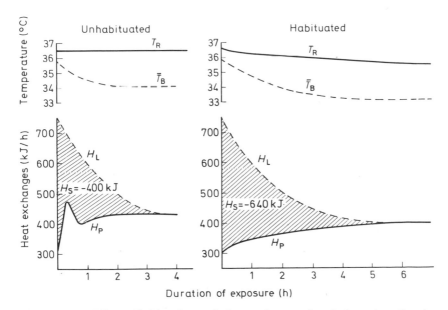

Figure 3.4 Effects of habituation on the heat exchanges of a naked man transferred from a temperature of 30 °C to 20 °C. H_P, H_L and H_S refer to heat production, loss and storage respectively. T_R is rectal temperature and $\bar{T}_B$, the average temperature of the tissues of the body (for further explanation see text)

cooling. The evidence at present suggests that *metabolic habituation* (what Hammel calls hypothermic acclimatisation) can develop to some extent in all individuals in appropriate circumstances, particularly when repeated cold stresses are applied at the time that the individual would normally expect to sleep. The capacity to sleep and shiver simultaneously is a clear indication of adaptation to cold.

The second physiological response, which Hammel called metabolic acclimatisation, is typified by the Eskimo, who eats well, has a high metabolic rate both in the cold and at thermoneutrality, but has a low tissue insulation, partly due to a relatively copious flow of blood through the extremities. Where cold stress is largely a local phenomenon affecting the extremities operator efficiency is preserved at the expense of a relatively high heat loss. Whether this second type of response, also seen in fishermen and others accustomed to severe local cooling, should be called metabolic acclimatisation is doubtful. The increased thermoneutral metabolic rate of these men in the cold is largely due to the inevitable biochemical consequences of increased food intake. Increased appetite in people exposed to cold is an adaptive response. An elevated thermoneutral metabolic rate that was not linked to increased food intake would have no adaptive significance to an individual exposed only intermittently to cold. On balance it would have a detrimental effect, expending calories unnecessarily, diminishing reserves of body fat and thereby reducing tissue insulation. The second type of response probably does not involve metabolic acclimatisation to cold at all, instead a diminished sympathetic vasoconstrictor response to local cooling. For this reason it might better be called *vasomotor habituation*.

3.4.3 Acclimatisation in domestic animals

Our knowledge of acclimatisation to cold in large domestic or wild mammals is much less than that which is known about man and small laboratory mammals like the laboratory rat. Most reviews[2, 10] describe field studies on winter survival in populations of large mammals and indicate how they adapt to cold by increasing the thermal insulation of the coat, adjusting the quality and quantity of food intake and by regulating the season of reproduction and the number of offspring born.

Laboratory experiments with large animals are not undertaken lightly. Nevertheless, the demands of the livestock industry for a better understanding of the effects of cold on the performance of domestic animals has prompted a number of studies with cattle, sheep and pigs. In this section, acclimatisation to cold in large mammals is considered almost entirely by reference to these three species, because they are economically important species in their own right and because their physiology is best understood (by me anyway).

Cattle, in common with most large mammals, have a thicker coat in the winter. Cattle breeds indigenous to the colder regions have longer shaggier coats than tropical and subtropical breeds. Although this suggests genetic adaptation, it certainly does not reflect natural selection since coat type in cattle, like every other criterion of type reflects the selection pressures of the owners rather than the animal population.

Growth of the coat in cattle[81] and sheep[82] is governed by daylight length, the most rapid growth occurring in the autumn when day length is decreasing and the rate of change of day length is at its greatest. Morris showed that growth of wool in sheep was unaffected by air temperatures ranging from moderate to hot, and we observed that total wool cover in sheep, and thus external insulation were the same whether the animals were kept indoors at 16 °C, outdoors during a Canadian winter at air temperatures from 0 °C to −40 °C or at a comparable intensity of cold indoors[50]. Thus hot or cold temperatures appear to have no effect on coat depth and external insulation in sheep. Decreasing day length in the autumn is the sole stimulus to increased wool growth and this has the effect of pre-adapting the animal to the cold stresses of the forthcoming winter. In the equatorial regions where there are no seasonal fluctuations in day length, the seasonal rhythm of wool growth disappears[82]. Whether the extreme fluctuations in day length in the polar regions would stimulate a greater total synthesis of wool per annum is not, I think, known.

Cattle grow thicker coats in the autumn, but, unlike most breeds of sheep, shed their winter coats each spring. Rate of hair growth in cattle has been shown to be related to photoperiod and yet it is common knowledge that cattle wintered outdoors have thicker coats than those kept inside. This suggests that cold stimulates hair growth in cattle. To test this assumption, we[81] measured total hair cover and growth of new hair in cattle kept indoors at 16 °C and wintered outdoors at air temperatures ranging from 0 °C to −40 °C. Total hair cover (mg/cm²) was measured by weighing the hair clipped from different sites at different times during the winter. Growth of new hair (mg/cm².24 h) was obtained by weighing clippings repeatedly made from the same site. We concluded that growth of new hair was inversely related to day length as expected (Figure 3.5), but was not influenced by acclimatisation to cold. Total hair cover was twice as great in the outwintered animals. Since cold had no effect on growth of new hair, we concluded that the effect of cold was to reduce shedding. This conclusion is reinforced by the familiar observation that thin, undernourished and therefore more cold sensitive cattle retain their winter coats much longer into the spring than well fed, sleeker animals.

The hair coat of pigs is sparse and effectively useless as a source of thermal insulation. Nevertheless, pigs raised in the cold are conspicuously hairier than those raised at thermoneutrality[83, 84]. Whether this is a function of increased growth, reduced shedding or both is not known.

The effect of coat depth on external insulation was discussed in the last chapter. Applying equation (2.15) from that chapter to the data in Figure 3.5 of this, values for the still air external insulation of warm and cold acclimatised cattle in January become 4.2 (17.6) and 5.5 (23.1) °C.m².24 h/MJ(Mcal) respectively, an increase of 31% attributable to the effects of acclimatisation.

We have been unable to demonstrate that acclimatisation to cold has an effect on tissue insulation in sheep[50] or cattle[81]. Changes in the depth of subcutaneous fat are obviously related to the balance between energy intake and energy expenditure in the cold. Thus animals that gain condition during the winter become progressively more cold tolerant, those that lose condition progressively more cold sensitive. Cold stress and starvation thus create a visious circle where each contrives to exacerbate the effects of the other.

The possibility that cold might induce morphological changes in the skin and subcutaneous tissues of domestic animals has not really been examined.

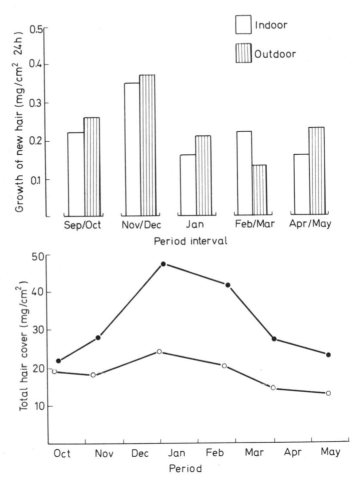

Figure 3.5 Rate of growth of new hair and total hair cover for cattle wintered indoors (○—○) and outdoors (●—●) (from Webster, Chlumecky and Young[81], by courtesy of *Can. J. Anim. Sci.*)

Sørenson[85] suggested that pigs chronically exposed to cold might preferentially deposit fat in subcutaneous tissues, but other careful studies have failed to confirm this[83].

The appetite of cattle, sheep and pigs increases during cold, dry weather although in miserably wet conditions their intake is reduced probably because of the physical discomfort involved in wading through deep mud to get at the food. When sheep were acclimated to low air temperatures, food intake increased rapidly and in proportion to the intensity of cold imposed[50]. Acclimatisation of sheep to severe but unpredictable weather conditions outdoors was associated with a gradual but persistent increase in food intake and thermoneutral metabolic rate. The increase appeared to be a function of the duration of the period of acclimatisation and unrelated to the intensity of cold experienced. The increases observed in thermoneutral metabolic rate in both acclimated and acclimatised sheep were calculated to be greater than would be expected from the increases in food intake.

In cattle wintered outside, food intake appeared to be related to how cold it was at the time, and changes in TMR could probably be attributed entirely to changes in food intake[81]. In pigs too, TMR, is probably unaffected by acclimatisation to cold if food intake is kept constant[84].

The other test of metabolic acclimatisation to cold is to measure the metabolic response to a standard cold stress. In sheep, this involves exposing shorn animals for several hours to an air temperature of $-20\,°C$ or below. Slee[86] tested three groups of sheep, previously kept at $30\,°C$ (warm acclimated) at $8\,°C$ (cold acclimated) or at $30\,°C$ but frequently subjected to brief cold shocks (1 h at $-10\,°C$). The animals acclimated to $8\,°C$ maintained rectal temperature best during the standard cold test, those acclimated to $30\,°C$ were intermediate and those which had received previous cold shocks were least able to maintain homeothermy. Females tended to be more cold tolerant than males.

We tested sheep with previous histories of warm acclimation (at $16\,°C$), cold acclimation and winter acclimatisation[50]. Both warm and cold acclimated sheep responded identically on exposure to $-25\,°C$, heat production rose sharply and rectal temperature was maintained. Winter acclimatised sheep, however, showed a delayed thermogenic response to cold and rectal temperature declined for about 2 h after the onset of exposure. This response was exactly comparable to that seen in habituated men (Figure 3.4). We concluded therefore that acclimatisation to winter conditions, but not acclimation to continuous cold, does confer upon sheep metabolic habituation comparable to that seen in man. The adaptive significance of this response for the sheep in its natural fleece and its natural environment is clear. Over winter direct stresses of cold are likely to be moderate and intermittent, but indirect stresses resulting from a shortage of food energy may be severe and prolonged.

Heitman, in continuing these investigations, has attempted to create in the laboratory a situation more closely resembling the patterns of cold stresses likely to be experienced out of doors. In addition to acclimating sheep to warm and constant cold, he included a third group, exposed to a daily rhythm of 12 h cold and 12 h at thermoneutrality (fluctuating cold group). The intensity of cold experienced by constant cold and fluctuating cold groups was kept the same by exposing the fluctuating cold group to twice the intensity of cold for half as long. His unpublished results are included with other published evidence in Table 3.4 which attempts to summarise what is and what is not known of acclimatisation to cold in sheep and cattle.

Sheep kept outside or under different patterns of cold in the laboratory all showed plasma protein bound iodine levels slightly higher than warm acclimated animals, even though iodine intakes were held constant in all groups. Mixed corticosteroids (cortisol and corticosterone) rose in both

Table 3.4 Physiological adjustments in sheep and cattle acclimated to constant or intermittent cold in the laboratory or acclimatised to winter conditions compared with animals kept inside at about 18 °C

	Sheep			Cattle	
Adjustments	Constant cold	Fluctuating cold	Outwintered	Outwintered	Outwintered
Insulative Coat growth					
Coat shedding	0	0	0	0	
External insulation	0	0	0	—	+
Tissue insulation	0	0	0	+	0
Metabolic Food intake					
Thermoneutral metabolic rate	++	+	gradual ++	++	++
Plasma PBI	++	?	gradual ++	++	++
Plasma corticosteroids	0	++	+?	+?	+(?)
Summit metabolism	0?	0?	0?	?	?
Habituation	0	0	++	?	?
Effect of adrenergic blockade					
α- receptors	—	+	?	?	?
β- receptors	0	0	0	0	?

Symbols: ++, increase (relative to warm groups); —, decrease; 0, no change; ?, uncertain

cold exposed groups at the beginning but returned to normal levels in the constant cold group. These results are similar to those seen by Heroux[51] in acclimated and acclimatised rats, and must, of course, be considered with similar reservations to those described earlier.

Although acclimation to constant cold enabled sheep to overcome the effects of a blockade with phenoxybenzamine (Figure 3.2) the fluctuating cold group were less able to maintain homeothermy at $-25\,°C$ after phenoxybenzamine than the warm acclimated animals. Moreover, they showed no signs of metabolic habituation comparable to that seen in outwintered animals. Exposure to fluctuating cold induced no metabolic changes that could be said to promote welfare or favour survival, indeed the sheep appeared to become rather less cold tolerant as a result of intermittent cold, an observation similar to that of Slee[86]. It would seem therefore that the physiological changes that accompany acclimatisation to natural winter environments in sheep and probably in other large mammals cannot be reproduced by exposing animals to controlled conditions of constant or intermittent cold in the laboratory.

The most precise description of the cold tolerance of a large animal is its critical temperature, the lower limit of the thermoneutral zone, which is determined by total thermal insulation and TMR. (Chapter 2, equation (2.11)). We were unable to demonstrate any difference in critical temperature between sheep kept warm or cold indoors or kept outside. There was thus no indication that the thermal comfort zone for sheep shifted as a result of acclimation or acclimatisation. The still air critical temperature of sheep in full fleece is, in fact, very low indeed, below $-25\,°C$[50].

In cattle however acclimatisation to winter conditions shifted critical temperature downwards by about $20\,°C$ (Figure 3.6a) principally as a result of changes in food intake and in thermal insulation[81]. At the same time the upper limits of the zone of thermal comfort were shifted downwards to the same extent. When acclimatised cattle were brought indoors in February from an air temperature of $-25\,°C$ to stand in a barn alongside their warm acclimated colleagues at $20\,°C$, their respiration rates increased to about $200/min$, they sweated, slavered and displayed all the classic symptoms of heat stress (Figure 3.6b). In April the difference between inwintered and outwintered cattle was conspicuously less as the effects of acclimatisation were wearing off. The downwards shift of $20\,°C$ in the zone of thermoneutrality observed in these experiments probably represents the extreme capacity of cattle to adapt to changing environments. January and June mean air temperatures at Edmonton, Alberta, Canada in the year when these experiments were performed were $-29\,°C$ and $+18\,°C$ (Figure 3.6a) a mean temperature range as large as that likely to be experienced by livestock anywhere.

3.5 HIBERNATION AND TORPOR

Adaptations to cold considered so far have principally been those which favour the maintenance of homeothermy in cold environments, the only exception being that of habituation which involves a slight relaxation in normal homeothermic mechanisms. A wide range of mammalian species can however permit body temperature, on occasions, to fluctuate within much wider limits. These are usually called the hibernators. The mechanisms of hibernation have been intensively studied and merit a more comprehensive

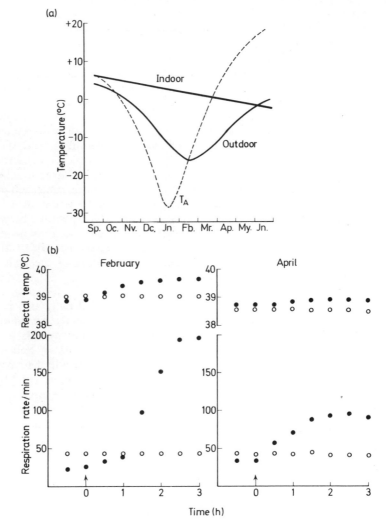

Figure 3.6 Effects of acclimatisation on the thermal comfort zone of cattle.
(a) Critical temperatures of cattle kept indoors and outdoors during a severely cold winter. Ambient temperature (T_A) is indicated by the broken line.
(b) Rectal temperatures and respiration rates of cattle measured at 20 °C in February and in April. Indoor group O, outdoor group ●; the outdoor group were exposed to 20 °C ambient at time 0 (from Webster, Chlumecky and Young[81] courtesy of *Can. J. Anim. Sci.*)

coverage by one more acquainted with the subject than me. This section is intended only to illustrate the importance to winter survival of this unique and extreme form of adaption to cold. It is drawn largely from the following articles[87-90] which make a good introduction to more detailed study.

Hibernation is, to my mind, best defined as 'a regulated, periodic phenomenon in which body temperatures become readjusted to new, lower levels approaching ambient, and heart rate, metabolic rate and other physiological functions show corresponding reductions from which spontaneous or induced arousal to normal levels is possible at all times'. Several refinements of this definition exist to deal with specific circumstances[88] and terms such as deep and shallow hibernation, obligate and permissive hibernation and even carnivorean lethargy have been suggested. Here hibernation will refer to any prolonged period of winter dormancy associated with a decreased body temperature. Torpor describes periods of reduced metabolic activity and body temperature which are of short duration, usually having a nychthemeral rhythm (c. 24 h).

Winter hibernation occurs in species within the orders insectivora (hedgehogs), rodentia (hamsters, dormice) and marmotina (ground squirrels, marmots). All these animals permit deep body temperature during the winter to fall close to ambient, which means in effect close to 0 °C. Larger mammals like the black bear (Ursus americanus) only permit body temperature to fall about 3–4 °C while they sleep in their winter burrows. There is no overwhelming reason to suppose that the mechanism of hibernation in this species differs from the others. The smaller fall in body temperature associated with the hypometabolic state may perhaps be explained simply by their larger mass to surface area ratio and greater thermal insulation. To establish whether the difference is more than one of degree, would involve a detailed study of the black bear in its natural winter environment and this is something which scientists, with certain heroic exceptions[11], have been unwilling to attempt.

At the other end of the spectrum of hibernators is the bat (Myotis sp.) which not only displays seasonal hibernation but also regularly exhibits torpor, permitting its body temperature to fall several degrees while it sleeps through a summer day.

Entry into hibernation is initiated by an active reduction in metabolic rate below the resting level which permits body temperature to fall. It is quite different therefore from the development of hypothermia in man, which results from a failure to sustain cold thermogenesis, usually due to exhaustion. At the end of the summer, for reasons that have been discussed at length[89,90] but are not really known for sure, the hibernator begins a series of 'test runs' preparatory to hibernation proper. In these, which are essentially the same as periods of torpor, heart rate is reduced by increasing the diastolic interval and by the introduction of missed beats[89]. Respiration rate and oxygen consumption decline. The consequent gradual decline in body temperature is usually interrupted by bursts of shivering during which all physiological processes tend to return to the active state. During the brief 'test runs', arousal takes place during one of these bursts of increased metabolic activity. Entry into deep and prolonged hibernation proceeds identically to the 'test runs'. Bursts of increased metabolic activity occur but do not reach an intensity sufficient to reverse the decline in body temperature. Although body temperatures remain fairly constant in deep hibernation, it is not a stable metabolic state. Periods of apnoea and cardiac asystole alternate with periods when the heart beats regularly and raises systolic blood pressure to about 60 mmHg, high enough to permit tissue respiration but probably not high enough to permit glomerular filtration, since urine flow from the kidneys appears to cease except during periods of arousal. On average, oxygen consumption and thus heat production are reduced to less than 10% of resting thermoneutral metabolic rate. During this controlled hypometabolic state body temperature in small mammals is within 3–4 °C of ambient. If ambient temperature falls to the point where deep body temperature approaches 0 °C, the animal can spontaneously arouse itself from hibernation by a massive increase in thermogenesis in muscles and in brown adipose tissue. Even when there is no immediate threat of freezing, hibernators in their winter burrows spontaneously arouse themselves from hibernation at frequent intervals throughout the winter. In the laboratory, hibernators can be roused at any time, often by the lightest of stimuli, such as gentle touch. However, generally speaking the intensity of stimulus required to induce arousal in midwinter is greater than that in autumn or spring.

The return of hibernators each spring to a free-living existence leads on from just one of the many normal periods of arousal, presumably at such time as the animal considers conditions favourable. Thus, the end, like the beginning of hibernation is not a single, irrevocable step but just one in a series of alternations between high temperature, free-living homeothermy and hypometabolism.

Seasonal changes in the endocrine system in hibernators are outside the scope of this chapter. Generally speaking, the pituitary and those endocrine glands which it controls appear to hypertrophy in the spring and regress in the fall. Pituitary hypertrophy begins while the animals are still asleep in their burrows so presumably is not dependent on day length. The role of the autonomic nervous system in hibernation is complex and somewhat paradoxical[89]. As a first approximation, one might say that entry into hibernation is associated with intense parasympathetic activity. Arousal is associated with intense sympathetic activity. Noradrenaline mediated non-shivering thermogenesis is vital to arousal in small hibernators, and noradrenaline injection can trigger arousal in the laboratory.

This very brief introduction to hibernation is intended only to show that hibernation is a unique, controlled, spontaneously reversible hypometabolic state which enables mammals to survive in climates where the direct stresses of cold are severe and no food is available during the winter. It differs from hypothermia and habituation in man in that it is initiated by a controlled reduction in metabolic rate. The only physiological state observed in man which is at all similar to entry into hibernation is the controlled hypometabolic state consciously induced during transcendental meditation or comparable yoga type practices[91]. Both processes appear to require a conscious control over the autonomic nervous system, and the cardiac and metabolic responses occurring during the early stages of both appear to be almost identical.

3.6 CONCLUSIONS: COMPARATIVE ASPECTS OF COLD TOLERANCE

This chapter was introduced by drawing attention to some commonsense principles that might influence the type of adaptive mechanism that would best promote welfare and favour survival of a particular species in a particular environment. Having described different adaptive mechanisms I now return to these simple principles to discuss the importance of each. Table 3.5 summarises the most common patterns of cold stress likely to be experienced by mammals in their natural habitat and lists the types of adaptive mechanisms invoked to combat these stresses. Small mammals indigenous to the maritime, cool temperate regions of, for example, Northern Europe, are mostly non-hibernators such as rats and mice. These animals have critical temperatures above 20 °C so that their metabolic rate is directly influenced by cold nearly all the time. When these small mammals are acclimated to cold in the laboratory, they develop an enhanced capacity for noradrenaline mediated cold thermogenesis, and also show an elevation in thermoneutral metabolic rate (usually measured at 30 °C, a temperature the animals would hardly ever experience in the wild). Since, in the wild, the metabolic rate of these animals is so dependent on air temperature it is not surprising to find that these species can adapt their thermoregulatory and non-thermoregulatory mechanisms of thermogenesis to the environment which they experience.

Air temperature in the maritime regions seldom falls far below 0 °C and periods of snow cover are not prolonged. These animal populations therefore face no real threat from cold injury or starvation, and therefore one would be unlikely to see adaptive mechanisms designed to counter these stimuli.

Primitive man sleeping naked in the desert is also under no threat of frostbite. The duration and intensity of the cold stresses to which he is exposed are brief and moderate but food may be in short supply. Here again, the type of adaptation observed is the type one would expect, increased tissue insulation and metabolic habituation, both designed to conserve energy.

Large ungulates in maritime climates are rarely stressed by cold. Nearly all species increase external insulation in the winter by growing thicker coats. The domestic sheep, which doesn't, is probably unique in this respect, having been selected by man not only for extreme thickness of coat but also for reduced shedding in the spring, with the result that its external insulation is much the same whatever its habitat. The other main factor contributing to the extreme cold tolerance of ungulates is their high thermoneutral metabolic rate resulting from the low efficiency with which they metabolise the end products of microbial fermentation in the gut. Ungulates also have very efficient mechanisms for preventing cold injury in the extremities in conditions of severe cold. Whether this is a genetic adaptation or whether it is influenced by physiological acclimatisation in the individual is not known.

Conditions on the edges of the Arctic ice caps, which appear severe to us, probably have no effect on the metabolism of aquatic mammals like the harbour seal[92] because of their very high tissue insulation. Small mammals living near the Arctic coasts or inland in continental regions with very severe winters are potentially vulnerable to all the direct and indirect stresses of cold; excessive heat loss, starvation and cold injury. Adaptive mechanisms

Table 3.5 Naturally occurring patterns of cold stress and the adaptive responses that they evoke

Climatic type	Mammalian species	Pattern of cold stress			Adaptation mechanism
		Direct		Indirect	
		General	Local	Food supply	
Cold Winters in maritime, cool temperate regions	Rodents and small mammals	Prolonged, moderate to severe	None	Adequate or scarce	Non-shivering cold thermogenesis elevated thermoneutral metabolism
Nights in continental, subtropical and desert regions	Primitive man	Intermittent, moderate	None	Adequate or scarce	Metabolic habituation increased tissue insulation
	Large ungulates	Intermittent, slight	None	Adequate or scarce	Increased external insulation metabolic habituation?
Very cold Winters on arctic coasts	Aquatic mammals	Probably slight	None	Plentiful	High tissue insulation
Winters in continental cool temperate and boreal regions	Rodents, marmots ground squirrels	Prolonged, severe	Moderate	Little or none	Hibernation, non-shivering cold thermogenesis
	Man	Intermittent, severe	Severe	Adequate	Improved local circulation (vasomotor habituation)
	Large ungulates	Frequent, moderate	Severe	Scarce	Improved local circulation improved external insulation metabolic habituation?

in these animals are hibernation and non-shivering cold thermogenesis, which together permit the animal first to reduce energy expenditure and thus energy requirement during the winter and secondly ensure that thermogenesis can be elevated rapidly to permit arousal whenever necessary.

Man can only exist in conditions of severe cold when provided with good housing, food and clothing. In polar regions, or on fishing boats in subarctic waters, man is liable to experience severe cold stresses, both general and local. Unadapted individuals may succumb to hypothermia due to exhaustion when general heat losses become excessive and prolonged. They are also prone to frostbite or at least incapacitating bouts of pain and numbness in the hands and feet that render them useless. Well fed, generally well covered men do acquire the ability to maintain circulation to the hands and feet to a degree adequate to avoid pain and injury and maintain function. This has been termed vasomotor habituation. Well fed, acclimatised men are also probably more resistant than unacclimatised individuals to hypothermia due to exhaustion of their capacity for cold thermogenesis. Since cold thermogenesis is essentially the same thing as exercise, it follows that a well trained individual can sustain cold thermogenesis for a longer period[93].

Adaptive changes observed in men are therefore also those which one would expect on common sense grounds. The types of adaptation that have *not* been demonstrated convincingly in man, i.e. increased basal metabolic rate and non-shivering cold thermogenesis are precisely those which would have little or no practical significance in the natural state. This may seem a blinding glimpse of the obvious. If it is, it has not apparently restricted the amount of time and effort expended in the search for cold induced changes in basal metabolism and non-shivering thermogenesis in man. The more important responses, cold induced vasodilatation and metabolic habituation are still incompletely understood. The latter, because of its potential importance in relation to hypothermia in old people[80], would seem on commonsense grounds to be particularly worthy of study.

References

1. Kleiber, M. (1961). *The Fire of Life*. (New York: John Wiley and Sons, Inc.)
2. Hart, J. S. (1964). Geography and season; mammals and birds. *Adaptation to the environment*, 295 (D. B. Dill, editor) (Washington: Amer. Physiol. Soc.)
3. Hammel, H. T. (1964). Terrestrial animals in cold: recent studies of primitive man. *Adaptation to the Environment*, 413 (D. B. Dill, editor) (Washington: Amer. Physiol. Soc.)
4. Budd, G. M. and Warhaft, N. (1966). Body temperature, shivering, blood pressure and heart rate during a standard cold stress in Australia and Antarctica. *J. Physiol (London)*, **186**, 216
5. Wyndham, C. M. and Loots, H. (1969). Responses to cold during a year in Antarctica. *J. Appl. Physiol.*, **27**, 696
6. Paik, K. S., Kang, B. S., Han, D. S., Rennie, D. W. and Hong, S. K. (1972). Vascular responses of Korean ama to hand immersion in cold water. *J. Appl. Physiol.*, **32**, 446
7. Leblanc, J. (1962). Local adaptation to cold of Gaspé fishermen. *J. Appl. Physiol.*, **17**, 950
8. Burton, A. C. and Edholm, O. G. (1955). *Man in a cold environment*. (London: Arnold)
9. Hafez, E. S. E. (1968). *Adaptation of domestic animals*. (Philadelphia: Lea and Febiger)
10. Hart, J. S. (1957). Climate and temperature induced changes in the energetics of homeotherms. *Rev. Can. Biol.*, **16**, 133

11. Folk, G. E. (1966). *Introduction to environmental physiology.* (London: Kimpton)
12. Prosser, C. L. (1958). *Physiological adaptation.* (Washington: Amer. Physiol. Soc.)
13. Smith, R. Em. and Hoejer, D. J. (1962). Metabolism and cellular function in cold acclimation. *Physiol. Rev.,* **42,** 60
14. Leduc, J. (1961). Catecholamine production and release in exposure and acclimation to cold. *Acta Physiol. Scand.,* **53,** Suppl. 183
15. Depocas, F. (1960). The calorigenic response of cold-acclimated white rats to infused noradrenaline. *Can. J. Biochem. Physiol.,* **38,** 107
16. Hseih, A. C. L. and Carlson, L. D. (1957). Role of adrenaline and noradrenaline in chemical regulation of heat production. *Amer. J. Physiol.,* **190,** 247
17. Heroux, O. (1960). Adjustments of the adrenal cortex and thyroid during cold acclimation. *Fed. Proc.,* **19,** 82
18. Schönbaum, E. (1960). Adrenocortical function in rats exposed to low environmental temperatures. *Fed. Proc.,* **19,** 85
19. Brown-Grant, K. (1956). Changes in thyroid activity of rats exposed to cold. *J. Physiol.,* **131,** 52
20. Cottle, M. and Carlson, L. D. (1956). Turnover of thyroid hormone in cold exposed rats determined by radioactive iodine studies. *Endocrinology,* **59,** 1
21. Straw, J. A. and Fregly, M. J. (1967). Evaluation of thyroid and adrenal-pituitary function during cold acclimation. *J. Appl. Physiol.,* **13,** 825
22. Boulouard, R. (1963). Effects of cold and starvation on adrenocortical activity of rats. *Fed. Proc.,* **22,** 750
23. Boulouard, R. (1966). Adrenocortical activity during adaptation to cold in the rat: role of Porter-Silber chromogens. *Fed. Proc.,* **25,** 1195
24. Swanson, H. E. (1956). Interrelations between thyroxine and adrenaline in the regulation of oxygen consumption in the albino rat. *Endocrinology,* **59,** 217
25. Shum, A., Johnson, G. E. and Flattery, K. V. (1969). Influence of ambient temperature on excretion of catecholamines and metabolites. *Amer. J. Physiol.,* **216,** 1164
26. Donhoffer, S., Sardy, F. and Szegvari, G. (1964). Brown adipose tissue and thermoregulatory heat production in the rat. *Nature (London),* **203,** 766
27. Smith, R. Em. and Horwitz, B. A. (1969). Brown fat and thermogenesis. *Physiol. Rev.,* **49,** 330
28. Reid, R. L. (1968). Physiopathology of undernourishment in the pregnant sheep, with particular reference to pregnancy toxaemia. *Advan. Vet. Sci.,* **12,** 163
29. Selye, H. (1950). *Stress,* (Montreal: Acta. Inc.)
30. Heroux, O. (1969). Diet and cold resistance. *Fed. Proc.,* **28,** 955
31. Heroux, O. (1969). Catecholamines, corticosteriods and thyroid hormones in non shivering thermogenesis under different environmental conditions. *Physiology and Pathology of Adaptation Mechanisms,* 347 (E. Bajusz, editor) (Oxford: Pergamon Press)
32. Cadot, Monique, Julien, M. F. and Chevillard, L. (1969). Estimation of thyroid function in rats exposed or adapted to environments at 5° and 30 °C. *Fed. Proc.,* **28,** 1228
33. Itoh, S., Hiroshige, T., Toshiyuki, K. and Nakatsugawa, T. (1966). Release of thyrotropin in relation to cold exposure. *Fed. Proc.* **25,** 1187
34. Sellers, E. A. and You, S. S. (1950). Role of the thyroid in metabolic responses to a cold environment. *Amer. J. Physiol.,* **163,** 81
35. Sellers, E. A., Flattery, K. V., Shum, A. and Johnson, G. E. (1971). Thyroid status in relation to catecholamines in cold and warm environments. *Can. J. Physiol. Pharmacol.,* **49,** 268
36. Davis, T. R. A. (1969). Physiological adjustments to cold. *Physiology and Pathology of Adaptation Mechanisms,* 366 (E. Bajusz, editor) (London: Pergamon Press)
37. Yousef, M. K., Cameron, R. D. and Luick, J. R. (1971). Seasonal changes in hydrocortisone secretion rate of reindeer, *Rangifer tarandus., Comp. Biochem. Physiol.,* **40,** 495
38. Yousef, M. K. and Johnson, H. D. (1965). Time course of thyroxine ^{131}I disappearance rates in cattle during exposure to hot and cold environments. *Life Sci.,* **4,** 1531
39. Webster, A. J. F., Heitman, J. H., Hays, F. L. and Olynyk, G. P. (1969). Catecholamines and cold thermogenesis in sheep. *Can. J. Physiol. Pharmacol.,* **47,** 719
40. Joy, R. J. T. (1963). Responses of cold acclimatised men to infused norepinephrine *J. Appl. Physiol.,* **18,** 1209
41. Bartunkova, R., Jansky, L. and Mejsnar, J. (1971). Non shivering thermogenesis and

cold adaptation. *Non shivering thermogenesis*, 39 (L. Jansky, editor) (Amsterdam: Swets and N. V. Zaitlinger)

42. Jansky, L. (1966). Body organ thermogenesis during exposure to cold and at maximum metabolic rate. *Fed. Proc.*, **25**, 1297
43. Leblanc, J. (1967). Adaptation to cold in three hours. *Amer. J. Physiol.*, **212**, 530
44. Bruck, K. (1970). Non shivering thermogenesis and brown adipose tissue in relation to age and their integration in the thermoregulatory system. *Brown adipose tissue*, 117 (O. Lindberg, editor) (London: Elsevier)
45. Lindberg, O. (1970). *Brown adipose tissue* (New York: Amer. Elsevier Co.)
46. Davis, T. R. A. (1961). Chamber cold acclimatisation in man. *J. Appl. Physiol.*, **16**, 1011
47. Sykes, A. R. and Slee, J. (1968). Acclimatisation of Scottish Blackface sheep to cold. 2. Skin temperature, heart rate, respiration rate, shivering intensity and skinfold thickness. *Anim. Prod.*, **10**, 17
48. Thompson, G. E. and Jenkinson, D. McE. (1969). Non shivering thermogenesis in the new-born lamb. *Can. J. Physiol. Pharmacol.*, **47**, 249
49. Alexander, G. (1970). Thermogenesis in young lambs. *Physiology of Digestion and Metabolism in the Ruminant*, 199 (A. T. Phillipson, editor) (Newcastle: Oriel Press)
50. Webster, A. J. F., Hicks, A. M. and Hays, F. L. (1969). Cold climate and cold temperature induced changes in the heat production and thermal insulation of sheep. *Can. J. Physiol. Pharmacol.*, **44**, 553
51. Heroux, O. (1963). Patterns of morphological, physiological and endocrinological adjustments under different environmental conditions of cold. *Fed. Proc.*, **25**, 789
52. Heroux, O. and Schönbaum, E. (1959). Comparison between seasonal and thermal acclimation in white rats III. Studies of the adrenal cortex. *Can. J. Biochem. Physiol.*, **37**, 1255
53. Leblanc, J., Robinson, D., Sharman, D. F. and Tousignant, P. (1967). Catecholamines and short-term adaptation to cold in mice. *Amer. J. Physiol.*, **213**, 1419
54. Sealander, J. A. (1952). The relationship of nest protection and huddling to survival of *Peromyscus* at low temperature. *Ecology*, **33**, 63
55. Girling, F. (1967). Seasonal changes in the physiological response of man to an acute cold stress. *Can. J. Physiol. Pharmacol.*, **45**, 13
56. Yoshimura, H. (1964). Organ systems in adaptation: the skin. *Adaptation to the environment*, 109 (D. B. Dill, editor) (Washington: Amer. Physiol. Soc.)
57. Brown, G. M. and Page, J. (1952). The effect of chronic exposure to cold on temperature and blood flow of the hand. *J. Appl. Physiol.*, **5**, 221
58. Miller, L. K. and Irving, L. (1962). Local reactions to air cooling in an Eskimo population. *J. Appl. Physiol.*, **17**, 449
59. Elsner, R. W., Nelms, J. D. and Irving, L. (1960). Circulation of heat to the hands of Arctic Indians. *J. Appl. Physiol.*, **15**, 662
60. Leblanc, J., Hildes, J. A. and Heroux, O. (1960). Tolerance of Gaspé fishermen to cold water. *J. Appl. Physiol.*, **15**, 1031
61. Nelms, J. D. and Soper, J. G. (1962). Cold vasodilatation and cold acclimatisation in the hands of British fish filleters. *J. Appl. Physiol.*, **17**, 444
62. Budd, G. M. and Warhaft, N. (1966). Cardiovascular and metabolic responses to noradrenaline in man, before and after acclimatisation to cold in Antarctica. *J. Physiol. (London)*, **186**, 233
63. Hampton, I. F. G. (1969). Effect of cold exposure in the Antarctic on heat elimination from the hands. *Fed. Proc.*, **28**, 1129
64. Krog, J., Folkow, B., Fox, R. H. and Andersen, K. L. (1960). Hand circulation in the cold of Lapps and north Norwegian fishermen. *J. Appl. Physiol.*, **15**, 654
65. Carlson, L. D. and Hsieh, A. C. L. (1965). Cold. *Physiology of Survival*, 15 (O. Edholm and A. L. Bacharach. editors) (London: Academic Press)
66. Carlson, L. D. (1966). The role of catecholamines in cold adaptation. *Pharmacol. Rev.*, **18**, 291
67. Pugh, L. G. C. and Edholm, O. G. (1955). Physiology of channel swimmers. *Lancet*, **269**, 761
68. Hart, J. S., Sabean, H. B., Hildes, J. A., Depocas, F., Hammel, H. T., Andersen, K. L., Irving, L. and Foy, G. (1962). Thermal and metabolic responses of coastal Eskimos during a cold night. *J. Appl. Physiol.*, **17**, 953
69. Milan, F. A., Hannon, J. P. and Evonuk, E. (1963). Temperature regulation of Eskimos Indians and Caucasians in a bath calorimeter. *J. Appl. Physiol.*, **18**, 378

70. Elsner, R. W. (1963). Comparison of Australian aborigines, Alacaluf Indians and Andean Indians. *Fed. Proc.*, **22**, 840
71. Wyndham, C. H., Williams, C. G. and Loots, H. (1968). Reactions to cold. *J. Appl. Physiol.*, **24**, 282
72. Spence, R. J., Rhodes, B. A. and Wagner, H. N. (1972). Regulation of arteriovenous anastomotic and capillary flow in the dog leg. *Amer. J. Physiol.*, **222**, 326
73. Hicks, C. S. (1964). Terrestrial animals in cold: exploratory studies of primitive man. *Adaptation to the environment*, 405 (D. B. Dill, editor) (Washington: Amer. Physiol. Soc.)
74. Kreider, M. B., Iampietro, P. F., Buskirk, E. R. and Bass, D. E. (1959). Effect of continuous cold exposure on nocturnal body temperatures of man. *J. Appl. Physiol.*, **14**, 43
75. Glaser, E. M. and Shephard, R. J. (1963). Simultaneous experimental acclimatisation to heat and cold in man. *J. Physiol. (London)*, **169**, 592
76. Skreslet, S. and Aarefjord, F. (1968). Acclimatisation to cold in man induced by frequent scuba diving in cold water. *J. Appl. Physiol.* **24**, 177
77. Davis, T. R. A. and Johnston, D. R. (1961). Seasonal acclimatisation to cold in man. *J. Appl. Physiol.*, **16**, 321
78. Sasaki, T. and Carlson, L. D. (1964). Seasonal changes in metabolic response to temperature change. *Proc. Soc. Exp. Biol. and Med.*, **117**, 332
79. Horvath, S. M., Radcliffe, C. E., Hutt, B. K. and Spur, G. B. (1955). Metabolic response of old people to a cold environment. *J. Appl. Physiol.*, **8**, 145
80. Watts, A. J. (1972), Hypothermia in the aged. A study of the role of cold sensitivity. *Environ. Res.*, **5**, 119
81. Webster, A. J. F., Chlumecky, J. and Young, B. A. (1970). Effects of cold environments on the energy exchanges of young beef cattle. *Can. J. Anim. Sci.*, **50**, 89
82. Morris, L. (1961). Photoperiodicity of seasonal rhythm of wool growth in sheep. *Nature (London)*, **190**, 102
83. Fuller, M. (1965). The effect of environmental temperature on the nitrogen metabolism and growth of the young pig. *Brit. J. Nutr.*, **19**, 531
84. Mount, L. E. (1968). The climatic physiology of the pig. *Monographs of the Physiol. Soc.* **18**. (London: Arnold)
85. Sørensen, P. H. (1962). Influence of climatic environment on pig performance. *Nutrition of pigs and poultry*, 88 (J. T. Morgan and D. Lewis, editors) (London: Butterworsth)
86. Slee, J. (1970). Resistance to body cooling in male and female sheep, and the effects of previous exposure to chronic cold, acute cold and repeated short cold shocks. *Anim. Prod.*, **12**, 13–21
87. Fisher, K. C., Dawe, A. R., Lyman, C. P., Schönbaum, E. and South, F. E. (1967). *Mammalian Hibernation III*, (London: Oliver and Boyd)
88. Hoffman, R. A. (1964). Terrestrial animals in cold: hibernators. *Adaptation to the environment*, 379 (D. B. Dill editor) (Washington: Amer. Physiol. Soc.)
89. Lyman, C. P. (1965). Circulation in mammalian hibernation. *Handbook of Physiology*, Sect. 2. *Circulation*, III, 1967 (P. Dow, editor) (Washington: Amer. Physiol. Soc.)
90. Lyman, C. P. and Dawe, A. R. (1960). Mammalian hibernation II. *Bull. Mus. Comp. Zool. Harv.*, **124**, 9
91. Wallace, R. K., Benson, H. and Wilson, A. F. (1971). A wakeful hypometabolic state. *Amer. J. Physiol.*, **221**, 795
92. Hart, J. S. and Irvine, L. (1959). Energetics of harbour seals in air and in water with special consideration of seasonal changes. *Can. J. Zool.*, **37**, 447
93. Adams, T. and Heberling, E. J. (1958). Human physiological responses to standard cold stress as modified by physical fitness. *J. Appl. Physiol.*, **13**, 226

4
Physiological Responses to Heat

J. R. S. HALES
C.S.I.R.O. Division of Animal Physiology, Ian Clunies Ross Animal Research
Laboratory, Prospect, N.S.W., Australia

4.1   INTRODUCTION

Many mammalian species control body-core temperature to within $\pm 1\,^{\circ}\text{C}$ despite wide variations in both external and internal heat loads, and there is relatively little difference between the 'normal' body temperature (*c.* $36-39\,^{\circ}\text{C}$) which is exhibited by highly different classes of mammals. Climatic conditions vary widely, for example, ambient dry bulb temperatures may range from about $-60\,^{\circ}\text{C}$ to $+50\,^{\circ}\text{C}$, and the effective thermal load can be even wider. The regulation of body temperature at a level close to the high end of this temperature range is probably related to optimal thermal conditions for biochemical processes, and might possibly be associated with temperature levels at which changes in the visceral structure of water occur.

The remarkable characteristic of homeotherms in regulating body temperature within relatively narrow limits entails the involvement of many 'physiological systems'. Right from the outset, behaviour greatly narrows the range of heat loads over which thermoregulation must rely upon autonomic functions. The importance of behavioural thermoregulation cannot be over-emphasised, and is discussed in Chapter 7 of this review. There is a considerable body of information concerning specific thermoregulatory reactions to heat stress, much of which was reviewed at an international symposium held in 1968[1]; interest in the control mechanisms involved therein is emphasised by the recent reviews and symposia on this topic[1-4]. However, a defined physiological system does not function in isolation from all the other systems, the actions of one often being intricately interrelated with the actions of another. For example, the circulatory system which has an important role in the transport of metabolites, is vitally important in convective heat exchange between the body core and tissues exposed to the external environment. Likewise, the panting mechanism used to control body temperature in many animals, employs processes which are also concerned in metabolic gaseous exchange. It is, therefore, surprising that so little attention has been paid to physiological responses to heat stress which are not specifically thermoregulatory, and to the interactions between thermoregulatory and other physiological systems. The present review gives emphasis to these interactions, as well as discussing major recent advances in our understanding of thermoregulatory mechanisms and their control. Because of restricted space, reference is frequently made only to recent reviews, symposia or major research papers from which references to a wider literature may be obtained. This discussion is concentrated on acute autonomic responses of the commonly studied adult mammals to heat. Three small sections concerning the perinatal period, phylogenesis of thermoregulatory mechanisms and physiological failure during heat stress are included, but endocrine functions and changes in body fluid and electrolyte status are virtually unmentioned because of their much greater relevance to adaptation (see Chapter 6). Further, because the actual control loops are considered in Chapter 1, the following discussion is confined to *responses* of the physiological systems and of receptors to heat.

4.2 SPECIFIC THERMOREGULATORY RESPONSES TO HEAT

Clearly, with such a precisely controlled parameter as '(mean?) body temperature' or 'body-heat content' (see Section 4.3.2) it should be possible to understand the relations between stimulus and response in quantitative terms. During the last 10 or 15 years much progress has been made towards quantitating the relative importance of the various heat-loss mechanisms in many different species, the relative importance of different thermoreceptor sites, and the interrelationships between the effectors and the controlling system.

4.2.1 Heat-loss mechanisms

When ambient temperature approaches deep-body temperature, or when metabolic heat production is high such as during exercise, evaporative heat loss is essential for homeothermy. There have been many studies of evaporative heat loss because of its importance and relative ease of measurement compared with non-evaporative heat loss. However, use of partitional calorimetry of the whole conscious animal, and in particular the use of gradient-layer calorimetry, has provided invaluable data for an understanding of the entire heat balance of an animal and of the complementary manner in which the various thermoregulatory mechanisms operate. Benzinger[3] has given a detailed description of gradient-layer calorimetry and its use together with tympanic thermometry in humans, in unravelling the role of peripheral and central thermoreceptors in the control of thermoregulatory mechanisms in man. Thus, for example, sweating in humans appears to be very closely controlled by central warm receptors operating in relation to a 'set-point' or 'reference' temperature. However, there are many experimental observations on man and other animals which are difficult to reconcile with the clear cut 'central warm and peripheral cold receptor control' proposed by Benzinger and co-workers. Gradient-layer calorimetry of animals which can be subjected to surgical procedures not possible with man, should be most rewarding. For example, McLean et al.[5] used chronically implanted thermodes in oxen to demonstrate that in an environment of 35 °C dry bulb (T_{db}) and 20 °C wet bulb (T_{wb}) temperature, spinal heating caused no change in non-evaporative whereas cutaneous and respiratory evaporative heat losses both increased by up to 65%.

A summary of data concerning the ability of various species to lose heat by evaporation from either the skin or respiratory tract is given in Table 4.1.

Table 4.1 Evaporative heat loss in different mammals (resting). The ambient conditions were such that maximal sweating was evoked but the control of body temperature was maintained. (Values have been either taken directly from or calculated from data in the references cited)

Species	Cutaneous moisture loss in heat (g m^{-2} h^{-1})	Cutaneous as a proportion of total evaporative heat loss (%)	Capacity to increase evaporative heat loss		
			Total	Cutaneous	Respiratory
Man[3, 223, 224]	200	92	× 14–28*		
Monkey[225]	68	82	× 5	× 9	× 2
Ox[6, 135, 226]	140–300*	62	× 4	× 7	× 1½
Sheep[18, 122, 227, 228]	30–60*	40	× 5	× 3	× 9
Pig[229]	30	52	× 2½	× 2	× 3
Dog[139, 143, 230]	8	10–20*	× 10–20*	× 1	× 10–20*
Cat[137]	24	30			× 7
Rabbit[231]	16	40	× 4	× 4	× 5

* range given because of variability between reports.

(Note that much higher sweating rates are generally possible during non-resting or pathological states). The complementary nature of sweating and panting between and within species is obvious. As is well known, the relative importance of sweating and panting within a given species varies with environmental temperature, and at low temperatures non-evaporative heat loss becomes important. However, to quantitate this is a considerable advance: with oxen in a gradient layer calorimeter, McLean and Calvert[6] have been able to show that with low humidity at an environmental temperature of 15 °C T_{db} heat loss by evaporation was 18% of the total heat loss whereas at 35 °C it was 84%; of this, 46% was due to cutaneous moisture loss at 15 °C, and 62% at 35 °C; these studies attribute greater significance to panting than did earlier studies[7].

The low sweating rate in the monkey (squirrel monkey, Saimiri sciureus) relative to man, is somewhat surprising because this is by far the most important channel of evaporative heat loss in this species. Presumably, the monkey is, therefore, less heat tolerant than man, for even if cutaneous moisture loss is expressed on a body weight basis, man has about a sevenfold advantage over the monkey. Thus, if one considers panting to be a more primitive thermoregulatory mechanism than sweating, as suggested by Bligh and Allen[8], it must be deduced, that whereas some primates (man) have evolved a highly developed sweating mechanism while losing the ability to pant, others (monkey) have lost the ability to pant without evolving sufficient sweating capacity to counteract this and would, therefore, be expected to be less heat tolerant. Another noteworthy point to be drawn from Table 4.1 is the relativly high contribution of cutaneous to total evaporative heat loss in the animals classically known as 'panters' (sheep, dog, cat, rabbit), although their ability to increase cutaneous moisture loss is not nearly so great as that of the 'sweaters'. The ultimate dependence of the ox on sweating has been demonstrated by its complete inability to control body temperature by panting in a moderately hot environment (40 °C T_{db}, 20 °C T_{wb}) when the animal is incapable of sweating (for unknown reasons)[9]. Likewise when respiratory evaporative heat loss in the sheep is blocked by supplying saturated air to a face mask, the control of body temperature is no longer possible in a moderately hot environment (Hales, unpublished observations). The relative importance of the various channels of heat loss also differs in the newborn of many species (see Section 4.4).

The question of the advantages and disadvantages of sweating compared with panting, which are such different physiological mechanisms, remains largely unresolved except in so far as it is now much more obvious that both have their roles in particular circumstances. Thus, in Robertshaw and Taylor's comparative study[10] of eight species of East African bovids, the ability to sweat was greatest in the larger animals. This might appear desirable because of a high energy cost of panting in large animals; however, this is not so (see Section 4.6). Animals which sweat poorly but have a high panting capacity would appear to have the advantage of absorbing less of the external heat load because of their high skin temperature, a factor also considered by Robertshaw and Taylor to be important. Similarly, insulation by a thick pelage is no disadvantage to the animal which can pant, and panting may provide preferential cooling to the brain (see Section 4.3.5). Apparent disadvantages of sweating are the loss of body electrolytes, possibly leading to fatigue, and the loss of body water as non-evaporated sweat. An obvious advantage of panting is that the animal provides its own air circulation over the areas significant for evaporative cooling, and almost all of the heat lost is drawn from within the body; however, evaporation of sweat is determined entirely by external conditions and heat loss may take place some distance above the skin surface. Under almost all environmental conditions there is no conflict between respiratory and thermoregulatory requirements of the respiratory system during panting (see Sections 4.7.2 and 4.7.3), however, when exercise is added to this, the situation may be different and the ability to sweat may be a considerable advantage (see also Chapter 5).

4.2.2 Salivation

The production of saliva increases in many species when subjected to heat stress, but this is often largely wasted, serving only to moisten the tongue and buccal cavity in most species. Schmidt-Nielsen[11] drew attention to the possible importance of the evaporation of saliva from the general body surface in small mammals, but it has commonly been regarded as a form of emergency temperature regulation. Recent studies of rats clearly demonstrate that the spreading of saliva is a normal and highly effective evaporative heat-loss mechanism[12,13]; it is integrated with other thermoregulatory mechanisms[222] and is likewise under hypothalamic control[12,14]. Thus, heat loss by evaporation of saliva in some species must now be regarded in the same light as sweating or panting in other species.

4.2.3 Sweating

An overall picture of the important role of cutaneous moisture loss was presented in Section 4.2.1. The name 'sweating' is often used synonomously with 'cutaneous moisture loss', although this is quite unjustified when it is recognised that, for example, 40% of the total evaporative heat loss may be from the skin of the rabbit (Table 4.1) and yet this species has no sweat glands[15]. Also, although the pig may show a twofold increase in cutaneous moisture loss during heat stress and it does have sweat glands, these glands arc not responsive to thermal stimulation[16].

In humans and oxen, variations in cutaneous moisture loss from different regions of the body surface are well known but little physiological significance appears to have been attributed to them. In the sheep, a noteworthy picture has evolved which illustrates the need for more studies involving partitional calorimetry of body regions: cutaneous moisture loss per unit surface area of the body is low (Table 4.1), covering the body with a plastic coat does not materially influence heat tolerance[17], and actual sweat-gland discharges may occur in a cold environment[8]. It therefore appears that evaporation from the general body surface may be of little thermoregulatory significance. However, recent studies in this laboratory[18] showed that up to 40% of the total evaporative heat loss could come from sources other than panting. Waites and Voglmayr[19] reported that in sheep, sweat glands are larger and more numerous in the skin of the leg than of the midside of the body, and glands of the scrotum are much larger still; moisture production by the scrotum may be as high as 208 g m^{-2} h^{-1}. The question arises as to the possible significance of regional variations in cutaneous moisture loss. There are numerous large arterio-venous anastomoses in the leg skin of sheep[20] and blood flow increases markedly during heat stress (see Section 4.8.2), which, together with a high local sweating rate (assuming the glands are functional), could constitute a highly significant heat-exchange system for the body as a whole. Sweating in the squirrel monkey appears to occur only from the feet, hands and perhaps the face, but not the body[21], and it would be particularly interesting to know whether there is sweating from the tail; all these areas might contribute to heat exchange in the manner suggested for the sheep's legs. On a more local basis, Hales and Hutchinson[22] have pointed out how the sweating capacity of the scrotum is sufficient to dissipate more than five times the heat produced by the testes; the scrotum acts as its own local thermostat and heat lost by evaporation is not wasted in cooling the rest of the body because heat exchange in the pampiniform plexus isolates thermally the scrotum and testicles from the rest of the body.

That many mammals differ in their ability to increase cutaneous moisture loss during heat exposure is demonstrated by the figures in Table 4.1. However, the ability to exhibit active thermal sweating and the mediating pathways involved also varies between species. The results of studies of sudomotor pathways involved in mediating sweat gland responses to thermal stress are summarised in Table 4.2. Particularly notable are the contributions by Robertshaw and co-workers, and Figure 4.1 illustrates their experimental approach, which generally included sympathectomy, splanchnicotomy and the use of various sympathomimetic, parasympathomimetic and autonomic blocking drugs. Note how, in Figure 4.1, Robertshaw and Taylor[23] were able to implicate the involvement of the adrenal medulla in the control of exercise-induced, but not purely heat-induced sweating. In the sheep, goat, donkey, pig and a number of wild bovids, the sweat gland response to thermal stress does not involve the adrenal medulla, and is mediated by adrenergic nerves, in contrast to cholinergic nerves in man and the cat; further, in some experiments, the involvement of adrenergic α-receptors was specifically demonstrated. The confusing picture of adrenergic and cholinergic effects on the eccrine sweat glands of man appears to have been resolved by Foster and Weiner[24]. Their studies of the effects of various nerve blocking agents on sweat gland activity in the human forearm and in the footpad of the cat, lead to the conclusion that only cholinergic sudomotor fibres are involved, and that an inhibition of neuroglandular transmission by antiadrenergic substances is due to interaction with cholinergic receptors in the glands. However, recently Robertshaw, Taylor and Mazzia (personal communication) have been able to demonstrate that in stump-tailed macaque monkeys (*Macaca speciosa*) circulating adrenaline, from the adrenal medulla, is responsible for the enhancement of cholinergic sweating during exercise. (See Chapter 5).

A marked decline in the sweating rate, or 'sweat gland fatigue', occurs in man during prolonged exposure to severe heat stress. This could be of considerable physiological significance, and it is therefore surprising to find that the cause is unknown. It has been suggested that this could be due to excessive skin hydration causing obstruction of the sweat gland ducts (see Ref. 25) or to a decline in activity of the secretory cells (see Ref. 26). Bligh[27] has described the mechanism of sweating in many species in terms of secretion of fluid into the gland lumen by secretory cells, and expulsion of the fluid by contraction of myoepithelial cells. Sweat gland fatigue as described in the sheep and goat[28] could be due to failure of either of these processes. However, Jenkinson and Robertshaw[29] found that as fatigue progresses in the goat, the volume of each active sweat gland shows a progressive decrease which is excessive in relation to the volume of sweat produced. That is, failure of the system is in the formation of the fluid, which is consistent with many results from human studies. However, the cause of this failure remains undetermined; it might be suggested that the provision of energy and/or 'raw materials' is limited by a reduction in skin blood flow which occurs during progressive heat stress (see Section 4.8.2). Alternatively, the entire effect might be due to antidiuretic hormone (ADH), the output of which

Table 4.2 Control of heat-induced sweating

Species	Response to heat exposure	Sympathetic innervation involved	Effect of adrenaline	Effect of noradrenaline	Effect of acetyl choline or pilocarpine	Adrenal medulla involved	Effect of bethanidine or phenoxy-benzamine	Effect of propranolol	Conclusion re. control
Man (eccrine)	+[24]	yes[24]	+[24]	+[24]	+[24]		−?[24]		cholinergic nerves[24]
Cat (eccrine)	+[24]	yes[24]	+[24]	+[24]	+[24]		−?[24]		cholinergic nerves[24]
Sheep	+[232]	yes[28]	+[28, 232, 233]	=[234] +?[232]	=[233]	no[28]	=[28]	=[28]	adrenergic α-receptor[28]
Goat	+[234]	yes[28, 234]	+[28, 234]	=[28]		no[28]	−[28]	=[28]	adrenergic α-receptor[28]
Equidae	+[235]	yes[23]	+[23, 235, 236]	=[23] ?[236]	+?[236]	no[23]	=[23] −[236]	−[236]	adrenergic nerves[23, 236]
Ox	+[237]	yes[238]	+[237, 238]	+[238]	=[238]	no[238]	−[238]	−[238]	adrenergic α-receptor[238]
Pig	=[16]	yes[16]	+[16]	+?[16]	=[16]				adrenergic nerves[16]
Wild bovids	+[10]	yes[10]	+[10]	=[10]		no[10]	−[10]		adrenergic nerves[10]

+, increased response; −, decrease or inhibition; =, no effect; ?, slight response, or variable, or effect only with high drug doses.

increases in the heat, and it has been shown to reduce eccrine sweating[30]. However, the time at which sweat gland fatigue begins in man may vary between body regions[26], and therefore if one accepts the likelihood that there would also be regional differences in skin temperature and/or blood flow, then the blood-flow hypothesis is more tenable than is the ADH hypothesis.

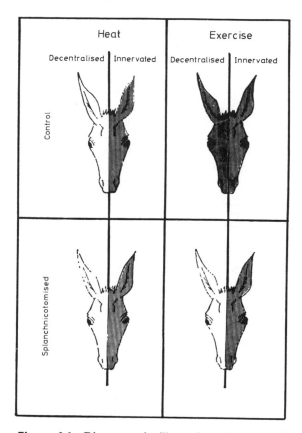

Figure 4.1 Diagrammatic illustration of an experimental approach to sudomotor mechanisms during heat and exercise. All animals were sympathetically decentralised on the right hand side of the head and one group of animals had also undergone bilateral splanchnicotomy; the control group had an intact adrenomedullary nerve supply. Shading denotes the occurrence of sweating. (From Robertshaw and Taylor[23], by courtesy of *J. Physiol. (London)* (1969))

There have been few studies directly orientated towards the relationship between skin blood flow and sweat gland function. This is mentioned above and in Sections 4.6 and 4.8. Senay *et al.*[31] estimated local skin blood flow using a photoelectric plethysmographic technique in men subjected to external heat stress, but obtained no evidence that sweat gland activity was related to cutaneous blood flow. However, there is evidence to the contrary during hypocapnic hyperventilation in man, sweating rate falls, and this has been attributed to the concurrent fall in skin blood flow estimated from plethysmograph records of hand blood flow[189]. Ingram et al.[33] showed that occluding the circulation to the shank of the ox prevented the usual increase in moisture vaporisation from the shank which occurs in response to local heating of the hypothalamus. Robertshaw and Taylor[23] concluded that cutaneous blood flow was important because adrenaline infusion in the donkey exposed to a cold environment would evoke sweating from denervated but not from innervated skin; however, temperature of the former was high whereas that of the latter was low, and therefore it is not possible to say whether it was the high temperature or the high blood flow which permitted the sweating response. Finally, histological studies of small areas of skin from which sweating rate had previously been measured in oxen, have demonstrated a direct correlation between capillary supply to the sweat gland and seasonal variations in performance of the gland[34]. Local circulation must supply substrates and energy for the formation and expulsion of sweat, and transport humoral agents and thermal information. It is therefore difficult to see how the circulation could fail to be a vital part of the system controlling sweating. The involvement of a single thermostat–effector system to regulate cutaneous circulation could be envisaged to fulfil the role of regulating both evaporative and non-evaporative heat loss.

Numerous studies leave no doubt that general or local sweating responses are strongly influenced by general or local skin temperature, and in fact, that sweating rate can be described mathematically in terms of body core and skin temperatures (e.g. Ref. 35). However the mode of action of the temperature changes is unknown. Is it on specific thermoreceptors which then act via a segmental reflex or higher centres? Is the local release of sudomotor transmitter directly modified? Is the activity of the gland cells directly modified? Or is the local blood flow (either total or the distribution between capillaries and arterio-venous anastomoses) altered by reflex or direct effects of temperature? Many studies favour the first explanation. The results reported by MacIntyre et al.[36] provide evidence for the second, but do not preclude the fourth explanation. In support of the fourth explanation is the evidence given above for the importance of local circulation in influencing sweat gland function, the known influence of local temperature on local circulation (see Sections 4.8.2 and 4.8.3) and the direct effect of temperature on blood vessels whether or not there is an intact nerve supply[37].

4.2.4 Panting

Richards[38] has reviewed the biology and comparative physiology of thermal panting. The important role played by panting in the regulation of body temperature of many species is well known, and our improved understanding of the relative importance of respiratory and non-respiratory evaporative heat loss based on quantitative measurements was discussed in Sections 4.2.1 and 4.2.3. The now largely resolved question of respiratory control during panting is discussed in Section 4.7.3.

Although reference is frequently made to 'heat loss from the lungs' during panting, the marked increase in respiratory minute volume which occurs, is restricted to the upper respiratory tract during true thermal polypnoea (see Section 4.7.2). Evaporative cooling from the upper respiratory tract has been demonstrated in the ox by a fall in the temperature of blood in the external jugular veins[39], which is magnified or attenuated with opening or closing of the mouth respectively[40]. A maximum of approximately 2% of the total respiratory heat loss is non-evaporative in the sheep[18], and, therefore, the large increases in blood flow to the upper respiratory tract[41] (Section 4.8.2) must be primarily involved in the supply of fluids and heat exchange with the surface of the tissues which have been cooled by evaporation. In considering the physics of evaporative heat loss in the upper respiratory passages during panting, it is clear that if the air were to be moved in and out through the mouth, complete saturation might be difficult. Further, if the air were to be moved in and out through the nasal passages, some of the heat lost to the air during inhalation might be recovered during exhalation. The latter form of panting would appear to be less of a problem than the former, and does not hinder the efficiency of panting in closed-mouthed panters such as the sheep and ox. However, this problem in an open-mouthed panter, the dog, has been described and resolved by Schmidt-Nielsen et al.[42]. By separately measuring oral and nasal air flow, it was demonstrated that most of the respired air usually enters through the nose and leaves through the mouth, but that this pattern may be varied.

Other than the demonstration some years ago that the dog often pants at a frequency corresponding to the natural frequency of the respiratory system[43, 44] there appear to have been no attempts to elucidate the mechanics or muscular activity involved in panting, even though an animal may show a respiratory frequency of over 500 breaths min^{-1} and a >tenfold increase in respiratory minute volume. In studies of the energy cost of panting, Hales and Findlay[45] concluded that panting must involve specifically adapted respiratory muscle function, and now Hales[46] has shown that the diaphragm and crus muscles (but not the intercostals) are involved in rapid shallow panting, and that during severe heat stress when panting changes to a slower deeper form, the intercostals also become involved (also see Sections 4.6 and 4.8.2). The ability of the respiratory muscles to contract at such a high frequency remains unexplained.

4.2.5 Vasodilatation

The transfer of heat from the body core to the body 'shell' for loss via non-evaporative or evaporative routes depends upon circulation in the 'shell', and this is discussed in Sections 4.8.2 and 4.8.3.

4.2.6 Conclusions

The relative importance of the various channels of heat loss in many mammals is now much better understood because of quantitative measurements often involving partitional calorimetry of the entire animal. Studies of the significance of regional variations in heat loss would appear to be warranted. Sudomotor function in many species is understood, but the mechanism of local effects of temperature and blood flow on sweat gland function, and the mechanism of sweat gland fatigue have yet to be clarified; the apparent absence of electron microscope studies of the sweat glands is surprising. The general process of panting and its control is well understood, but much remains to be learnt about the mechanics of panting. Finally, the evolutionary significance of the existence of both sweating and panting remains an interesting question.

4.3 THERMORECEPTORS CONTROLLING HEAT-LOSS MECHANISMS

The role of the temperature sensitivity of the hypothalamus and of receptors located on or near the outer surface of the body in controlling heat-loss mechanisms has been reviewed in depth by Bligh[2], Benzinger[3] and Hellon[47], and at recent symposia (Hardy et al.[1]; Bligh and Moore[4]). The marked influence of spinal cord temperature on thermoregulatory mechanisms has more recently become well established and was considered in the latter three of the above publications. Advances since that time include quantitating the effects of the various thermoreceptors, the demonstration of intra-abdominal warmth receptors, and extending information regarding thermoregulatory responses, interactions between thermoreceptors at different sites, role of the circulation in transmitting thermal information, neuronal responses of the receptors, and the characterisation of neurotransmitters involved in thermo-regulatory responses. The first item in this list is covered in Chapter 1, and the remaining six items are discussed in the following sections.

4.3.1 Intra-abdominal thermoreceptors

When it became obvious that a number of experimental observations on mammals were inexplicable in terms of peripheral (skin) and brain tempera-tures, experiments involving the independent manipulation of the temperature of the head and body were performed using heat exchangers (e.g. Ref. 48) or cross-circulated animals[49]. The former of these studies led to the discovery of the spinal cord as an important thermoreceptor site (see Ref. 50), and the results of the latter study were explained in terms of 'powerful extracerebral temperature receptors'.

Rawson and co-workers[51,52] have used electrical heaters sutured to the inside surface of the abdominal wall of sheep to elicit heat-loss responses which were well correlated with the level of heat input and persisted despite a marked decline in hypothalamic temperature. Specific thermoreceptors appear to lie within the walls of the rumen and intestine and possibly the mesenteric veins, with an afferent pathway in the splanchnic nerves[53]. The stimulation of these receptors provides an explanation for a number of previous experimental observations, for example, the enhanced or depressed panting which follows ingestion of warm or cold water respectively[54]. Thus there is good evidence for the existence of specific deep-body extracerebral temperature receptors besides those in the spinal cord, and the major task which lies ahead would appear to be evaluation of the importance of these receptors compared with thermoreceptors at other sites.

4.3.2 Thermoregulatory responses to core and peripheral temperature

Local heating of the hypothalamus will stimulate vasodilatation, sweating and panting and the responses are modified by ambient, and therefore presumably peripheral thermoreceptor temperature. The effect of hypothalamic heating may be very potent, for example, in causing a 10 °C fall in deep-body temperature[55]; however, in some species at least, hypothalamic thermo-sensitivity may not be as crucial in the control of body temperature as has been long supposed. Thus, Hales[56] reported that normal panting and sweating responses of the ox subjected to moderate heat stress were not altered when the rise in hypothalamic temperature which normally accompanies these responses was artificially prevented. Also, heating the scrotum of the ram results in depressed metabolic rate, peripheral vasodilatation and panting which continue even though core temperature is caused to fall by 1 °C or more[22,57]. Even more remarkable are the results shown in Figure 4.2(a and b). Jessen et al.[58] demonstrated that steady heating of the spinal cord of the ox will cause heat-loss mechanisms to persist and cause a fall in core temperature by 5 °C or more. As these authors pointed out, it was also clear that the importance of the thermal information from the spinal cord relative to the whole temperature sensing system increased as spinal temperature increased, and that this would continue until spinal cord control completely dominated negative feed-back signals and deep-body temperature fell to lethal levels.

The relative importance of hypothalamic and spinal cord thermoreceptors in controlling heat-loss responses is difficult to judge in that the overall validity of comparing responses evoked by altering the temperature of a large section of the spinal cord with responses evoked by altering hypothalamic temperature may be questioned. It is therefore not surprising that results to date conflict in some respects. Simultaneous heating of both regions has an additive effect with respect to panting in the anaesthetised rabbit (Guieu and Hardy[59]) and conscious dog (Jessen and Ludwig[60]), and in increasing peripheral blood flow in the conscious pig (Ingram and Legge[61]). However, whereas Guieu and Hardy's study[59] implicates a more dominant role for the hypothalamus in controlling panting, the studies by Jessen and Mayer[62] and Jessen and Simon[63] show that responses of equal magnitude may be evoked from either site and that heating one site will over-ride the effect of cooling the other. Some illustrative results are given in Figure 4.3, and it must be concluded from these particular results that each site has identical and interchangeable functions. This conforms with the earlier discussion of the intense hypothermia which can be produced by persistent heating of either the hypothalamus or the spinal cord (or specific peripheral regions, which is

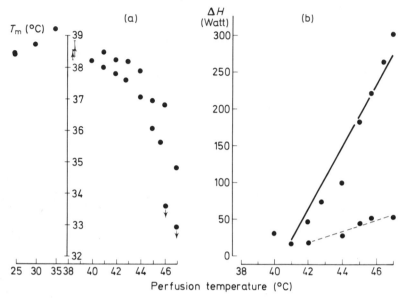

Figure 4.2 Relationship between the perfusion temperature of thermodes in the spinal canal of the ox and (a) the final steady level of body core (meatal) temperature (T_m) the two arrowed points being experiments in which no steady temperature was reached, and (b) the increase in total heat loss (ΔH) during the first hour of spinal cord heating. The broken line represents the thermal power transferred directly from the thermode to the animal (From Jessen et al.[58], by courtesy of *Amer. J. Physiol.* (1972))

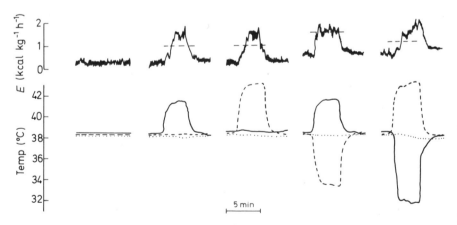

Figure 4.3 Respiratory evaporative heat loss responses (E) to selective and simultaneous heating and cooling of the hypothalamus and spinal cord of a conscious dog. Ambient temperature, 29 °C. Vertebral canal temperature (———), hypothalamic temperature (– – – –), rectal temperature (. . . . .). (From Jessen and Simon[63], by courtesy of Springer–Verlag (1971))

discussed further in the following section), and as Jessen and Simon pointed out, the data are consistent with the view that core thermoreceptors are much more sensitive to heating than to cooling[3, 64]. The discrepancy between the results from Guieu and Hardy[59] and Jessen and co-workers[60, 62, 63] may be due to the fact that the vertebral canal thermodes passed only between T_1 and T_6 in the former work, but between C_2 and the cauda equina in the latter work. (It should be emphasised that the same situation does not exist with respect to heat production.) Shivering and vasomotor activity can be mediated at the spinal level[50], and observations on paraplegic man[65] indicate that sweating can be mediated at the spinal level. However, panting has been shown to be mediated by diencephalic structures[66].

In the preceding discussion, only passing reference has been made to the importance of thermoreceptors at the periphery (in or near the skin, or membranes of the nasobuccal cavity, or tongue, ears or digits) because it has been so well established. For example, the magnitude of the panting response to increments in temperature of the hypothalamus[67, 68] or spinal cord[69] increases as ambient temperature increases. However, with respect to different heat-loss mechanisms, recent evidence indicates variability in the importance of the peripheral input relative to hypothalamic and spinal cord temperature changes. Thus, during exposure to low ambient temperatures, hypothalamic heating will elicit peripheral vasodilatation, very little or no panting[67, 68, 70], and no sweating[33]. In contrast, under comparable conditions, heating the spinal cord will elicit peripheral vasodilatation and vigorous panting, but no sweating (see Ref. 71 and Figure 4.4).

The question of the importance of regional variations in peripheral warm-sensitivity does not appear to have received the attention warranted by some earlier studies. Variations in the distribution of temperature receptors between different peripheral regions is well known (see Ref. 72) and yet, for example, it was not until 1971 that Mitchell et al.[73] showed that in terms of the sweating response from a reference area of skin, the face was much more sensitive than the chest, thigh or abdomen. Bligh[74] showed that panting activity in sheep could be markedly influenced by selectively warming or humidifying inspired air, however, whether this response is due to the transmission of thermal information via the circulation or to the stimulation of temperature receptors is unknown; with respect to the latter possibility, the existence of specific warm receptors in the nasal region of cats has recently been demonstrated[75], although they have long been known for the tongue[72] and from the discussion in Section 4.3.5 it seems that the circulatory pathway is also likely to be involved. The recent report by Kluger et al.[76] indicates a greater thermal sensitivity of the ears than the body skin of the rabbit, a feature of obvious survival value to the animal. The activity of all thermoregulatory mechanisms is markedly altered by changes in temperature of the scrotum or mammary glands of the sheep and goat[22, 57, 77, 78]. Waites[57] showed that heating a region of body skin equal in area to that of the scrotum evoked only a very weak response, indicating a high sensitivity of the scrotal thermoreceptors which has now been proven by electrophysiological studies[79]. Harking back to the original question, it seems significant that although the scrotal thermoreceptors appear to provide the input for a local thermostat, they can also result in a lowering of the 'set-point' temperature for the whole body[22].

In a closely-shorn sheep which has been exposed to a cool environment, the onset of panting on exposure to heat is delayed[80], and the panting response to scrotal heating is absent[57]. Bligh[80] postulated that the inhibition of panting was due to a persistent block between warm receptors and the respiratory centres due to stimulation of peripheral cold receptors. However, the situation

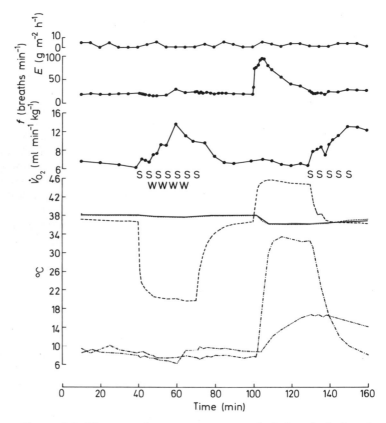

Figure 4.4 Thermoregulatory responses to manipulation of spinal cord temperature in the ox in an environment of 0 °C T_{db}. Cutaneous moisture loss (E), respiratory frequency (f), oxygen consumption ($\dot{V}_{O_2}$), visible shivering (S), 'walking on the spot' (W), temperature of the vertebral canal (– – –), rectum (——), hypothalamus (. . . . . .), ear skin (– . – . –) and skin 1 cm above a hind hoof (– . . . – . . . –). (Hales and Jessen, unpublished observations).

with scrotal heating appears to be explicable on the basis of changes in metabolic rate and vasomotor activity[22]. Whether this applies to Bligh's results remains unknown, as Phillips and Raghavan[81] have shown that established panting in a warm environment can be rapidly inhibited by cooling a 900 cm² area of body skin to 10 °C. As Bligh and Allen[8] have pointed out, the solution of this problem may have significance pertaining to the evolutionary change in respiratory function from panting to non-panting animals, if such a change has occurred.

4.3.3 Electrical responses from thermoreceptor sites

There have been numerous, detailed descriptions of electrical activity of nerve fibres from cutaneous thermoreceptors (see reviews in Refs. 72, 82, 83. Of major significance, particularly with regard to regional variations in gross peripheral thermosensitivity referred to in the preceding section, is the implication of differences in specific warm receptor sensitivity. Some studies of the cat have shown that the face is more sensitive than the leg[75, 84], but another report denies this[85]. Further, it has been shown[79] that the scrotal nerve of the rat contains large numbers of warm receptor units; these, like those in the face and leg of the cat referred to above, exhibit a very markeo increase in impulse

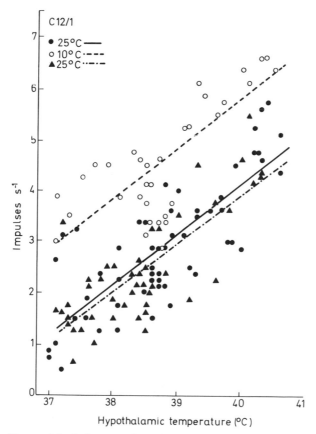

Figure 4.5 Influence of ambient temperature on the responses of a hypothalamic neurone to changes in hypothalamic temperature in an anaesthetised cat. (From Hellon[47], courtesy of Springer–Verlag (1971))

frequency when their temperature exceeds about 38–40 °C, and a peak is reached at about 40–45 °C. This temperature of peak activity approximates the upper critical level for body temperature regulation and falls into the 'possible secondary level of thermoregulation' discussed by Bligh[2]. It would seem therefore, that any differences in the thermosensitivity of various regions of the skin appear to be related to the density of warm receptors and not to differences in the impulse-frequency characteristics of the thermal response of individual receptors.

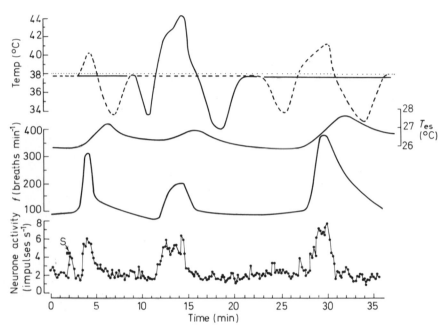

Figure 4.6   Effects of manipulating preoptic hypothalamic and spinal cord temperature on thermoregulatory mechanisms and electrical activity of a preoptic neurone in an anaesthetised rabbit. Preoptic temperature (– – – –), vertebral canal temperature (———), rectal temperature (. . . . . . .), respiratory frequency (f), and ear skin temperature (T_{es}). This unit responded to stroking of the fur (s). (From Guieu and Hardy[87], courtesy of *J. Appl. Physiol.* (1970))

Eleven years ago[82] there was no direct evidence for either the role of hypothalamic thermoreceptors as 'specific' temperature receptors by exhibiting specifically temperature-dependent neuronal activity, or for the possibility that the hypothalamus acted as a centre of convergence and integration. (That thermoregulatory responses could be evoked by alterations in hypothalamic temperature was of course well known, but this was open to a number of different interpretations.) There is now considerable evidence that the hypothalmus must be credited with both of these characteristics, and Hellon[47], who has been responsbile for much of the work in this field, has presented a detailed discussion of the subject. Three classes of neurones appear to act as specific sensors of local temperature, while a fourth class may be considered to fulfil the role of an 'interneurone', the latter responding to temperature changes in the mesencephalon[86] and spinal cord[87].

Wünneberg and Brück[88] and Simon and Iriki[89] have described proportional responses of spinal cord neurones to local temperature. This may be indicative of the presence of specific temperature receptors, which surely must be present because of the thermoregulatory responses (e.g. shivering) which can be elicited independently of the existence of supraspinal CNS structures. However, in view of Guieu and Hardy's demonstration of the influence of spinal cord temperature on hypothalamic neuronal activity[87] (see Figure 4.6), there is an obvious need for more work in this area.

Crucial evidence on the functioning of these control systems was provided by the demonstration that peripheral temperature will influence the firing rate of some hypothalamic neurones[47, 90], and that thermoregulatory responses could be correlated with the neuronal activity[87]; Figures 4.5 and 4.6 illustrate these phenomena.

4.3.4 Putative neurotransmitters involved in thermoregulation

There is now considerable evidence supporting the proposal that 5-hydroxy-tryptamine (5-HT) and noradrenaline (NA) act as transmitters in the hypothalamus, to mediate thermoregulatory responses. (See reviews in Refs. 91–94).

Attempts to clarify this aspect of the thermoregulatory control system have been confounded by reports of opposite effects of the drugs in different species. Bligh et al.[95] have tabulated these results. (Note that there was an error in their table, NA injected into the anterior hypothalamus of the cat causes a fall in body temperature.) Thus, in general, NA results in a fall and 5-HT in a rise of body temperature in the monkey, cat and dog, and the reverse holds for the rabbit, sheep, goat and rat. Both drugs cause body temperature of the mouse and ox to fall. Despite this variation between representatives of the placental mammals, if this concept of temperature regulation is to be fully exploited then studies of other animal groups seems warranted. Hales and Baird[96] have reported that a monotreme, the echidna (*Tachyglossus aculeatus*) responds to both the drugs by a fall in body temperature.

The transmitters supposedly act in the pathways between thermoreceptors and effectors, and, therefore, the influence of administered drugs must depend upon the existing state of activity of the pathway under investigation. It has taken some time for full realisation of the need to carefully control ambient environmental temperatures. For example, Bligh et al.[95] showed that NA caused a rise in body temperature of the sheep, goat and rabbit in warm environments, and a fall in cold environments, supposedly because this substance acts to inhibit thermoregulatory mechanisms. Further, the expected importance of hypothalamic temperature[97] and of spinal cord temperature (Bligh and Maskrey, personal communication) has now been demonstrated. An additional point frequently neglected, is the need to correlate responses of thermoregulatory effectors with body temperature changes. It has been observed in this laboratory that the expected changes in thermoregulatory mechanisms accompany the changes in body temperature in the rat, sheep and echidna, but that the cat frequently exhibits a 'deranged' response; for example, although 5-HT and prostaglandins E_1 and E_2 invariably evoke a rise in body temperature, there is often concurrent peripheral vasodilatation, increased respiratory frequency, and sometimes piloerection and shivering in the cat (Baird, Hales and Lang, unpublished observations).

Besides the biogenic amines supposedly acting in neuronal pathways between warmth and cold receptors and effector mechanisms, the involvements of a cholinergic pathway from cold receptors has also been implicated[95, 98, 99].

Considerable interest was recently aroused when it was reported that a number of prostaglandins (PG), particularly E_1 and E_2 evoked a marked rise in body temperature in the cat, rat and rabbit. These three species normally vary in their responses to the biogenic amines, and it, therefore, seemed that 'an ideal general mediator for raising temperature' might have been found[100-102]. The above results were all obtained in an approximately thermoneutral environment, and have also been found to hold true for the sheep[103]. In this latter study, PGE_1, E_2, F_{2a} and F_{1a}, were also shown to increase body temperature in a warm environment by inhibiting panting and sometimes evoking shivering, and in a cool environment by increasing the intensity of shivering. It was, therefore, concluded that the PGs act as though they are involved in the pathway from cold receptors to heat production, with an inhibitory pathway to heat loss mechanisms, i.e. as if in the cholinergic pathway referred to above. To date, the only results which do not conform with this picture for the prostaglandins, have come from observations on the echidna, in which PGs caused a fall in body temperature[96, 141].

The widely adopted experimental approach to this subject has been based on the injection of simulator drugs into a lateral cerebral ventricle, although the use of various agents to block the release or uptake of transmitter, as well as microinjections into the hypothalamus and 'push-pull' hypothalamic cannulae have also been employed. Such approaches might be considered as being somewhat crude, and considerable scepticism has arisen about the exact mode of action of the drugs. The obvious possibility of local changes in hypothalamic temperature and/or blood flow has been discounted[104-106].

Three, possibly more subtle approaches, would appear to be available. The putative transmitters referred to above, all occur naturally in brain tissue. Thus, if they are involved in a particular thermoregulatory pathway, then the turnover rate should alter when that pathway is activated. Simmonds[107, 108] has demonstrated that the rate of turnover of NA and 5-HT in various regions of the brain, particularly the hypothalamus, increased during heat stress of the rat; however, this was not in a manner entirely predictable on the basis of changes in the thermoregulatory system. Probably the most significant results obtained by this approach have come in relation to the prostaglandins: Holmes[109] perfused the cerebral ventricles of dogs, and found that intraventricular 5-HT caused a fourfold increase in the release of PGE, but adrenaline or NA had no effect. This conforms with the proposed role of 5-HT in cholinergic pathways from cold receptors[98, 99], and with the previously discussed effects of intraventricular injections of PGs; however, it is difficult to reconcile with the concept of 5-HT involvement in a pathway from warm receptors.

A second approach involves the cross-perfusion of cerebrospinal fluid (CSF). By this means it has been shown that when CSF is transferred from a cold donor to a thermoneutral recipient monkey, shivering is evoked in the latter (see Myers' review[92]).

The most elegant approach to the question of neurotransmitters would appear to be to locate specific 'thermoregulatory' neurones and then observe the response of the neurone to direct application of drugs by micro-iontophoresis. In fact, Beckman and Eisenman[110] have attempted this approach, but these early results were disappointing because of the small number of cells which responded. For example, only 2 out of 25 thermodetector-type cells showed amine sensitivity. However, some warm-sensitive 'interneurones' had their discharge rate increased by acetylcholine and decreased by NA. Some cold-sensitive 'interneurones' were excited by NA but depressed by 5-HT. Both rats and cats responded similarly, and therefore the results for cats do not conform with theories based on intraventricular injections of the drugs.

In conclusion, it appears highly probable that 5-HT, NA, acetylcholine and PGs are involved in neurotransmission within the thermoregulatory centres of the central nervous system (CNS). Implications of this appear even more significant when, for example, the mechanisms of pyrogen action, and the inhibited production of PGs by aspirin are taken into account (e.g. see Refs. 11 and 12). However, the precise means of involvement of the transmitters remains to be determined. It is difficult to accept the existence of 'true species differences' and it is even surprising that such apparent advancements in this concept of temperature regulation have been made, when the commonly employed experimental methods are taken into account: thermoregulatory responses may vary with the drug dose level, peripheral and core temperatures, not to mention possible interference with many CNS functions. More studies employing the approach described immediately above are required, because, for example, the supposed inverse responses of the cat and rat were no longer present.

4.3.5 Specific circulatory influences on thermoregulation

Awareness by researchers of the possible role of the circulating blood in the transmission of thermal information is not always obvious.

The frequently reported divergence between brain and extracerebral temperature in many animals (particularly those which pant) during exposure to various environmental conditions, now has a basis for an explanation. Of prime importance is the cooling of brain afferent arterial blood as it passes through the carotid rete, by nasal efferent venous blood as it passes through the cavernous sinus[113, 114]. It further appears that in the dog, the amount of blood by-passing the cavernous sinus by way of the facial vein may be varied[115], and that blood draining nasal regions via the angularis oculi veins of sheep may enter not only the cavernous sinus, but also the straight and transverse sinuses[116]. The presence or absence of the carotid rete in many animal species has been documented[117].

A mechanism such as that described above for preferentially cooling the brain is likely to contribute significantly to the high heat tolerance of, for example, some African antelopes[118] and the Australian Merino sheep[119] in natural environments. It is also feasible that this same mechanism is involved in the changes in panting which occur with alterations in temperature or humidity of inspired air, or during sudden cooling following heat stress (see Section 4.3.2).

It was clear in the earlier discussion of sweating (see Section 4.2.3) that many aspects of local control of sweat gland activity which have been attributed to the activity of thermoreceptors, require re-examination to separate the possible role of the local microcirculation.

Finally, the circulation as a whole must convey information about the thermal status of tissues to specific thermoreceptors, and as pointed out by Cremer and Bligh[91], this must provide important feed-back from effectors to sensors.

There are a number of reports in which the results would be explicable on the basis of heat transfer by the blood, and others in which circulatory rather than nervous pathways for the transmission of thermal information may be readily implicated. Many studies need to be repeated, or at least reappraised with this in mind.

4.3.6 Conclusions

The integrated responses of thermoregulatory effector mechanisms to heat, and available information concerning hypothalamic neuronal activity and neurotransmitters, lead one back to a former concept that it is *mean* body temperature which is being regulated. However, some neurones in the hypothalamus respond only to local temperature, some to temperature changes in other areas of the brain and in the spinal cord, some to peripheral temperature, and some respond to more than one of these factors; thus there would appear to be the provision for convergence and integration in the preoptic region of the hypothalamus. The role of the circulating blood in conveying thermal information commands wider recognition and requires further examination.

4.4 THERMOREGULATION IN THE PERINATAL PERIOD

In the newborn of the majority of mammals, fully effective temperature regulation develops over a number of days, and therefore one frequently reads that 'the newborn is incompetent with respect to the regulation of body temperature', or even that it is 'poikilothermic'.

Because of a relatively high ratio of body surface area to volume, the newborn has a high metabolic demand for the normal maintenance of body temperature, and as a consequence, may not respond to heat until ambient temperature has reached a relatively high level, only a few degrees below that of the body. Therefore, heat loss by radiation, convection and conduction soon become insignificant and evaporative heat loss mechanisms assume paramount importance. Thus the newborn dog does not pant when exposed to heat, until about 3 days of age and panting is not really effective until about 3 weeks of age[120]. The newborn pig is similarly vulnerable to heat, lacking the ability to sweat and exhibiting weak panting responses relative to the adult[121]. In contrast to the newborn pup and piglet, the lamb and calf have well developed evaporative heat-loss mechanisms. In the newborn lamb panting during exposure to hot environments enables a tolerance similar to that of adult sheep[122]. The calf has extremely well-developed sweating and panting mechanisms, and recent studies by Bianca and Hales[9] led to the conclusion that the newborn calf is more heat tolerant than the one-year-old calf, probably because of greater sweating capacity per unit of metabolic body size; these newborn calves were capable of a 20-fold increase in cutaneous moisture loss during heat stress. With respect to the maturation of heat-loss mechanisms, Hey and Katz[123] have recently dispelled previous beliefs that the newborn human baby cannot sweat (Figure 4.7). The baby appears

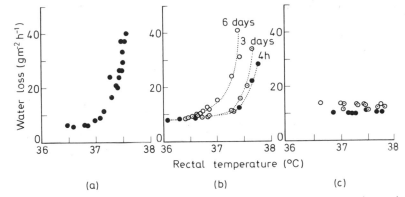

Figure 4.7 Relationship between total evaporative water loss and rectal temperature (a) Response on the day of birth, of a girl born 2 weeks before term. (b) Response of a girl born 3 weeks before term (●:age 4 h; ☉:3 days; ○:6 days). (c) Response on three separate occasions during the first 10 days of life, of a girl born 6 weeks before term. (From Hey and Katz[123], courtesy of *J. Physiol.* (*London*) (1969))

to hold an intermediate position compared with the above species. On the day of birth the ability to sweat is present, but only a 3–5-fold increase in cutaneous moisture loss is possible during heat stress (compared with 14–28 in adult man, Table 4.1), although this increases significantly even over the first few days of life.

The total number of sweat glands is fixed at birth, and the number per unit area of skin therefore decreases directly in inverse proportion to the increasing body surface area with body growth. However, there appears to be species differences in changes in sweat gland function with age. Hales et al.[124] showed that in oxen 4–20 h, 6 months and 12 months old, sweat gland density decreased from 3824 to 1795 to 1350 glands cm^{-2} while moisture loss per gland during mild heat stress increased from 4.3×10^{-6} to 9.0×10^{-6} to 11.0×10^{-6} g h^{-1} for the three groups respectively, thereby resulting in insignificant differences in total moisture loss per unit area of body surface. However, Foster *et al.*[125] showed that in humans 7–10 days and 17–34 years old, the number of sweat glands activated in an area of skin decreased from 98 to 48 glands, and the volume of sweat produced increased from 5.3×10^{-3} to 76×10^{-3} µl gland^{-1} for the two groups respectively, thereby resulting in a sevenfold increase in total moisture loss per unit area of body surface. Therefore, sweat glands of the adult compared with those of the newborn, are approximately three times as productive in oxen, and approximately 14 times as productive in humans.

When one considers the stability of the intrauterine thermal environment of the foetus, the high degree of maturation of autonomic thermoregulatory effector mechanisms in the newborn of many species could be somewhat surprising. Indications of an increase in placental blood flow during exposure of the pregnant ewe to a warm environment have led to the suggestion that the mother is sensitive to foetal temperature[126]. However, the stage of gestation at which thermoreceptors and thermoregulatory effector mechanisms become responsive in the foetus is not definitely established. Brück[127] has reported that babies born 2–3 months before term are able to control skin blood flow effectively, however, as shown in Figure 4.7, the ability to sweat is present 3 weeks but not 6 weeks before term. Further, the relatively high thyroxine level normally found in the foetal lamb, decreases sharply 5–10 days before parturition[128], which might be indicative of maturation of some facet of the thermoregulatory system. Thus in the above studies, the presence of vasomotor responses corresponded to the elapse of approximately 70% of the gestation period in the human, whereas the sweating responses in the human and thyroxine changes in the lamb corresponded to the elapse of approximately 94% of the gestation period. These results appear to be indicative of differences in the gestational stage at which various heat-regulating mechanisms become effective, rather than there being an absence of thermosensitivity. An outstanding omission in our knowledge is the lack of explanations for apparent thermoregulatory incompetence in the newborn of many species. For instance, does central and peripheral thermosensitivity change with age? (Figure 4.7 indicates a decrease in the threshold rectal temperature at which sweating was detected during the first 10 days after birth of the baby). Does the newborn conserve energy by being more tolerant of bradythermia?

4.5 PHYLOGENESIS OF THERMOREGULATORY MECHANISMS

If body temperature regulation in its broad sense is to be fully understood then there is an obvious need to study not only different species of placental mammals, but also all other animal groups. For example, recent studies demonstrating the importance of behavioural thermoregulation and indicating that this probably preceded the evolution of autonomic mechanisms has led to more attention being paid to the role of behaviour in regulating body temperature in 'higher' mammals (see Chapter 7). It is beyond the scope of the present review to cover this topic in which research has advanced so rapidly in recent years[8, 38, 129-131].

4.6 ENERGY COST OF HEAT-LOSS PROCESSES

The efficiency of a thermoregulatory process can be thought of as the total energy expended by the process relative to the fraction of this energy which has actually benefited the animal.

4.6.1 Vasodilatation and sweating

There have been no attempts to estimate the energy cost of increasing blood flow through dilated peripheral blood vessels, probably because it is reasonable to assume that the energy cost would be negligibly small. Work involved would be done by the heart, and during mild heat stress, when blood flow to regions of heat loss is at or near maximum levels[41], it has been shown[132] that neither right nor left ventricular work are altered in the ox. Further, total body oxygen consumption does not change either under these conditions although there is marked panting, or during maximal cutaneous vasodilatation and moderate panting induced by selective heating of the spinal cord in a cold environment (Figure 4.4).

Likewise, the energy cost of sweating is difficult to estimate. Ohara[133] made *in vitro* measurements of the oxygen consumption of skin slices and of isolated sweat glands of humans. Activation of the glands by adding pilocarpine to the incubation medium caused about a threefold increase in oxygen consumption. It was also noted that apocrine glands consumed two or three times more oxygen than did eccrine glands. Depending upon whether estimates of the oxygen cost of sweating in cattle are based on Ohara's data, or on the energy cost of urine and saliva formation[134], $>10\%$ or approximately 0.5% (respectively) of the total oxygen consumption is attributable to the energy cost of sweating. Because one estimate indicates that the energy cost of sweating could be quite significant, there is a need for further experimentation.

4.6.2 Panting

Previous reviewers[7, 82, 134] have unanimously concluded that the animal which relies on panting as an avenue of heat loss must be at a disadvantage with respect to energy expenditure, when compared with the animal which relies on sweating. This conclusion is based primarily on the fact that voluntary hyperventilation in man involves a considerable oxygen cost. However, voluntary hyperventilation in man and CO_2-induced hyperventilation in man and animals involves a much greater increase in depth than in frequency of breathing, and therefore contrasts markedly with the rapid, shallow form of respiration seen during panting. The difference in oxygen cost of the two types of hyperventilation in the ox is illustrated in Figure 4.8a. Hales and Findlay[45] reported that with approximately a fourfold increase in total respiratory ventilation in the ox, oxygen consumption was increased by approximately 48% during CO_2-induced hyperventilation but there was no significant change during thermally-induced hyperventilation (panting).

In oxen and sheep, the oxygen cost of panting during moderate heat stress appears to be so small that it is immeasurable[18, 41, 45, 46, 135, 136]. During severe heat stress of oxen, 7% of the total oxygen consumption has been attributed the energy cost of panting at the peak of the first phase of rapid shallow panting, and 11–25% during maximal slower deeper panting (see Section 4.7.2 for a description of these panting phases)[45,136].

Data concerning the oxygen cost of breathing are summarised in Table 4.3. Note that the oxygen cost of panting in the ox (which would be associated with a six- to eight-fold increase in total respiratory ventilation) is much lower than in the dog or pig, and approximates the oxygen cost of eupnoea in

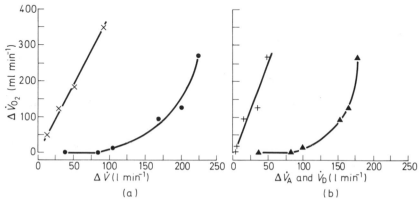

Figure 4.8 (a) Relationship between the change in oxygen consumption ($\Delta \dot{V}_{O_2}$) and change in total respiratory ventilation ($\Delta \dot{V}$) of oxen during panting under severe heat stress (●) or while respiration was stimulated by CO_2 (×). (b) Relationship between the change in oxygen consumption and change in alveolar ($\dot{V}_A$, +) and dead space ventilation ($\dot{V}_D$, ▲) during panting under severe heat stress. (From Hales and Findlay[45], courtesy of North Holland Pub. Coy.

man. Also, although the oxygen cost of CO_2-induced hyperventilation in man is less than that of voluntary hyperventilation, panting still involves a much lower oxygen cost than does CO_2-induced hyperventilation in the ox. It appears that the oxygen cost of panting is low in the cat[137] and high in the goat[138] but available data does not permit direct comparison with the above species.

Compared with the ox and sheep, the relatively high oxygen cost of panting in the dog (Hammel et al.[139] and Albers and co-workers[140-142]) is surprising, as Hull and Long[43] and Crawford[44] have shown that the dog often pants at a frequency approximating the resonant frequency of the respiratory system. This was largely supported by Hammel et al. but not by the results of Albers and co-workers. The latter appear to be more correct, because if the change in oxygen consumption measured by Hammel et al. were attributable to a Q_{10} effect, as the authors stated, a Q_{10} of >2 would have to be assumed. However, Albers directly estimated the coefficient of the Arrhenius equation, which led to their use of a Q_{10} of considerably <2. The relationship between alveolar and dead-space ventilation, and oxygen consumption during panting is illustrated in Figure 4.8b. This indicates the relatively low oxygen cost of dead-space ventilation (the important factor in the panting animal) compared with the high oxygen cost of alveolar ventilation, and may help in explaining the above differences in the oxygen cost of breathing. During panting, alveolar ventilation of the dog and goat increase to a much greater extent than does that of the sheep or ox (see Section 4.7.2), and CO_2-induced or voluntary hyperventilation involve a relatively large tidal volume. In view of the many studies of the oxygen cost of panting in the dog by Albers and co-workers, it appears, that there is a genuine difference between the energy cost of panting in the dog, ox and sheep. The higher oxygen cost of the slower deeper panting may be due in part to hypocapnia[142] and very likely involves variations in respiratory muscle activity[45, 46].

Table 4.3 Oxygen cost of breathing*

Species	Condition	O_2 cost of breathing (ml O_2/litre ventilation)	Reference
Man	Eupnoea	0.5–1.0	239
Man	Moderate voluntary hyperventilation	2–4	240
Man	Maximal voluntary hyperventilation	3–8	240
Man	CO_2-induced hyperventilation	1–3	239
Dog	Panting (anaesthetised)	1.2–1.6	142
Pig	Panting (maximal rapid shallow)	<2.1	153
Ox	Panting (maximal rapid shallow)	0.5	45
Ox	Panting (maximal slow deep)	<1.2	45
Ox	CO_2-induced hyperventilation	3–4	45

* for further data see Ref. 142

The above studies did not investigate the energetic efficiency of panting as a thermoregulatory mechanism, i.e. the degree to which the heat lost by the process of panting is offset by the heat produced in performing the work of panting. Thiele and Albers[143] have shown that in the dog, efficiency of panting at respiratory frequencies of from approximately 100 to 300 breaths/min is approximately 60%. However, as predictable from the lower energy cost of panting in the sheep, the efficiency is higher in this species, namely 100% with respiratory frequencies of from 100 to 270 breaths/min[18]. These results are puzzling since it is obvious that work must be done to increase respiratory ventilation. An explanation for the apparent absence of any energy cost might lie in a change in the metabolic rate of various tissues relative to one another, an increase in metabolic rate of respiratory muscles being offset by a decrease in other tissues; in fact, recent experiments indicate that this is what occurs (Hales[46] and see Figures 4.13 and 4.14) also see 'Note added in proof'.

In conclusion, it appears that the question of the energy cost and efficiency of panting has been resolved for some mammals, but there is a need for further studies on the energy cost of sweating and possibly of vasodilatation.

4.7 RESPIRATORY FUNCTION DURING HEAT STRESS

4.7.1 Respiration in man

Unlike animals which rely on panting for evaporative heat loss, man exhibits little change in respiration if resting in a hot environment. If deep body temperature is raised by up to $3\,°C$ by severe external heat stress[144], or in a pathological state[145] (Chapot, et al. personal communication), total respiratory ventilation increases by only approximately 30%. However, this increase is primarily due to increased tidal volume[146, 147], and therefore causes a fall in arterial or venous P_{CO_2} by 10–20 mmHg[147] (Chapot et al. personal communication). Although Cunningham and O'Riordan[144] showed that the increase in ventilation during external heat stress is much greater (approx. sixfold) if hypocapnia is prevented, there is a persistent hypocapnia in chronic fever which shows a highly significant straight line correlation with body temperature (Chapot et al. personal communication). The significance of this hypocapnia might be recognised in terms of its possible influence on the circulation and on sweating (see Sections 4.8 and 4.2.3). It is apparent that the regulation of blood gas and acid-base status retains considerable significance compared with temperature effects on respiration in man, in contrast to the panting animal in which thermoregulatory functions may force the sacrifice of blood gas and acid-base regulation. In fact, during hyperthermia, respiratory sensitivity to CO_2 is doubled in man[144] but is reduced to one third in the dog[148].

4.7.2 Respiratory ventilation and blood gases during panting

In the panting animal, the respiratory system is subjected to conflicting demands: the need for increased heat loss from the respiratory tract calls for an increase in respiratory ventilation via the thermoregulatory drive, while 'normal' respiratory control mechanisms must at the same time attempt to maintain alveolar ventilation at the level required to meet the body's metabolic needs. These requirements could be met by reducing the tidal volume while respiratory frequency is increased, thereby restricting the increasing total respiratory ventilation to the respiratory dead space. The existence of such a situation has been largely assumed, although some measurements of tidal volume and the carbon dioxide content of blood provided supporting evidence. However, changes in respiratory activity of the panting animal are marked, and therefore only with modern techniques has it been possible to evaluate respiratory function during panting, with minimal disturbance to the animal.

The most detailed studies have been in the ox (Ref. 149 and see this for earlier references). During severe heat stress (approximately $40\,°C$ T_{db} and $38\,°C$ T_{wb}), there are two phases in the respiratory response, while deep-body temperature increases from approximately 38.5 to $42\,°C$ over a period of 2–3 h. Respiratory frequency first increases to approximately ten times the control level and then decreases to approximately seven times the control or 70% of the peak level. Concurrently, tidal volume first decreases to approximately 60% of the control value and then increases to approximately equal or sometimes even exceed control levels. These changes result in more than a fivefold increase in respiratory minute volume at the peak of the first phase of rapid shallow panting, and up to an eightfold increase during the second phase of slower deeper panting. Similar changes occur in the sheep, but with respiratory frequency commonly increasing to 15 times the control level and tidal volume decreasing to 25% (as little as 18%) of the control level[150]. The situation appears similar in the conscious dog[151], but in the anaesthetised animal, respiratory minute volume decreases during the phase of slower deeper panting[152]. The pig appears to rely heavily on panting for evaporative heat loss, and yet up to a deep-body temperature of 42 °C, respiratory minute volume shows only about a threefold increase due to almost an 18-fold increase in respiratory frequency while tidal volume is reduced to approximately 20% of the control level; the pig does not show the change to slower deeper panting[153]. Mild heat stress of the above species results in respiratory activity typical of the early stages of severe heat stress.

Total respiratory ventilation has been partitioned into alveolar and dead-space ventilation in the anaesthetised dog[152], conscious sheep[150], and conscious ox[149] (Figure 4.9). During mild heat stress of the ox, dead space ventilation increases at a rate 15 times greater than does alveolar ventilation. Under these conditions, the changes in arterial P_{CO_2}, P_{O_2} and pH are very slight and probably physiologically insignificant; oxygen consumption changes little (see Section 4.6.2). Thus there is a marked increase in respiratory ventilation associated with the control of body temperature within about 0.5 °C of control levels, and at the same time normal metabolic functions of the respiratory system experience little disturbance. There is therefore a balance between the thermoregulatory and respiratory drives on the respiratory system. However, during severe heat stress, although the increase in ventilation is initially largely restricted to the respiratory dead space, respiratory frequency eventually increases out of proportion to the reduction in tidal volume. At the peak of rapid shallow panting in the ox there is more than a sevenfold increase in dead-space ventilation but alveolar ventilation is less than doubled. Hales and Webster[150] reported a threefold increase in dead-space ventilation but only a 60% increase in alveolar ventilation of the sheep; in the dog, alveolar ventilation is approximately doubled even during relatively mild panting[141]. Dead-space ventilation was not measured in this latter study, but Albers[152] had reported that in the anaesthetised dog, dead-space ventilation increases to approximately 14 times and alveolar ventilation to approximately five times control levels at the peak respiratory frequency. The efficiency of the panting mechanism with respect to the distribution of ventilation between the alveoli and dead space is therefore much higher in the ox and sheep than in the dog, as previously discussed[149]. In this respect, the goat seems least efficient, since alveolar ventilation increases when respiratory frequency increases, even under very mild heat stress[138].

During the second phase of slower deeper panting, alveolar ventilation in the ox and sheep increases to four or five times control levels, and results in a severe respiratory alkalosis. Arterial P_{CO_2} may be less than 10 mmHg and pH may exceed 7.7 units[41, 149, 150, 154]. Thus, during panting in severe heat, there is ultimately a breakdown in the balance between respiratory and thermoregulatory demands on the respiratory system; this begins when tidal volume starts to increase, and becomes particularly marked a short time later when respiratory frequency begins to decrease. Control of this pattern of panting is considered in the following section.

Ventilation of the alveoli is maintained or slightly increased during rapid shallow panting even though tidal volume is often less than the anatomical dead space of the respiratory tract[149, 150]. Probably of prime importance in

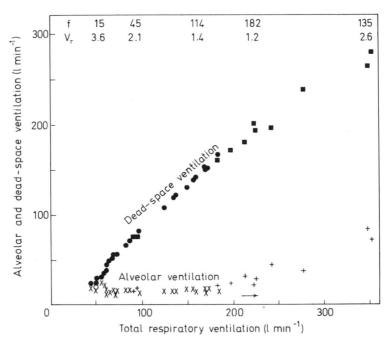

Figure 4.9 The changes in alveolar and dead-space ventilation with increasing total respiratory ventilation during panting. Results from eight experiments on two oxen in environments of 40 °C T_{db}, 28 °C T_{wb} (●, ×), 40 °C T_{db}, 38 °C T_{wb} (■, +) and 16 °C T_{db}, 14 °C T_{wb} (the ten points of lowest ventilation which each represent the mean of three control measurements). The arrow indicates the transition from rapid, shallow to slower, deeper panting; f, average respiration rate (breaths min⁻¹); V_t, average tidal volume (litres). (From Hales[221], courtesy of *J. Physiol.* (*London*) (1967))

controlling this is the cyclic raising and lowering of mid-respiratory position and intermittent periods of slower, deeper panting which both seem to be typical of panting. If tidal air moved through the respiratory passages in the form of a cone-shaped front, allowing a portion to penetrate deeply, this could also be a contributing factor.

Alterations in physiological dead space of the respiratory system during panting must have an important bearing on the alveolar ventilation. Physiological dead space decreases linearly with tidal volume during rapid shallow panting[149, 152], and the straight line depicting this relationship moves in a clockwise manner during slower deeper panting (regression lines calculated from the data of Hales and Findlay[149]). These changes could be due partly to changes in anatomical dead space (since this varies directly with lung volume and increases during hyperventilation[149]), or to specific adaptations such as the ability to ventilate the paranasal sinuses as has been reported for the wildebeest[155]. Further, during severe heat stress there is a decrease in mean pulmonary arterial pressure and an increase in central blood volume in the ox[132] and sheep[41], and when these facts are considered along with the very big increase in total and alveolar ventilation it seems reasonable to expect changes in ventilation/perfusion ratios in the lungs which would influence physiological dead space; the alveolar dead space must be greatly increased. In fact, both anatomical and physiological dead space increase during hypocapnia, possibly due to changes either in the composition of lung gases or in temperature (see Ref. 149).

Blood oxygenation changes little during mild heat stress but ultimately alters markedly under severe heat stress. As would be expected, the hyperventilation that occurs under the latter conditions results in a very marked increase in arterial oxygen tension (P_{O_2}) in the sheep, while the percentage oxygen saturation (S_{O_2}), which is already near maximum levels, increases slightly[41]. In the ox, arterial P_{O_2} increases throughout heat exposure but S_{O_2} remains essentially unchanged[154], but in the conscious dog, arterial P_{O_2} reaches its highest level at the peak of rapid shallow panting and then decreases so that it is equal to or even slightly less than the control level, while S_{O_2} remains raised by approximately 3%[151]. This must represent a difference in the relative importance of the effect of temperature and of CO_2 on the oxyhaemoglobin dissociation curve of the dog as compared with the ox and sheep: the curve is moved to the left in the dog and therefore must be more influenced by the low P_{CO_2} (Bohr effect), and to the right in the ox and sheep and therefore must be more influenced by the high temperature. This means that oxygen will be more readily available to the tissues of the ox and sheep. Further, the normally low blood oxygen capacity and content in sheep relative to many other species, means that there will be a greater independence between oxygen transport and pH, and this would benefit the alkalotic animal during panting. Despite enhanced oxygenation of arterial blood in the sheep, mixed venous P_{O_2} and S_{O_2} decrease. This might reflect tissue hypoxia, which has been indicated by increased levels of 'excess lactate' in the dog[156], ox[157] and sheep (Hales and Mabon, unpublished observations). Blood lactate and pyruvate concentrations may increase as a result of hypocapnia[158], and excess lactate levels during hypoxia are elevated by hypocapnia[159]. However, in the hyperthermic ox with panting inhibited by anaesthesia and blood gases and pH artificially controlled, excess lactate does not vary significantly from zero; furthermore, if hypocapnia and alkalosis of comparable magnitude to that seen during slower deeper panting is induced by artificial hyperventilation, lactate and pyruvate concentrations increase but excess lactate again remains essentially unchanged (Hales and Mabon, unpublished observations). Thus the excess lactate occurring during severe heat stress cannot be attributed to either hypocapnia and alkalosis or to hyperthermia *per se*, but must be associated with the respiratory muscle activity or circulatory changes which occur in the conscious panting animal.

4.7.3 Control of respiration in the panting animal

The question of specific thermoreceptor activity has been considered in Section 4.3. Aspects of the control of panting which may be considered more specifically related to respiration than to thermoregulation have received little attention in previous reviews. There are two questions to be considered, namely, (a) the control of rapid shallow panting during mild heat stress and the initial stages of severe heat stress, and (b) the control of slower deeper panting during severe heat stress.

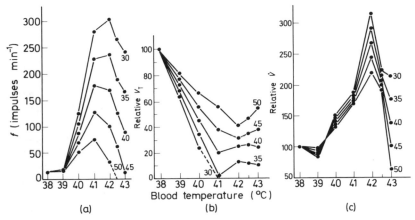

Figure 4.10 Inter-related effects of blood temperature and P_{CO_2} (mmHg) on (a) 'respiratory frequency' (f), (b) 'tidal volume' (V_T) and (c) 'total respiratory ventilation' ($\dot{V}$), these functions being estimated from electrical activity of the phrenic nerve in the vagotomised, anaesthetised dog. (From Pleschka[162], courtesy of Springer–Verlag (1969))

A uniform concept embracing all details of the control of panting should not be of paramount concern, and quite possibly does not even exist, especially when interspecies differences discussed in earlier sections are recalled. Thus, although it is generally accepted that vagal afferent fibres from the lungs play an important role in the regulation of respiratory rate and depth, any possible role of this nervous pathway in the control of panting must vary widely between species; panting is largely unaffected by vagotomy in the dog, cat, rabbit and lamb[38], but is abolished in the rat and guinea-pig[160].

Nevertheless, the first question posed above might be largely resolved in terms of direct influences of temperature on nervous pathways involved in pulmonary control, and a paradoxical CO_2 effect (Figure 4.10). Thus, the phrenic nerve (anaesthetised dog)[161, 162] and more specifically, fibres associated with the slowly adapting pulmonary stretch receptors (anaesthetised rat)[163] exhibit an increase in discharge with raised temperature, and this effect is augmented by hypocapnia. This possible role of the phrenic and associated receptors in stimulating respiratory frequency accords nicely with the observed initiation of panting by raising the temperature of the body of a dog while its head is perfused with blood from a normothermic donor[49]. However, it is probably unnecessary to attribute any specific role to the phrenic or vagus nerves and associated receptors in the normal initiation of panting; against this would be the reported influences of vagotomy mentioned above, and the repeated demonstration (see Ref. 2) that structures high in the brain stem mediate the panting response to temperature changes. For example, Von Euler et al.[164] showed that increased temperature will cause respiratory frequency to increase in the cat whether it is vagotomised or intact, but the brain stem, particularly the upper areas, must be intact. This thermal effect contrasts notably with CO_2 stimulation of respiratory frequency which requires intact vagus nerves. It appears that the Hering–Breuer reflex

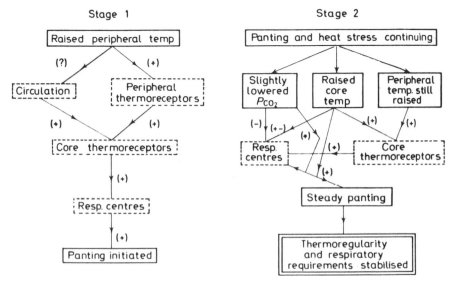

Figure 4.11 Schematic representation of a proposed two-stage system for the control of panting. Inhibition (—), and stimulation (+). Specific phenomena are enclosed by solid lines, and pathways by broken lines

normally controls respiratory frequency and in the absence of the pneumo-taxic centre, maintains a relatively constant depth; the pneumotaxic centre normally controls the respiratory depth and in the absence of the Hering–Breuer reflex, maintains a relatively constant rate[165]. Further, although respiration in normothermia is depressed by hypocapnia, the responses of specific neurones in the respiratory centres to changes in CO_2 varies consider-ably, and in fact, reciprocal responses to CO_2 have been reported[166].

A scheme for the control of rapid shallow panting which takes into account both thermoregulatory and respiratory influences as outlined above, might be represented by a two-stage process as depicted in Figure 4.11. That is, specific thermoregulatory pathways are responsible for the initiation of panting but then specific pulmonary pathways decrease the depth and further increase the frequency of breathing. A further contributing factor could be the cyclic changes in depth of breathing and in mid-respiratory position described earlier, as this could result in oscillations in arterial P_{CO_2}.

The cause of the apparent breakdown in the balance between thermo-regulatory and respiratory demands on the respiratory system with the change from rapid shallow to slower deeper panting during severe heat stress and the drive to increase ventilation in the face of a worsening alkalosis is not clear. Because the phase of slower deeper panting quickly reverts to the rapid shallow form on reduction of ambient heat load[40], many past explana-tions are untenable, namely heat damage to central mechanisms, muscle fatigue, alterations in respiratory mechanics, the regulation of alveolar ventilation to meet oxygen requirements, and tissue hypoxia[45, 150, 157].

In view of the severity of the respiratory alkalosis which develops, the driving force must be extremely powerful. The respiratory sensitivity to CO_2 is reduced[148], and for example, Pleschka et al.[167] were unable to produce classical post-hyperventilation apnoea in anaesthetised dogs even with arterial P_{CO_2} as low as 5 mmHg, when body temperature was above about 40 °C. One might suggest that the chemoreceptors of the medulla oblongata (so important in the regulation of respiration) are buffered from the changes which occur in the blood, by changes in brain blood flow and/or brain metabolism. Recent measurements of these latter two functions show that they are unlikely to be involved[168]. Examination of the CSF has revealed smaller and slightly slower changes in gas and acid-base status compared with those in the blood, and a decrease in CSF $[HCO_3^-]$ during slower deeper panting[169]. Thus the chemosensitive areas of the brain are probably not subjected to as marked a degree of inhibition as had previously been deduced from blood analysis, and the decreasing CSF $[HCO_3^-]$ might even participate in the stimulation of ventilation.

Possibly the nervous pathways involved in pulmonary control, and the paradoxical CO_2 effects discussed earlier, are again involved with the change to slower deeper panting. As illustrated in Figure 4.10, all patterns of electrical activity in the phrenic nerve of the anaesthetised dog become reversed when blood temperature exceeds 41–42 °C, and this conforms with the pattern of respiratory activity described by Albers[152]. Further, in the study of the anaesthetised rat by Schoener and Frankel[163], six of the 30 slowly adapting pulmonary stretch receptors examined exhibited a temperature response only above a critical temperature level of 40–43.5 °C; also, in the 13 receptors in which a generally progressive facilitation of activity occurred with increas-ing temperature, the effect was markedly greater with a change from 41 to 42 °C than at lower levels of temperature. The cause of these changes appears unexplained, but the concept is readily acceptable since similar multiphasic responses occur in, for example, peripheral thermoreceptors (see Refs. 72 and 82), and some temperature sensitive hypothalamic neurones are only affected above a threshold temperature[47].

Normally, the carotid body chemoreceptors play an extremely important role in the regulation of respiration, and there are at least four possible avenues by which they might be stimulated during panting. Firstly, a decrease in the internal P_{O_2} could result from a decrease in blood flow induced by the hypocapnia[170]. Secondly, the increased temperature might cause stimulation by either direct or indirect means[171]. Thirdly, there is the excitatory effect of increased sympathetic activity[172]. Fourthly, the stimulating effects on respiration of adrenaline and noradrenaline have been shown to occur via the carotid bodies[173]; plasma levels of the catecholamines increase markedly in the ox when body temperature exceeds about 40.5 °C[174].

The effect of temperature on the medulla oblongata is not clear, and neither is the mechanism of action. Holmes *et al.*[175] reported that there was a heat sensitive region in the medulla oblongata from which an increase in tidal volume could be elicited, but Chai *et al.*[176] recorded a decrease in respiratory frequency and tidal volume during local heating of the medulla. In both laboratories, participation of more rostral areas of the brain was excluded, but possible effects of temperature on chemosensitive areas of the medulla[177] were not, and therefore this latter mode of action of the temperature remains a possibility.

Work on the ox and sheep indicated that the pattern of panting is due to the hypothalamus attaining a critical temperature level of approximately 40.5 °C, and that skin temperature is less likely to be involved[40, 67, 178]. Panting in the anaesthetised animal does not begin until body temperature approximates this level, and it seems reasonable to accept this as representing the upper level of broad-band temperature control in the two-tiered temperature regulating system proposed by Bligh[2] and referred to in Section 4.3. As suggested previously, at temperatures above 40.5 °C the regulation of body temperature may take precedence over the regulation of acid-base balance, and during post-heat cooling when brain temperature is falling very rapidly, the regulation of acid-base balance may resume its predominance[178]. At this latter time the rapid shallow respiratory movements might be considered to represent a compromise between the inhibition of breathing by the low P_{CO_2} (as in post-hyperventilation apnoea) and the remaining thermal stimulus to panting; the form of breathing is indicative of a decrease in alveolar ventilation, and in fact, arterial P_{CO_2} in the ox 3 min after removal from the heat was approximately 23 mmHg compared with 10 mmHg at the end of heat exposure (Hales, unpublished observations). To test the hypothesis that the regulation of hypothalamic temperature was critical, Findlay and Hales[179] used chronically implanted thermodes to manipulate the temperature of the hypothalamus of the conscious ox during severe heat stress. However, no change in the pattern of panting could be evoked. More recent preliminary experiments have indicated that heating the spinal cord can cause a change from rapid shallow to slower deeper panting when the animal is in a moderately hot environment and hypothalamic temperature is 39.4–40.6 °C[5]. Thus in view of the various factors discussed in Section 4.3.1 and 4.3.2, and the conclusion in Section 4.3.6 that *mean* body temperature was the regulated variable, it seems likely that the drive to slower, deeper panting could be found here.

4.7.6 Conclusions

Detailed descriptions of respiratory function during panting are now available for some species, and although all factors involved in the control of rapid shallow panting are not entirely proven, a tenable picture is available. However, with respect to the phase of slower deeper panting which develops during severe heat stress, many questions remain to be answered. For example, would vagotomy prevent slower deeper panting or post-heat rapid shallow panting? There is the need for the repetition in the conscious animal, of Chapot[161] and of Pleschka's[162] work concerning temperature and CO_2 effects on pulmonary nervous pathways. Possible roles of the carotid bodies and medulla oblongata have yet to be clarified. Finally, further experiments involving manipulation of the temperature of 'prime sites' of deep-body thermoreceptors appear to be warranted. An excellent demonstration of the extreme potency of thermal stimuli with respect to the control of respiration has come from observations on the anaesthetised cat by Dr M. E. Schläfke (personal communication). Thus, if body temperature is raised, respiratory activity is still observed after section of the sinus and vagus nerves and cold blockade of chemosensitive areas of the medulla oblongata; apnoea is induced in normothermic animals.

4.8 CARDIOVASCULAR ADJUSTMENTS TO HEAT

There are many and varied changes in gross cardiovascular function and in the blood flow ($\dot{Q}$) through specific tissues during acute heat stress. The prime function of many changes is direct involvement in the regulation of heat loss from the body, other changes indirectly sub-serve that prime function, while still other changes are secondary consequences of, for example, alterations in body temperature, blood gas and acid-base status, and hormone status.

4.8.1 Gross cardiovascular function

The effects of exposure to heat without the complication of exercise do not appear to have been studied in any great detail in man. When body temperature is raised by 0.5 °C or more, cardiac output increases by 30–75%, but blood pressure changes little due to a decrease in total peripheral resistance which is involved in the increase in cutaneous blood flow (see following section). The increase in cardiac output is initially due mainly to accelerated heart rate[180, 181] although an increase in stroke volume may assume importance as the duration of heat stress is extended. Studies of man and other mammals almost invariably (excluding the goat[138]) show an increase in heart rate with increasing body temperature, an expected consequence of the excitatory effect of increased temperature on the sino-atrial node, and of direct enhancement of cardiac muscle contraction even independently of the pacemaker influence. The effect of hyperthermia on heart rate of the ox and chicken, in which cardiac regulation differs considerably, is explicable entirely in terms of the increase in body temperature[182]. As pointed out by Guyton[183], the results from Brendel et al.[184] illustrated in Figure 4.12, provide a clear demonstration of the intimate relationship between cardiac output and body metabolism (in the anaesthetised dog) the Q_{10} of both being approximately 2.5; although this is so, other factors must be borne in mind in considering the conscious animal[41, 132]. Thus, in the severely heat-stressed ox, when rectal temperature increases from 40.5 to 41.5 °C, the increase in cardiac output is only half that in heart rate because of a proportional decrease in stroke volume; in the sheep, there is only an insignificant increase in cardiac output despite a 30% increase in heart rate. Such apparent variation in the influence of temperature may be attributable to effects of the respiratory alkalosis[185] and variations in intrathoracic pressure in the conscious panting animal. However, Colton and Frankel[186] have reported

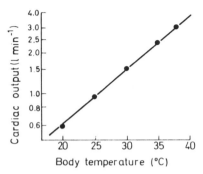

Figure 4.12 Semi-logarithmic plot of the relationship between body temperature and cardiac output in the anaesthetised dog. (From Guyton[183], derived from the data of Brendel *et al.*[184], courtesy of Springer–Verlag and W. B. Saunders & Co.

blood pressure and heart rate changes in hyperthermic, artificially normocapnic dogs which were essentially the same as those which occurred when hypocapnia was permitted to develop[156]; these results therefore illustrate the powerful influence of temperature.

4.8.2 Regional circulation

Obvious alterations in $\dot{Q}$ specifically involved in the regulation of body heat loss would be expected to involve an increase to the skin, to the nasobuccal regions particularly in panting animals, and to the respiratory muscles in panting animals (Figures 4.13 and 4.14).

One of the most important functions of the circulation is the transfer of heat from deep to superficial body tissues. The existence of a marked increase in cutaneous $\dot{Q}$ during heat stress has been demonstrated in man and other animals by plethysmographic techniques, or by the measurement of tissue heat conductance or of skin temperature. Although the results from such studies are not disputed, direct absolute measurements have only recently been made using radioactive krypton in the anaesthetised rabbit[187] and radioactive microspheres in the conscious sheep[41]. A shortcoming of the latter study is that only capillary $\dot{Q}$ was measured, and since arteriovenous anastomoses (AVAs) are present in these tissues and likely to be patent (see Section 4.8.3), total $\dot{Q}$ was most probably greater than that reported.

Nevertheless, in this study it was possible not only to separate the $\dot{Q}$ to underlying fat and deep skeletal muscle, as was often imprecise in past studies, but with respect to body skin, to separate the $\dot{Q}$ to panniculus muscle which adheres very closely to the true skin and lies only about 2 mm below

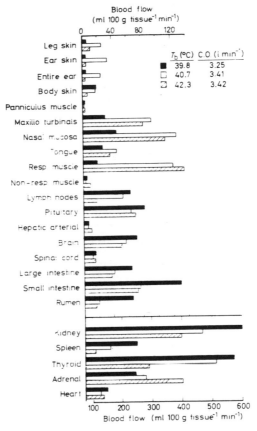

Figure 4.13 Absolute tissue blood flow in the conscious sheep in a thermo-neutral environment (■, 16 °C T_{db} and 12 °C T_{wb}) and during severe heat stress (exposure to 42 °C T_{db} and 39 °C T_{wb}), at the peak of rapid shallow panting (□) and during maximal slower deeper panting (▨). T_b, deep body temperature; C.O. cardiac output from data of Hales[41], courtesy of Springer–Verlag (1973)

the outer surface of the body. Also, the simultaneous measurement of $\dot{Q}$ to all other body tissues has been possible, and the results are shown in Figure 4.13. The decline in panniculus muscle $\dot{Q}$ while the overlying skin $\dot{Q}$ increases during mild heat stress should be noted; this might have considerable implications for heat transfer. Also, the temperature of skin of the extremities at the peak of rapid shallow panting was not significantly different from that during mild heat stress and yet $\dot{Q}$ was much greater[41]. This illustrates the possible independence between skin temperature and skin $\dot{Q}$, as was contended by Aschoff[188]. Also, there was a highly significant decrease in skin $\dot{Q}$ during advanced stages of severe heat stress. This might be taken to represent 'heat-vasoconstriction', a concept that would be consistent with the decreased percentage of cardiac output passing through AVAs in some severely heat-stressed animals[41], and with the eventual decrease in conductance in the heat-stressed dog[139]. This could be interpreted as a specific response to reduce the uptake of heat from the external environment during severe heat stress, or it could also be a consequence of the prevailing hypocapnia and alkalosis[189] or increased levels of catecholamines[190].

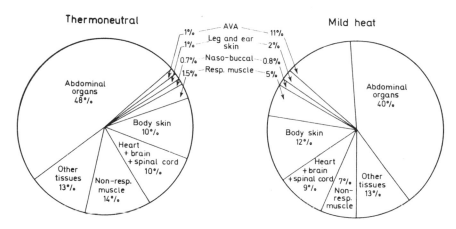

Figure 4.14 Distribution of cardiac output in the conscious sheep in a thermoneutral environment (16 °C T_{db} and 12 °C T_{wb}) and during mild heat stress (40 °C T_{db} and 26 °C T_{wb}). There was no change in the absolute value of cardiac output. (Compiled from data of Hales[41,46], courtesy of Springer–Verlag (1973))

Very few studies of skin $\dot{Q}$ in the heat have been orientated towards aspects other than its role in heat transfer. However, there are probably other functions of considerable importance as discussed in Sections 4.2.3 and 4.3.5.

The nasopharyngeal and buccal regions are well known to be important in heat loss, particularly in the panting animal. This knowledge has arisen from direct measurements of the temperature of tissues and respired air, and from the observed stimulatory effect of raised humidity on panting. Evidence of changes in $\dot{Q}$ in the nasopharyngeal region was indirect[191] until the measurements shown in Figure 4.13. On the basis of Ederstrom's[192] measurements of venous outflow from the tongue of the anaesthetised dog, it has been commonly stated that blood flow to the tongue increases during panting. However, the increase does not occur during mild heat stress[41], but only when deep-body temperature reaches about 41 °C (Ref. 192; Figure 4.13). The respiratory muscles of the panting animal are another tissue in which a change of $\dot{Q}$ might be expected as a specific part of a heat-loss response. As described in Section 4.6, $\dot{Q}$ to the diaphragm and crus muscles shows a >threefold increase during mild heat stress and almost an eightfold increase during advanced stages of severe heat stress; respective figures for the intercostals were zero and almost fourfold (Figure 4.13).

Besides the above changes in tissue $\dot{Q}$ which are specifically and directly involved in thermoregulation, other changes occur which might be regarded in two categories. Firstly, changes in $\dot{Q}$ which might reflect alterations in metabolic activity of the tissue. Secondly, $\dot{Q}$ may decrease in some regions to make blood available for increasing or maintaining $\dot{Q}$ in other regions. such changes are illustrated in Figures 4.13 and 4.14. The decrease in thyroid $\dot{Q}$ correlates with reduced thyroid activity, and the increased adrenal $\dot{Q}$ correlates with increased adrenal activity which occurs under these conditions. Neither hepatic arterial (Figure 4.12) nor total hepatic $\dot{Q}$[193] change during heat stress.

Blood flow to the spinal cord in the conscious sheep shows no change during mild heat stress, but there is a transient but statistically significant decrease during severe heat stress[168]. Whether this has any particular physiological significance is unknown, although it might be assumed that the maintenance of normal $\dot{Q}$ is desirable to retain normal functioning. Brain $\dot{Q}$ is considered in Section 4.9.

Decreased $\dot{Q}$ to the kidneys and splanchnic areas in man has previously been described[32, 194, 195]. Decreased $\dot{Q}$ to non-respiratory skeletal muscle would also appear to be important in sheep during mild heat stress, and the overall picture (Figure 4.14) is one of a redistribution of cardiac output to meet the situation confronting the organism. An analogous situation occurs during haemorrhagic shock[196] and during cold exposure[197]. It is noteworthy that although cardiac output is increased during heat stress of man and most other mammals studied, there is no significant change in the sheep, and therefore the increases in $\dot{Q}$ required for body temperature regulation in this species are brought about entirely by a redistribution of cardiac output.

4.8.3 Blood flow through arterio-venous anastomoses

It is widely accepted[191] that a major role of AVAs in many tissues is the regulation of heat exchange with the environment. Their existence, with a diameter of 5–150 µm in the skin, nasal mucosa and tongue, has been well established. The extreme efficiency of even small AVAs in heat transfer was illustrated in 1895 by Stewart, whose work has been presented by Krogh in 1936[198]. Thus, 1 mm³ of blood takes over 6 h to pass a capillary of 10 µm diameter when flowing at the high rate of 0.5 mm s⁻¹. For the thermal equilibration of 1 mm³ of blood with surrounding tissue, 1 s is probably more than sufficient, and this would be provided in a vessel of 100 µm diameter when the flow rate was 12 mm s⁻¹.

In view of the apparent significance of $\dot{Q}$ through AVAs, and the numerous anatomical and histological studies, it is surprising that so little attention has been paid to their physiology with respect to body temperature regulation (see Piiper[199] and Thauer[191]). Studies of the hindleg of the anaesthetised dog led Piiper to conclude that 'no heat exchange worth mentioning occurs in the AVAs owing to unfavourable heat exchange conditions (short flow time, small surface area, thick walls). It is probable that the major part of the heat exchange occurs in the small veins into which the AVAs flow.' Unfortunately, most of Piiper's preparations were denervated, and this together with the effects of anaesthesia could grossly influence the results. Piiper's conclusions do not necessarily contradict the preceding discussion; the AVAs may provide a low resistance pathway for high $\dot{Q}$ to the veins where heat exchange occurs, as well as permitting heat exchange within themselves.

Radioactive microspheres have been recently used in the conscious sheep[41] to show that the fraction of the total cardiac output passing through AVAs >15 μm in diameter was approximately 1% in a thermoneutral environment and 11% during mild or severe heat stress (Figure 4.14). It would appear that all AVAs are opened under mild heat stress, however, the maximum values recorded in individual animals were 14.5% in mild heat and 22.2% in severe heat. This blood is not supplying nutrients to tissues, and therefore the significance of these figures should be emphasised.

4.8.4 Control of cardiovascular changes during heat stress

Despite the almost universal rule that cardiac output parallels the level of whole body metabolism, or that local tissue $\dot{Q}$ parallels local metabolic requirements[183], it is clear from the foregoing discussion that during heat-stress cardiac output and its distribution in terms of $\dot{Q}$ through various tissues is under the influence of many factors. The major controlling factors might be grouped into three major categories, namely metabolic, specific thermoregulatory, and secondary thermoregulatory. It is beyond the scope of the present review to cover this entire topic, and some influencing factors (e.g. the effect of temperature on cardiac function) have already been mentioned.

Peripheral and central nervous control of the cutaneous circulation has been reviewed by Thauer[191] and Shepherd and Webb-Peploe[194]. The existence of sympathetic and parasympathetic vasoconstrictor and vasodilator fibres with possible antagonism by sudomotor (sympathetic) induced dilatation, is well established, as is the vasodilator response which follows hypothalamic heating or changes in local skin temperature. A most significant recent advancement has been the demonstration of spinal cord thermoreceptor participation in the control of $\dot{Q}$ to peripheral tissues[61, 200, 201]. Besides demonstrating that spinal cord heating elicits increased $\dot{Q}$ to the skin, it has also been shown that the activity of cutaneous sympathetic nerves decreases[202]; a converse situation exists with respect to the intestines. Such changes conform with the redistribution of $\dot{Q}$ within the body during external heat stress (Figures 4.12 and 4.13). Thermal stimulation of the hypothalamus gives similar results[201, 203, 204], and these workers have suggested 'that the sympathetic nervous system may perform under special conditions a sort of "reciprocal innervation" of functionally antagonistic autonomic effector systems'. It surely only requires that AVAs in the two regions should be under reciprocal control.

An important aspect of the control of all the thermoregulatory mechanisms is the interaction between various sites of thermoreceptors within the body core and in the body 'shell' (see Sections 4.3.1 and 4.3.2). Whittow[205] showed that the magnitude of the fall in total peripheral resistance elicited by hypothalamic heating depends upon ambient (skin?) temperature. Ingram and Legge[61] have made the first comprehensive approach to this problem with respect to the circulation. Peripheral $\dot{Q}$, as measured plethysmographically in the tail of the pig, could be varied in a predictable manner by artificial manipulation of hypothalamic, spinal cord or skin temperature.

As with specific thermoregulatory responses discussed in Section 4.2, gross cardiovascular function is influenced by temperature changes in the hypothalamus, spinal cord and medulla oblongata[175, 176, 200, 201, 205], and is therefore probably similarly related to *mean* body temperature. The fineness of the controls involved is illustrated by the cyclic changes in blood pressure and total peripheral resistance which parallel typical cyclic panting activity[206]; this might be due to cyclic changes in brain temperature induced via the circulation (see Section 4.3.5).

In the above discussion of the control of cardiovascular changes during heat stress, only apparently specific thermoregulatory factors have been considered. However, many 'secondary' consequences of the heat stress are likely to exert significant influences. Thus, Whittow[207] has shown that the pressure wave in the right ventricle and aorta may be considerably distorted during vigorous panting in the ox; this appears to be caused by the respiratory movements, and could affect cardiac function. The marked increase in blood levels of catecholamines which occurs during hyperthermia in some species, and the hypocapnia and alkalosis which develops in man and other species (see Section 4.7.2) all have obvious implications for control of the circulation.

4.8.5 Conclusions

Effects of heat stress on gross cardiovascular function in man and some other species, and on the regional distribution of cardiac output in the sheep are clear. However, because of apparently large species differences, extrapolation of results between species should be done with extreme caution. Blood flow to certain tissues has been shown to be influenced by hypothalamic and spinal cord temperature, but these studies require extension to many other tissues, and to the role of thermoreceptors in other areas and of 'secondary' consequences of heat stress. Clarification of the precise role and control of blood flow through arterio-venous anastomoses is required, and further information is needed on blood flow to regions of the skin in relation to regional heat exchange and the control of sweating.

4.9 BRAIN BLOOD FLOW AND METABOLISM DURING HEAT STRESS

The effects of heat on the brain has received little attention until recently, despite the knowledge that brain $\dot{Q}$ is markedly decreased during hypothermia and that brain $\dot{Q}$ is highly sensitive to changes in P_{CO_2} (which decreases markedly during severe heat stress). In the anaesthetised dog[208, 209] and conscious sheep[168], mild heat stress does not cause any significant change in brain $\dot{Q}$. However, with progressive hyperthermia the results of different studies appear to be conflicting. Thus, Demers *et al.*[208] found that when rectal temperature of the anaesthetised dog is raised by approximately 3.7 °C, the brain $\dot{Q}$ at a given level of arterial P_{CO_2} is raised, however, if the normal development of hypocapnia is taken into account, then there is no significant change in $\dot{Q}$. This is broadly supported by Nemoto and Frankel's[209] work on anaesthetised dogs with rectal temperature raised by approximately 4.2 °C. Later work by Colton and Frankel[186] illustrates the over-riding role of hypocapnia. In this latter study, brain $\dot{Q}$ during hyperthermia was not significantly different from that during normothermia if the animals were hypocapnic under both conditions, however, hyperthermia resulted in raised brain $\dot{Q}$ if the animals were normocapnic or hypercapnic; the sensitivity of brain $\dot{Q}$ to changes in P_{CO_2} was increased. In the conscious sheep with rectal temperature raised by approximately 1 or 2.5 °C, and marked hypocapnia, brain $\dot{Q}$ was decreased to approximately 75% of control levels (Figure 4.13). A much greater decrease would be expected to result from the hypocapnia, and therefore there is presumably a buffering influence of the hyperthermia. Cerebral vascular resistance was reduced in the anaesthetised dog[209] whereas it remained unchanged in the conscious sheep[168]. Total cerebral oxygen consumption was increased in the anaesthetised dog[208, 210] whereas oxygen consumption by the cerebral hemispheres either decreased slightly or was essentially unchanged in the conscious sheep[168].

An explanation for the discrepancies between results of the above studies is not clear; it may lie in the different techniques used for assessing brain $\dot{Q}$. Use of anaesthetic agents in the dogs might have influenced results, as Cranston and Rosendorff[211] have shown that pentobarbitone anaesthesia depresses $\dot{Q}$ in the cerebral cortex, but not in the hypothalamus, and these authors also pointed out the apparently variable effects of anaesthesia on total brain $\dot{Q}$. Finally it seems notable that the body-temperature changes provoked in the anaesthetised dogs were extremely severe.

Because of the different functions of regions of the brain, and the demonstrated regional variations in brain temperature, studies of regional $\dot{Q}$ in the brain were essential, however, the results obtained to date[168] may be considered disappointing. Thus, relative to control levels, $\dot{Q}$ decreased to 77% in the cerebellum, 56% in the pons, and approximately 67% in all other regions. The percentage of total brain $\dot{Q}$ received by the pons decreased and that received by the cerebellum increased during severe heat stress, and no other changes were significant. In these studies, only discrete measurements of $\dot{Q}$ were made, and therefore a technique enabling continuous monitoring of $\dot{Q}$ might provide more enlightening results.

4.10 PHYSIOLOGICAL FAILURE DURING HEAT STRESS

The ambiguity of the title of this section is intentional as the limited scope of this review permits only brief mention of two topics about which so much has been written, namely (a) the assessment of thermal stress and (b) physiological failure during exposure to extreme heat stress including pathological states which lead to failure of homeothermy.

Because the deep-body temperature of animals with which we are most commonly concerned is usually found to lie within narrow limits, the widely held view that the ability to control body temperature near the 'normal' level indicates heat tolerance, is understandable. However, the ability to tolerate wide deviations in body temperature is surely advantageous with respect to the conservation of energy (e.g. see Ref. 118). It appears therefore, that an index of heat strain should be orientated more towards the secondary effects of thermoregulatory responses or the effects of the temperature load *per se* on vital physiological systems. For example, in panting animals, the time at which blood gas and acid-base status become altered should represent an important stage in thermoregulatory reactions. In view of the many roles played by the circulation in combating heat stress (probably in many species), some readily assessable index of circulatory function would seem desirable; thus heart rate, which usually increases with heat exposure (see Section 4.8.1) may be a useful index of stress. Many aspects of the assessment of thermal stress were discussed at a recent symposium[1]. The ultimate test of the significance of the heat stress must be productivity, in terms of work or mental activity in man, and production of meat, milk, etc., by animals: for example exposure to high temperatures for only 1–3 h can induce infertility in the ram[212]. More studies orientated towards the assessment of heat stress in terms of 'secondary' alterations in physiological functions appear to be warranted.

Tetany or carpopedal spasms occur readily in man during respiratiory alkalosis whether or not it is associated with heat stress. Tetany has not been observed in the panting dog[213] and extremely rarely in the ox[149]. Although a fall in ionised calcium is commonly cited as the cause of tetany, this is by no means proven in man and does not appear to have been examined in panting animals.

Heat stroke is an extremely dangerous 'failure' of the thermoregulatory system which usually terminates in death unless there is external cooling. In a survey of 36 healthy young men engaged in strenuous physical excrtion, it was found[214] that at the onset of unconsciousness, many cases showed disseminated intravascular coagulation, and in fatal cases, autopsy revealed gross haemorrhages, congestion and cellular degeneration. In this regard the electron-microscope study by Sohal *et al.*[215] appears to be particularly important. Their results indicated that endothelial cell damage due to an elevated body temperature may be the triggering mechanism of disseminated intravascular coagulation. Also, the endothelial damage was sufficiently extensive to account for the extravasation of blood and fluids, which is a significant manifestation of fatal hyperpyrexia. These authors point out that the early recognition of these derangements as being a sign of heat stroke could provide an opportunity to intervene therapeutically.

There have been many studies orientated towards elucidating the actual mechanism of heat stroke, but attention is drawn to only one because of its apparent conformity with current concepts of CNS thermoregulatory mechanisms as discussed in Section 4.3.4. During convulsions induced by leptazol or strychnine in cats, a prostaglandin-like substance is released into the cerebrospinal fluid[216]. If this is so, then the apparent role of prostaglandins in stimulating heat production, causing vasoconstriction and inhibiting heat-loss mechanisms, together with the antagonistic effect of aspirin (see Section 4.3.4), conform with the clinical picture of convulsions and the beneficial effect of aspirin. Shibolet et al.[214] found that all but one of their subjects were profusely sweating at the onset of unconsciousness. Because this conflicts with the above commonly observed clinical picture, the possibility that basic mechanisms involved in heat stroke might vary depending upon the cause of the condition should be borne in mind.

4.11 FACTORS INFLUENCING PHYSIOLOGICAL RESPONSES TO HEAT

Specific thermoregulatory and 'non-specific' physiological responses to short-term heat stress are influenced by many factors that can only be mentioned briefly. It is hoped that earlier studies will be reviewed with these possible limitations in mind and that future studies will take them into account. Passing reference to many influential factors has already been made in preceding sections. Anaesthetics, particularly the barbiturates, depress or derange most physiological systems. For example, sweating and panting in response to heat can be completely suppressed by anaesthesia; $\dot{Q}$ to different regions of the brain is differentially influenced (see Section 4.9), $\dot{Q}$ to skeletal muscle is reduced while that to skin is unaltered[217] and the proportion of the cardiac output passing through AVAs is increased[218]. The temperature threshold for stimulation of a thermoregulatory mechanism and the level at which that mechanism and body temperature are regulated are modified by adaptation to hot or cold environments and show both circadian and seasonal variations. An important topic which has received considerable attention is the influence of water restriction: sweating and panting are markedly depressed, and the sudden increase in evaporative heat loss which is often seen when body temperature exceeds a certain level (e.g. Bianca[7] and Taylor[118, 219]) might be taken to indicate that the set-point temperature for the thermoregulatory system has been raised. It is particularly noteworthy from Taylor's work, that the relative contribution of panting and sweating is altered in the dehydrated state. The post-prandial state, acid-base status and insulation by the pelage and tissues, all influence responses.

Finally, the important differences between responses to natural outdoor environments and to artificial laboratory environments should be given greater consideration; for example, sweating rates from cattle are much higher in the field than in supposedly comparable laboratory environments, and cutaneous moisture loss in the laboratory is increased following a few hours exposure to sunlight[220]. Further, when the rectal temperature of sheep approximates 41 °C, they are quite distressed in the laboratory but appear to be undisturbed in the field, and under these conditions, there is an inverse correlation between rectal temperature and respiratory frequency[119].

4.12 EXPERIMENTAL METHODS AND TECHNOLOGY

A chapter such as this would be incomplete without acknowledgement of the remarkable changes in experimental methods and the technological achievements which in many instances have been largely responsible for advances in our understanding of aspects of thermal physiology. It is surprising that the electron microscope has played little part in research in this field. Attention to many of the factors listed in the preceding section (such as the use of conscious subjects when feasible, perhaps with chronic surgical implants, and attempts to establish physiological responses to natural environments), are leading to a re-thinking of many earlier concepts. Telemetry technology is advancing rapidly and will probably reveal many surprises. For obvious reasons, laboratory experiments remain essential, but one cannot help but wonder, for example, how different autonomic thermoregulatory reactions might be if behavioural thermoregulation was not almost universally prevented. Perfusion of the cerebral ventricles of the conscious animal is no longer uncommon, and even cross-perfusion between animals has been employed. The measurement of blood flow by ultrasonic, electromagnetic, radioactive gas and radioactive particle techniques is enabling detailed studies of circulatory dynamics. Only with the refinement of spirometry and pneumotachometry have reasonably sound studies of respiratory function during panting been possible. Refinements of whole-body partitional calorimetric techniques including development of the gradient-layer calorimeter, are providing the quantitative information so essential for a precise understanding of the complete physiological response. The provision of this sort of information, together with the data from so many other approaches, such as studies at the neuronal level, has led to the formulation of models of the biological control systems (e.g. see Bligh and Moore[4]). It would seem that only by using these models, aided by computers, will we eventually understand the systems with which we are concerned.

Acknowledgements

The author is grateful to Messrs J. W. Bennett and A. A. Fawcett for their assistance in preparation of the manuscript and to many colleagues for their critical reviewing of the manuscript.

Note added in proof

In the studies referred to in Section 4.6.2, the *energy cost of panting* was estimated by measuring the increase in energy expenditure associated with panting, and correcting this for factors known to also influence energy expenditure, such as the Q_{10} effect. Recent work[41, 46] has shown that the total physiological response to heat stress involves marked alterations in the metabolic rate of many tissues. Therefore, the above method for estimating the energy cost of panting is invalid in so far as it does not provide an estimate of the energy expenditure due to increased respiratory activity; rather, an estimate of the *net energy balance during panting* is obtained[18].

References

1. Hardy, J. D., Gagge, A. P. and Stolwijk, J. A. J. (1970). *Physiological and Behavioral Temperature Regulation* (Springfield: Thomas)
2. Bligh, J. (1966). The thermosensitivity of the hypothalamus and thermoregulation in mammals. *Biol. Rev.*, **41**, 317

3. Benzinger, T. H. (1969). Heat regulation: homeostasis of central temperature in man. *Physiol. Rev.*, **49**, 671
4. Bligh, J. and Moore, R. E. (1972). *Essays on Temperature Regulation* (Amsterdam: North-Holland)
5. McLean, J. A., Hales, J. R. S., Jessen, C. and Calvert, D. T. (1970). Influences of spinal cord temperature on heat exchange of the ox. *Proc. Australian Physiol. Pharmacol. Soc.*, **1**, No. 2, 32
6. McLean, J. A. and Calvert, D. T. (1972). Influence of air humidity on the partition of heat exchanges of cattle. *J. Agric. Sci.*, **78**, 303
7. Bianca, W. (1965). Cattle in a hot environment. *J. Dairy Res.*, **32**, 291
8. Bligh, J. and Allen, T. E. (1970). A comparative consideration of the modes of evaporative heat loss from mammals. In *Physiological and Behavioral Temperature Regulation*, 97 (J. D. Hardy, A. P. Gagge and J. A. J. Stolwijk, editors) (Springfield: Thomas)
9. Bianca, W. and Hales, J. R. S. (1970). Sweating, panting and body temperatures of newborn and one-year-old calves at high environmental temperatures. *Brit. Vet. J.*, **126**, 45
10. Robertshaw, D. and Taylor, C. R. (1969). A comparison of sweat gland activity in eight species of East African bovids. *J. Physiol.* (*London*), **203**, 135
11. Schmidt-Nielsen, K. (1964). Terrestrial animals in dry heat: desert rodents. In *Handbook of Physiology Section 4: Adaptation to the Environment*, 493 (D. B. Dill, E. F. Adolph and C. G. Wilber, editors) (Washington, D.C.: Amer. Physiol. Soc.)
12. Hainsworth, F. R. and Epstein, A. N. (1966). Severe impairment of heat-induced saliva-spreading in rats recovered from lateral hypothalamic lesions. *Science*, **153**, 1255
13. Hainsworth, F. R. (1967). Saliva spreading, activity and body temperature regulation in the rat. *Amer. J. Physiol.*, **212**, 1288
14. Stricker, E. M. and Hainsworth, F. R. (1970). Evaporative cooling in the rat: effects of hypothalamic lesions and chorda tympani damage. *Can. J. Physiol. Pharmacol.*, **48**, 11
15. Jenkinson, D. McE. (1970). The distribution of nerves, monamine oxidase and cholinesterase in the skin of the guinea pig, hamster, mouse, rabbit and rat. *Res. Vet. Sci.*, **11**, 60
16. Ingram, D. L. (1967). Stimulation of cutaneous glands in the pig. *J. Comp. Pathol. Therap.*, **77**, 93
17. Hutchinson, J. C. D. (1962). Adaptation of domestic animals to the tropics. *Biometeorology*, 55 (S. W. Tromp editor) (Oxford: Pergamon)
18. Hales, J. R. S. and Brown, G. D. (1973). Net energetic and thermoregulatory efficiency during panting in the sheep. *Pflügers Arch.*, (in press)
19. Waites, G. M. H. and Voglmayr, J. K. (1962). Apocrine sweat glands of the scrotum of the ram. *Nature*, (London) **196**, 965
20. Molyneux, G. S. (1965). Observations on the structure, distribution and significance of arterio-venous anastomoses in sheep skin. In *Biology of the Skin and Hair Growth*, 591 (A. G. Lyne and B. F. Short, editors) (Sydney: Angus and Robertson)
21. Nadel, E. R. and Stitt, J. T. (1970). Control of sweating in the squirrel monkey. *Physiologist* (*Washington*), **13**, 267
22. Hales, J. R. S. and Hutchinson, J. C. D. (1971). Metabolic, respiratory and vasomotor responses to heating the scrotum of the ram. *J. Physiol.* (*London*), **212**, 353
23. Robertshaw, D. and Taylor, C. R. (1969). Sweat gland function of the donkey (*Equus asinus*). *J. Physiol.* (*London*), **205**, 79
24. Foster, K. G. and Weiner, J. S. (1970). Effects of cholinergic and adrenergic blocking agents on the activity of the eccrine sweat glands. *J. Physiol.* (*London*), **210**, 883
25. Collins, K. J. and Weiner, J. S. (1962). Observations on arm-bag suppression of sweating and its relationship to thermal sweat gland 'fatigue'. *J. Physiol.* (*London*), **161**, 538
26. Peter, J. and Wyndham, C. H. (1966). Activity of the human eccrine sweat gland during exercise in a hot humid environment before and after acclimatisation. *J. Physiol.* (*London*), **187**, 583
27. Bligh, J. (1967). A thesis concerning the processes of secretion and discharge of sweat. *Environ. Res.*, **1**, 28

28. Robertshaw, D. (1968). The pattern and control of sweating in the sheep and the goat. *J. Physiol.* (*London*), **198**, 531
29. Jenkinson, D. McE. and Robertshaw, D. (1971). Studies on the nature of sweat gland 'fatigue' in the goat. *J. Physiol.* (*London*), **212**, 455
30. Fasciolo, J. C., Totel, G. L. and Johnson, R. E. (1969). Antidiuretic hormone and human eccrine sweating. *J. Appl. Physiol.*, **27**, 303
31. Senay, L. C., Prokop, L. D., Cronau, L. and Hertzman, A. B. (1963). Relation of local skin temperature and local sweating to cutaneous blood flow. *J. Appl. Physiol.*, **18**, 781
32. Robinson, S. (1963). Circulatory adjustments of men in hot environments. In *Temperature, Its Measurement and Control in Science and Industry*, Vol. 3, Part 3, 287 (J. D. Hardy, editor) (New York: Reinhold)
33. Ingram, D. L., McLean, J. A. and Whittow, G. C. (1963). The effect of heating the hypothalamus and the skin on the rate of moisture vaporisation from the skin of the ox (*Bos taurus*). *J. Physiol.* (*London*), **169**, 394
34. Schleger, A. V. and Bean, K. G. (1971). Factors determining sweating competence of cattle skin. *Australian J. Biol. Sci.*, **24**, 1291
35. Nadel, E. R., Bullard, R. W. and Stolwijk, J. A. J. (1971). Importance of skin temperature in the regulation of sweating. *J. Appl. Physiol.*, **31**, 80
36. MacIntyre, B. A., Bullard, R. W., Banerjee, M. and Elizondo, R. (1968). Mechanism of enhancement of eccrine sweating by localised heating. *J. Appl. Physiol.*, **25**, 255
37. Grant, R. T., Bland, E. F. and Camp, P. D. (1932). Observations on the vessels and nerves of the rabbit's ear with special reference to the reaction to cold. *Heart*, **16**, 69
38. Richards, S. A. (1970). The biology and comparative physiology of thermal panting. *Biol. Rev.*, **45**, 223
39. Ingram, D. L. and Whittow, G. C. (1962). The effects of variations in respiratory activity and in the skin temperatures of the ears on the temperature of the blood in the external jugular vein of the ox (*Bos taurus*), *J. Physiol.* (*London*), **163**, 211
40. Hales, J. R. S. (1969). Changes in respiratory activity and body temperature of the severely heat-stressed ox and sheep. *Comp. Biochem. Physiol.*, **31**, 975
41. Hales, J. R. S. (1973). Effects of exposure to hot environments on the regional distribution of blood flow and on cardiorespiratory function in sheep. *Pflügers Arch.* (in press)
42. Schmidt-Nielsen, K., Bretz, W. L. and Taylor, C. R. (1970). Panting in dogs: unidirectional air flow over evaporative surfaces. *Science*, **169**, 1102
43. Hull, W. E. and Long, E. C. (1961). Respiratory impedance and volume flow at high frequency in dogs. *J. Appl. Physiol.*, **16**, 439
44. Crawford, E. C. (1962). Mechanical aspects of panting in dogs. *J. Appl. Physiol.*, **17**, 249
45. Hales, J. R. S. and Findlay, J. D. (1968). The oxygen cost of thermally-induced and CO_2-induced hyperventilation in the ox. *Resp. Physiol.*, **4**, 353
46. Hales, J. R. S. (1973). Effects of heat stress on blood flow in respiratory and non-respiratory muscles in the sheep: An explanation of the apparent high efficiency of panting. *Pflügers Arch.* (in press)
47. Hellon, R. F. (1971). Central thermoreceptors and thermoregulation. *Handbook of Sensory Physiology*, Vol. 3 Part 1, 161 *Enteroceptors* (E. Neil, editor) (Berlin: Springer–Verlag)
48. Rautenberg, W., Simon, E. and Thauer, R. (1963). Die Bedeutung der Kerntemperatur für die chemische Temperaturregulation beim Hund in leichter Narkose I. Isolierte Senkung der Rumpfkerntemperatur. *Pflügers Arch.*, **278**, 337
49. Hales, J. R. S., Kao, F. F., Mei, S. S., Wang, C. and Gretenstein, M. (1970). Panting in heated cross-circulated dogs. *Amer. J. Physiol.*, **218**, 1389
50. Thauer, R. (1970). Thermosensitivity of the spinal cord. In *Physiological and Behavioral Temperature Regulation*, 472 (J. D. Hardy, A. P. Gagge and J. A. J. Stolwijk, editors) (Springfield: Thomas)
51. Rawson, R. O., Quick, K. P. and Coughlin, R. F. (1969). Thermoregulatory responses to intra-abdominal heating of sheep. *Science*, **165**, 919
52. Rawson, R. O. and Quick, K. P. (1970). Evidence of deep-body thermoreceptor response to intra-abdominal heating of the ewe. *J. Appl. Physiol.*, **28**, 813
53. Rawson, R. O. and Quick, K. P. (1972). Localisation of intra-abdominal thermoreceptors in the ewe. *J. Physiol.* (*London*), **222**, 665

54. Bianca, W. (1964). Thermoregulatory responses of the dehydrated ox to drinking cold and warm water in a warm environment. *Res. Vet. Sci.*, **5,** 75

55. Andersson, B., Ekman, L., Gale, C. C. and Sundsten, J. W. (1963). Control of thyrotrophic hormone (TSH) secretion by the "heat loss center". *Acta Physiol. Scand.*, **59,** 12

56. Hales, J. R. S. (1970). Hypothalamic control of heat loss mechanisms in the ox. *Proc. Australian Physiol. Pharmacol. Soc.*, **1,** No. 1, 43

57. Waites, G. M. H. (1962). Effect of heating the scrotum of the ram on respiration and body temperature. *Quart. J. Exp. Physiol.*, **47,** 314

58. Jessen, C., McLean, J. A., Calvert, D. T. and Findlay, J. D. (1972). Balanced and unbalanced temperature signals generated in spinal cord of the ox. *Amer. J. Physiol.*, **222,** 1343

59. Guieu, J. D. and Hardy, J. D. (1970). Effects of preoptic and spinal cord temperature in control of thermal polypnea. *J. Appl. Physiol.*, **28,** 540

60. Jessen, C. and Ludwig, O. (1971). Spinal cord and hypothalamus as core sensors of temperature in the conscious dog II. Addition of signals. *Pflügers Arch.*, **324,** 205

61. Ingram, D. L. and Legge, K. F. (1971). The influence of deep body temperatures and skin temperatures on peripheral blood flow in the pig. *J. Physiol. (London)*, **215,** 693

62. Jessen, C. and Mayer, E. Th. (1971). Spinal cord and hypothalamus as core sensors of temperature in the conscious dog I. Equivalence of responses. *Pflügers Arch.*, **324,** 189

63. Jessen, C. and Simon, E. (1971). Spinal cord and hypothalamus as core sensors of temperature in the conscious dog III. Identity of functions. *Pflügers Arch.*, **324,** 217

64. Hellstrøm, B. and Hammel, H. T. (1967). Some characteristics of temperature regulation in the unanesthetised dog. *Amer. J. Physiol.*, **213,** 547

65. Randall, W. C. (1963). Sweating and its neural control. In *Temperature, Its Measurement and Control in Science and Industry*, Vol. 3, Part 3, 275 (J. D. Hardy, editor) (New York: Reinhold)

66. Kosaka, M., Simon, E., Thauer, R. and Walther, O.-E. (1969). Effect of thermal stimulation of spinal cord on respiratory and cortical activity. *Amer. J. Physiol.*, **217,** 858

67. Ingram, D. L. and Whittow, G. C. (1962). The effect of heating the hypothalamus on respiration in the ox (*Bos taurus*). *J. Physiol. (London)*, **163,** 200

68. Baldwin, B. A. and Ingram, D. L. (1968). The influence of hypothalamic temperature and ambient temperature on thermoregulatory mechanisms in the pig. *J. Physiol. (London)*, **198,** 517

69. Jessen, C. (1967). Auslösung von Hecheln durch isolierte Wärmung des Rückenmarks am wachen Hund. *Pflügers Arch.*, **297,** 53

70. Jacobson, F. H. and Squires, R. D. (1970). Thermoregulatory responses of the cat to preoptic and environmental temperatures. *Amer. J. Physiol.*, **218,** 1575

71. Hales, J. R. S. and Jessen, C. (1969). Increase of cutaneous moisture loss caused by local heating of the spinal cord in the ox. *J. Physiol. (London)*, **204,** 40

72. Zotterman, Y. (1959). Thermal sensations. In *Handbook of Physiology Section 1: Neurophysiology*, Vol. 1, 431 (J. Field, H. W. Magoun and V. E. Hall, editors) (Washington D.C.: Amer. Physiol. Soc.)

73. Mitchell, J. W., Nadel, E. R. and Stolwijk, J. A. J. (1971). Thermal sensitivity coefficients of different skin areas. *Proc. Int. Union Physiol. Sci.*, **9,** 1175

74. Bligh, J. (1963). The receptors concerned in the respiratory response to humidity in sheep at high ambient temperature. *J. Physiol. (London)*, **168,** 747

75. Hensel, H. and Kenshalo, D. R. (1969). Warm receptors in the nasal region of cats. *J. Physiol. (London)*, **204,** 99

76. Kluger, M. J., Gonzalez, R. R. and Hardy, J. D. (1972). Peripheral thermal sensitivity in the rabbit. *Amer. J. Physiol.*, **222,** 1031

77. Waites, G. M. H. and Voglmayr, J. K. (1963). The functional activity and control of the apocrine sweat glands of the scrotum of the ram. *Australian J. Agr. Res.*, **14,** 839

78. Linzell, J. L. and Bligh, J. (1961). Polypnoea evoked by heating the udder of the goat. *Nature (London)*, **190,** 173

79. Iggo, A. (1969). Cutaneous thermoreceptors in primates and subprimates. *J. Physiol. (London)*, **200,** 403

80. Bligh, J. (1963). Inhibition of thermal polypnoea in the closely shorn sheep. *J. Physiol. (London)*, **168,** 764

81. Phillips, G. D. and Raghavan, G. V. (1970). Responses of unshorn and shorn sheep to thermal stress. *J. Physiol. (London)*, **208**, 317
82. Hardy, J. D. (1961). Physiology of temperature regulation. *Physiol. Rev.*, **41**, 521
83. Iggo, A. (1970). The mechanisms of biological temperature reception. In *Physiological and Behavioral Temperature Regulation*, 391 (J. D. Hardy, A. P. Gagge and J. A. J. Stolwijk, editors) (Springfield: Thomas)
84. Kenshalo, D. R., Duncan, D. G. and Weymark, C. (1967). Threshold for thermal stimulation of the inner thigh, footpad and face of cats *J. Comp. Physiol. Psychol.*, **63**, 133
85. Stolwijk, J. A. J. and Wexler, I. (1971). Peripheral nerve activity in response to heating the cat's skin. *J. Physiol. (London)*, **214**, 377
86. Nakayama, T. and Hardy J. D. (1969). Unit responses in the rabbit's brain stem to changes in brain and cutaneous temperature. *J. Appl. Physiol.*, **27**, 848
87. Guieu, J. D. and Hardy, J. D. (1970). Effects of heating and cooling of the spinal cord on preoptic unit activity. *J. Appl. Physiol.*, **29**, 675
88. Wünnenberg, W. and Brück, K. (1970). Studies on the ascending pathways from the thermosensitive region of the spinal cord. *Pflügers Arch.*, **321**, 233
89. Simon, E. and Iriki, M. (1971). Sensory transmission of spinal heat and cold sensitivity in ascending spinal neurons. *Pflügers Arch.*, **328**, 103
90. Wit, A. and Wang, S. C. (1968). Temperature-sensitive neurons in preoptic/anterior hypothalamic region: effects of increasing ambient temperature. *Amer. J. Physiol.*, **215**, 1151
91. Cremer, J. E. and Bligh, J. (1969). Body temperature and responses to drugs. *Brit. Med. Bull.*, **25**, 299
92. Myers, R. D. (1970). The role of hypothalamic transmitter factors in the control of body temperature. In *Physiological and Behavioral Temperature Regulation*, 684 (J. D. Hardy, A. P. Gagge, and J. A. J. Stolwijk, editors) (Springfield: Thomas)
93. Feldberg, W. (1970). Monoamines of the hypothalamus as mediators of temperature response. In *The Hypothalamus*, 1 (L. Martini, M. Motta and F. Fraschini, editors) (New York: Academic Press)
94. Hellon, R. F. (1972). Central transmitters and thermoregulation. In *Essays on Temperature Regulation*, 71 (J. Bligh and R. E. Moore, editors) (Amsterdam: North-Holland)
95. Bligh, J., Cottle, W. H. and Maskrey, M. (1971). Influence of ambient temperature on the thermoregulatory responses to 5-hydroxytryptamine, noradrenaline and acetylcholine injected into the lateral cerebral ventricles of sheep, goats and rabbits. *J. Physiol. (London)*, **212**, 377
96. Hales, J. R. S. and Baird, J. A. (1972). Effects of 5-hydroxytryptamine, noradrenaline, cholinomimetic substances and prostaglandins E_1 and E_2 on thermoregulation in the echidna. *Proc. Int. Union Physiol. Sci.* in *Proc. Australian Physiol. Pharmacol. Soc.*, **3**, No. 2, 172
97. Maskrey, M. and Bligh, J. (1971). Interactions between the thermoregulatory responses to injections into a lateral cerebral ventricle of the Welsh Mountain sheep of putative neurotransmitter substances and of local changes in anterior hypothalamic temperature. *Int. J. Bioclimatol. Biometeorol.*, **15**, 129
98. Myers, R. D. and Yaksh, T. L. (1969). Control of body temperature in the unanaesthetised monkey by cholinergic and aminergic systems in the hypothalamus. *J. Physiol. (London)*, **202**, 483
99. Avery, D. D. (1972). Thermoregulatory effects of intrahypothalamic injections of adrenergic and cholinergic substances at different environmental temperatures. *J. Physiol. (London)*, **220**, 257
100. Milton, A. S. and Wendlandt, S. (1971). Effects on body temperature of prostaglandins of the A, E and F series on injection into the third ventricle of unanaesthetised cats and rabbits. *J. Physiol. (London)*, **218**, 325
101. Feldberg, W. and Saxena, P. N. (1971). Further studies on prostaglandin E_1 fever in cats. *J. Physiol. (London)*, **219**, 739
102. Potts, W. J. and East, P. F. (1972). Effects of prostaglandin E_2 on the body temperature of conscious rats and cats. *Arch. Int. Pharmacodyn.*, **197**, 31
103. Hales, J. R. S., Bennet, J. W., Baird, J. A. and Fawcett, A. A. (1973). Thermoregulatory effects of prostaglandins E_1, E_2, F_{1a} and F_{2a} in the sheep. *Pflügers Arch.* **339**, 125

104. Findlay, J. D. and Thompson, G. E. (1968). The effect of intraventricular injections of noradrenaline, 5-hydroxytryptamine, acetylcholine and tranylcypromine on the ox (*Bos taurus*) at different environmental temperatures. *J. Physiol.* (*London*), **194**, 809
105. Hassler, C. R. and McCook, R. D. (1971). Hypothalamic blood flow in cats during injection of biogenic amines. *Amer. J. Physiol.*, **220**, 196
106. Rosendorff, C. and Cranston, W. I. (1971). Effects of intrahypothalamic and intraventricular norepinephrine and 5-hydroxytryptamine on hypothalamic blood flow in the conscious rabbit. *Circulation Res.*, **28**, 492
107. Simmonds, M. A. (1969). Effect of environmental temperature on the turnover of noradrenaline in the hypothalamus and other areas of rat brain. *J. Physiol.* (*London*), **203**, 199
108. Simmonds, M. A. (1970). Effect of environmental temperature on the turnover of 5-hydroxytryptamine in various areas of rat brain. *J. Physiol.* (*London*), **211**, 93
109. Holmes, S. W. (1970). The spontaneous release of prostaglandins into the cerebral ventricles of the dog and the effect of external factors on this release. *Brit. J. Pharmacol.* **38**, 653
110. Beckman, A. L. and Eisenman, J. S. (1970). Microelectrophoresis of biogenic amines on hypothalamic thermosensitive cells. *Science*, **170**, 334
111. Myers, R. D. (1971). Hypothalamic mechanisms of pyrogen action in the cat and monkey. In *Ciba Foundation Symposium on Pyrogen and Fever*, 131 (G. E. W. Wolstenholme and J. Birch, editors) (London: Churchill)
112. Tomlinson, R. V., Ringold, H. J., Qureshi, M. C. and Forchielli, E. (1972). Relationship between inhibition of prostaglandin synthesis and drug efficacy: support for the current theory on mode of action of aspirin-like drugs. *Biochem. Biophys. Res. Commun.*, **46**, 552
113. Hayward, J. N. and Baker, M. A. (1969). A comparative study of the role of the cerebral arterial blood in the regulation of brain temperature in five mammals. *Brain Res.*, **16**, 417
114. Baker, M. A. (1972). Influence of the carotid rete on brain temperature in cats exposed to hot environments. *J. Physiol.* (*London*), **220**, 711
115. Magilton, J. H. and Swift, C. S. (1969). Response of veins draining the nose to alarfold temperature changes in the dog. *J. Appl. Physiol.*, **27**, 18
116. Hales, J. R. S. (1972). Chronic catheterisation for sampling venous blood from the brain of the sheep. *Pflügers Arch.*, **337**, 81
117. Klosovskii, B. N. (1963). *Blood Circulation in the Brain*. (Translated by A. D. Behmoaram). (Jerusalem: Israel Program for Scientific Translations)
118. Taylor, C. R. (1969). The eland and the oryx. *Sci. Amer.*, **220**, 89
119. Brown, G. D. (1971). The responses of sheep and kangaroos to climate in a natural environment using multichannel telemetry. *Symposium on Biotelemetry*, **285**, 1 (CSIR 1971: Pretoria)
120. Jensen, C. and Ederstrom, H. E. (1955). Development of temperature regulation in the dog. *Amer. J. Physiol.*, **183**, 340
121. Mount, L. E. (1968). *The Climatic Physiology of the Pig*. (London: Edward Arnold)
122. Alexander, G. and Williams, D. (1962). Temperature regulation in the new-born lamb VI. Heat exchanges in lambs in a hot environment. *Australian J. Agr. Res.*, **13**, 122
123. Hey, E. N. and Katz, G. (1969). Evaporative water loss in the newborn baby. *J. Physiol.* (*London*), **200**, 605
124. Hales, J. R. S., Findlay, J. D. and Robertshaw, D. (1968). Evaporative heat loss mechanisms of the newborn calf, *Bos taurus*. *Brit. Vet. J.*, **124**, 83
125. Foster, K. G., Hey, E. N. and Katz, G. (1969). The response of the sweat glands of the new-born baby to thermal stimuli and to intradermal acetylcholine. *J. Physiol.* (*London*), **203**, 13
126. Hales, J. R. S., Hopkins, P. S. and Thorburn, G. D. (1972). Decreased blood P_{CO_2} in the ovine foetus during hyperthermia: implications for increased placental blood flow. *Experientia*, **28**, 801
127. Brück, K. (1961). Temperature regulation in the newborn infant. *Biol. Neonatorum*, **3**, 65
128. Hopkins, P. S. and Thorburn, G. D. (1971). Plasma thyroxine and cortisol concentrations of the foetal lamb. *Abstr. Fourth Asia and Oceania Congr. of Endocrinol.*, 170

129. Whittow, G. C. (1970). *Comparative physiology of thermoregulation*, **1**, (New York: Academic Press)
130. Richards, S. A. (1970). Physiology of thermal panting in birds. *Ann. Biol. Animale Biochim. Biophys.*, **10**, 151
131. Dawson, T. J. (1972). Primitive mammals and patterns in the evolution of thermoregulation. In *Essays on Temperature Regulation*, 1 (J. Bligh and R. E. Moore editors) (Amsterdam: North-Holland)
132. Whittow, G. C. (1965). The effect of hyperthermia on the systemic and pulmonary circulation of the ox (*Bos taurus*). *Quart. J. Exp. Physiol.*, **50**, 300
133. Ohara, K. (1951). Studies on the oxygen consumption of human skin tissues, with special reference to that of sweat glands. *Japan. J. Physiol.*, **2**, 1
134. Macfarlane, W. V. (1964). Terrestrial animals in dry heat: ungulates. In *Handbook of Physiology Section 4: Adaptation to the Environment*, 509 (D. B. Dill, E. F. Adolph and C. G. Wilber, editors) (Washington D.C.: Amer. Physiol. Soc.)
135. McLean, J. A. (1963). The partition of insensible losses of body weight and heat from cattle under various climatic conditions. *J. Physiol.* (*London*), **167**, 427
136. Whittow, G. C. and Findlay, J. D. (1968). Oxygen cost of thermal panting. *Amer. J. Physiol.*, **214**, 94
137. Adams, T., Morgan, M. L., Hunter, W. S. and Holmes, K. R. (1970). Temperature regulation of the unanesthetised cat during mild cold and severe heat stress. *J. Appl. Physiol.*, **29**, 852
138. Heisey, S. R., Adams, T., Hofman, W. and Riegle, G. (1971). Thermally-induced respiratory responses of the unanesthetised goat. *Resp. Physiol.*, **11**, 145
139. Hammel, H. T., Wyndham, C. H. and Hardy, J. D. (1958). Heat production and heat loss in the dog at 8–36 °C environmental temperature. *Amer. J. Physiol.*, **194**, 99
140. Albers, C. (1961). Der Mechanismus des Wärmehechelns beim Hund. II. Der respiratorische Stoffwechsel während des Wärmehechelns. *Pflügers Arch.*, **274**, 148
141. Siemon, G., Pleschka, K. and Albers, C. (1966) Die alveolar-arterielle Sauerstoffdifferenz (AaD O₂) und die alveolare Ventilation beim wachen Hund in Abhängigkeit von der Umgebungstemperatur. *Pflügers Arch.*, **289**, 255
142. Spaich, P., Usinger, W. and Albers, C. (1968). Oxygen cost of panting in anaesthetized dogs. *Resp. Physiol*, **5**, 302
143. Thiele, P. and Albers, C. (1963). Die Wasserdampfabgabe durch die Atemwege und der Wirkungsgrad des Wärmehechelns beim wachen Hund. *Pflügers Arch.*, **278**, 316
144. Cunningham, D. J. C. and O'Riordan, J. L. H. (1957). The effect of a rise in the temperature of the body on the respiratory response to carbon dioxide at rest. *Quart. J. Exp. Physiol.*, **42**, 329
145. Moser, K. M., Perry, R. B. and Luchsinger, P. C. (1963). Cardiopulmonary consequences of pyrogen-induced hyperpyrexia in man. *J. Clin. Invest.*, **42**, 626
146. Senay, L. C. and Christensen, M. L. (1967). Respiration of dehydrating men undergoing heat stress. *J. Appl. Physiol.*, **22**, 282
147. Gaudio, R. and Abramson, N. (1968). Heat-induced hyperventilation. *J. Appl. Physiol.*, **25**, 742
148. Kappey, F., Albers, C. and Schmidt, R. (1962). Die ventilatorische CO₂-Reaktion des Hundes während der Wärmetachypnoe. *Pflügers Arch.*, **275**, 312
149. Hales, J. R. S. and Findlay, J. D. (1968). Respiration of the ox: normal values and the effects of exposure to hot environments. *Resp. Physiol.*, **4**, 333
150. Hales, J. R. S. and Webster, M. E. D. (1967). Respiratory function during thermal tachypnoea in sheep. *J. Physiol.* (*London*), **190**, 241
151. Hales, J. R. S. and Bligh, J. (1969). Respiratory responses of the conscious dog to severe heat stress. *Experientia*, **25**, 818
152. Albers, C. (1961). Der Mechanismus des Wärmehechelns beim Hund. I. Die Ventilation und die arteriellen Blutgase während des Wärmehechelns. *Pflügers Arch.*, **274**, 125
153. Ingram, D. L. and Legge, K. F. (1969). The effect of environmental temperature on respiratory ventilation in the pig. *Resp. Physiol.*, **8**, 1
154. Findlay, J. D. and Whittow, G. C. (1966). The role of arterial oxygen tension in the respiratory response to localised heating of the hypothalamus and to hyperthermia. *J. Physiol.* (*London*), **186**, 333
155. Taylor, C. R., Robertshaw, D. and Hofmann, R. (1969). Thermal panting: a comparison of wildebeest and zebu cattle. *Amer. J. Physiol.*, **217**, 907

156. Frankel, H. M., Ellis, J. P. and Cain, S. M. (1963). Development of tissue hypoxia during progressive hyperthermia in dogs. *Amer. J. Physiol.*, **205**, 733

157. Hales, J. R. S., Findlay, J. D. and Mabon, R. M. (1967). Tissue hypoxia in oxen exposed to severe heat. *Resp. Physiol.*, **3**, 43

158. Eichenholz, A., Mulhausen, R. O., Anderson, W. E. and MacDonald, F. M. (1962). Primary hypocapnia: a cause of metabolic acidosis. *J. Appl. Physiol.*, **17**, 283

159. Cain, S. M. (1968). Effect of P_{CO_2} on the relation of lactate and excess lactate to O_2 deficit. *Amer. J. Physiol.*, **214**, 1322

160. Richards, S. A. (1968). Vagal control of thermal panting in mammals and birds. *J. Physiol.* (*London*), **199**, 89

161. Chapot, G. (1967). Action de la température et de FA_{CO_2} sur les décharges du nerf phrénique. *Pflügers Arch.*, **296**, 196

162. Pleschka, K. (1969). Der Einfluss der Temperatur auf dir elektrische Aktivität des Nervus phrenicus. *Pflügers Arch.*, **308**, 357

163. Schoener, E. P. and Frankel, H. M. (1972). Effect of hyperthermia and Pa_{CO_2} on the slowly adapting pulmonary stretch receptor. *Amer. J. Physiol.*, **222**, 68

164. Von Euler, C., Herrero, F. and Wexler, I. (1970). Control mechanisms determining rate and depth of respiratory movements. *Resp. Physiol.*, **10**, 93

165. Tang, P. C. (1967). Brain stem control of respiratory depth and rate in the cat. *Resp. Physiol.*, **3**, 349

166. Cohen, M. I. (1968). Discharge patterns of brain-stem respiratory neurons in relation to carbon dioxide tension. *J. Neurophysiol.*, **31**, 142

167. Pleschka, K., Albers, C. and Heerd, E. (1965). Der Einfluss der Temperatur auf die CO_2-Schwelle des Atemsystems. *Pflügers Arch.*, **286**, 142

168. Hales, J. R. S. (1973). The effects of heat stress on total and regional blood flow in the brain and spinal cord of the sheep. *Pflügers Arch.* (*London*), (in press)

169. Hales, J. R. S., Bligh, J. and Maskrey, M. (1970). Cerebrospinal fluid acid-base balance during respiratory alkalosis in the panting animal. *Amer. J. Physiol.*, **219**, 469

170. Purves, M. J. (1970). The effect of hypoxia, hypercapnia, and hypotension upon carotid body blood flow and oxygen consumption in the cat. *J. Physiol.* (*London*), **209**, 395

171. Eyzaguirre, C. and Lewin, J. (1961). Effect of different oxygen tensions on the carotid body *in vitro*. *J. Physiol.* (*London*), **159**, 238

172. Purves, M. J. (1970). The role of the cervical sympathetic nerve in the regulation of oxygen consumption of the carotid body of the cat. *J. Physiol.* (*London*), **209**, 417

173. Joels, N. and White, H. (1968). The contribution of the arterial chemoreceptors to the stimulation of respiration by adrenaline and noradrenaline in the cat. *J. Physiol.* (*London*), **197**, 1

174. Robertshaw, D. and Whittow, G. C. (1966). The effect of hyperthermia and localised heating of the anterior hypothalamus on the sympathoadrenal system of the ox (*Bos taurus*) *J. Physiol.* (*London*), **187**, 351

175. Holmes, R. L., Newman, P. P. and Wolstencroft, J. H. (1960). A heat-sensitive region in the medulla. *J. Physiol.* (*London*), **152**, 93

176. Chai, C. Y., Mu, J. Y. and Brobeck, J. R. (1965). Cardiovascular and respiratory responses from local heating of medulla oblongata. *Amer. J. Physiol.*, **209**, 301

177. Mitchell, R. A., Loeschcke, H. H., Massion, W. H. and Severinghaus, J. W. (1963). Respiratory responses mediated through superficial chemosensitive areas on the medulla. *J. Appl. Physiol.*, **18**, 523

178. Findlay, J. D. and Ingram, D. L. (1961). Brain temperature as a factor in the control of thermal polypnoea in the ox (*Bos taurus*). *J. Physiol.* (*London*), **155**, 72

179. Findlay, J. D. and Hales, J. R. S. (1969). Hypothalamic temperature and the regulation of respiration of the ox exposed to severe heat. *J. Physiol.* (*London*), **203**, 651

180. Koroxenidis, G. T., Shepherd, J. T. and Marshall, R. J. (1961). Cardiovascular response to acute heat stress. *J. Appl. Physiol.*, **16**, 869

181. Rowell, L. B., Brengelmann, G. L. and Murray, J. A. (1969). Cardiovascular responses to sustained high skin temperature in resting man. *J. Appl. Physiol.*, **27**, 673

182. Whittow, G. C. (1971). Cardio-acceleration in the ox (*Bos taurus*) during hyperthermia. *Res. Vet. Sci.*, **12**, 495

183. Guyton, A. C. (1963). *Circulatory physiology: cardiac output and its regulation*, (Philadelphia: Saunders)

184. Brendel, W., Albers, C. and Usinger, W. (1958). Der Kreislauf in Hypothermie. *Pflügers Arch.*, **266**, 341
185. Suutarinen, T. (1966). Cardiovascular response to changes in arterial carbon dioxide tension. *Acta Physiol. Scand.*, **67**, Suppl. 266
186. Colton, J. S. and Frankel, H. M. (1972). Cerebrovascular response to CO_2 during hyperthermia. *Amer. J. Physiol.*, **223**, 1041
187. Thorburn, G. D., Casey, B. H. and Molyneux, G. S. (1966). Distribution of blood flow within the skin of the rabbit with particular reference to hair growth. *Circulation Res.*, **28**, 650
188. Aschoff, J. (1958). Hauttemperatur und Hautdurchblutung im dienst der Temperaturregulation. *Klin. Wochenchr.*, **36**, 193
189. Robinson, S. M. and King, A. B. (1971). Hypocapnia-induced increases in rectal temperature in man during heat exposure. *J. Appl. Physiol.*, **31**, 656
190. Nagasaka, T. and Carlson, L. D. (1971). Effects of blood temperature and perfused norepinephrine on vascular responses of rabbit ear. *Amer. J. Physiol.*, **220**, 289
191. Thauer, R. (1965). Circulatory adjustments to climatic requirements. In *Handbook of Physiology Section 2: Circulation*, Vol. 3, 1921 (W. F. Hamilton and P. Dow, editors) (Washington, D.C.: Amer. Physiol. Soc.)
192. Ederstrom, H. E. (1954). Blood flow changes in the dog during hyperthermia. *Amer. J. Physiol.*, **176**, 347
193. Spurr, G. B. and Dwyer, N. J. (1972). Hepatic blood flow and indocyanine green disappearance in hyperthermia and endogenous fever. *J. Appl. Physiol.*, **32**, 362
194. Shepherd, J. T. and Webb-Peploe, M. M. (1970). Cardiac output and blood flow distribution during work in heat. In *Physiological and Behavioral Temperature Regulation*, 237 (J. D. Hardy, A. P. Gagge and J. A. J. Stolwijk, editors) (Springfield: Thomas)
195. Rowell, L. B., Detry, J-M. R., Profant, G. R. and Wyss, C. (1971). Splanchnic vasoconstriction in hyperthermic man—role of falling blood pressure. *J. Appl. Physiol.*, **31**, 864
196. Kaihara, S., Rutherford, R. B., Schwentker, E. P. and Wagner, H. N. (1969). Distribution of cardiac output in experimental hemorrhagic shock in dogs. *J. Appl. Physiol.*, **27**, 218
197. Alexander, G., Bell, A. W. and Hales, J. R. S. (1973). The effect of cold exposure on tissue blood flow in the new-born lamb. *J. Physiol. (London)* (in press)
198. Krogh, A. (1936). *The Anatomy and Physiology of Capillaries*, 104 (New Haven: Yale University Press)
199. Piiper, J. (1959). Durchblutung der arterio-venösen Anastomosen und Wärmeaustausch an der Hundeextremität. *Pflügers Arch.*, **268**, 242
200. Kullmann, R., Schönung, W. and Simon, E. (1970). Antagonistic changes of blood flow and sympathetic activity in different vascular beds following central thermal stimulation 1. Blood flow in skin, muscle and intestine during spinal cord heating and cooling in anesthetized dogs. *Pflügers Arch.*, **319**, 146
201. Schönung, W., Jessen, C., Wagner, H. and Simon, E. (1971). Regional blood flow antagonism induced by central thermal stimulation in the conscious dog. *Experientia*, **27**, 1291
202. Walther, O.-E., Iriki, M. and Simon, E. (1970). Antagonistic changes of blood flow and sympathetic activity in different vascular beds following central thermal stimulation II. Cutaneous and visceral sympathetic activity during spinal cord heating and cooling in anesthetized rabbits and cats. *Pflügers Arch.*, **319**, 162
203. Schönung, W., Wagner, H., Jessen, C. and Simon, E. (1971). Differentiation of cutaneous and intestinal blood flow during hypothalamic heating and cooling in aneasthetized dogs. *Pflügers Arch.*, **328**, 145
204. Iriki, M., Riedel, W. and Simon, E. (1971). Regional differentiation of sympathetic activity during hypothalamic heating and cooling in anesthetised rabbits. *Pflügers Arch.*, **328**, 320
205. Whittow, G. C. (1968). Cardiovascular response to localized heating of the anterior hypothalamus. *J. Physiol. (London)*, **198**, 541
206. Dampney, R. A. L. (1973). Cardiovascular alterations associated with panting in the conscious dog. *Proc. Int. Union Physiol. Soc.*, In Proc. Australian Physiol. Pharmacol. Soc., **3**, No. 2, 217

207. Whittow, G. C. (1970). Respiratory variations of blood pressure in the ox (*Bos taurus*) during panting. *Brit. Vet. J.*, **126,** 652
208. Demers, H. G., Spaich, P. and Usinger, W. (1969). Der Hirnkreislauf bei erhöhter Körpertemperatur. *Verhandl. Deut. Ges. Kreislaufforsch.*, **35,** 340
209. Nemoto, E. M. and Frankel, H. M. (1970). Cerebrovascular response during progressive hyperthermia in dogs. *Amer. J. Physiol.*, **218,** 1060
210. Nemoto, E. M. and Frankel, H. M. (1970). Cerebral oxygenation and metabolism during progressive hyperthermia. *Amer. J. Physiol.*, **219,** 1784
211. Cranston, W. I. and Rosendorff, C. (1971). Local blood flow, cerebrovascular autoregulation and CO_2 responsiveness in the rabbit hypothalamus. *J. Physiol. (London)*, **215,** 577
212. Waites, G. M. H. (1970). Temperature regulation and the testis. In *The Testis*, **1,** 241 (A. D. Johnson, W. R. Gomes and N. L. Vandemark, editors) (New York: Academic Press)
213. Iampietro, P. F., Fiorica, V., Higgins, E. A., Mager, M. and Goldman, R. F. (1966). Exposure to heat: comparison of responses of dog and man. *Int. J. Bioclimatol. Biometeorol.*, **10,** 175
214. Shibolet, S., Coll, R., Gilat, T. and Sohar, E. (1967). Heat stroke: its clinical picture and mechanism in 36 cases. *Quart. J. Med.*, **36,** 525
215. Sohal, R. S., Shih, C. S., Colcolough, H. L. and Burch, G. E. (1968). Heat stroke. An electron microscopic study of endothelial cell damage and disseminated intravascular coagulation. *Arch. Internal Med.*, **122,** 43
216. Beleslin, D. B., Radmanović, B. Ž. and Rakić, M. M. (1971). Release during convulsions of an unknown substance into the cerebral ventricles of the cats. *Brain Res.*, **35,** 625
217. Forsyth, R. P. and Hoffbrand, B. I. (1970). Redistribution of cardiac output after sodium pentobarbital anesthesia in the monkey. *Amer. J. Physiol.*, **218,** 214
218. Kaihara, S., Van Heerden, P. D., Migita, T. and Wagner, H. N. (1968). Measurement of distribution of cardiac output. *J. Appl. Physiol.*, **25,** 696
219. Taylor, C. R. (1970). Dehydration and heat: effects on temperature regulation of East African ungulates. *Amer. J. Physiol.*, **219,** 1136
220. Murray, D. M. (1966). A comparison of cutaneous evaporation rates in cattle exposed to heat in a climate laboratory and in the field. *J. Agr. Sci.*, **66,** 175
221. Hales, J. R. S. (1967). The partition of respiratory ventilation of the panting ox. *J. Physiol. (London)*, **188,** 45
222. Stricker, E. M. (1971). Evaporative cooling in the rat: interaction with heat loss from the tail. *Quart. J. Exp. Physiol.*, **56,** 231
223. Stolwijk, J. A. J. and Hardy, J. D. (1966). Partitional calorimetric studies of responses of man to thermal transients. *J. Appl. Physiol.*, **21,** 967
224. Mitchell, J. W., Nadel, E. R. and Stolwijk, J. A. J. (1972). Respiratory weight losses during exercise. *J. Appl. Physiol.*, **32,** 474
225. Stitt, J. T. and Hardy, J. D. (1971). Thermoregulation in the squirrel monkey (*Saimiri sciureus*) *J. Appl. Physiol.*, **31,** 48
226. McLean, J. A. (1963). Measurement of cutaneous moisture vaporisation from cattle by ventilated capsules. *J. Physiol. (London)*, **167,** 417
227. Brook, A. H. and Short, B. F. (1960). Sweating in Sheep. *Australian J. Afr. Res.*, **11,** 557
228. Brockway, J. M., McDonald, J. D. and Pullar, J. D. (1965). Evaporative heat-loss mechanisms in sheep. *J. Physiol. (London)*, **179,** 554
229. Morrison, S. R., Bond, T. E. and Heitman, H. (1967). Skin and lung moisture loss from swine. *Trans. Amer. Soc. Agr. Engr.*, **10,** 691, 696
230. Taylor, C. R., Schmidt-Nielsen, K., Dmi'el, R. and Fedak, M. (1971). Effect of hyperthermia on heat balance during running in the African hunting dog. *Amer. J. Physiol.*, **220,** 823
231. Gonzalez, R. R., Kluger, M. J. and Hardy, J. D. (1971). Partitional calorimetry of the New Zealand white rabbit at temperatures 5–35 °C. *J. Appl. Physiol.*, **31,** 728
232. Bligh, J. (1961). The synchronous discharge of apocrine glands of the Welsh Mountain sheep. *Nature (London)*, **189,** 582
233. Hayashi, H. (1968). Functional activity of the sweat glands in the hairy skin of the sheep. *Tohoku J. Exp. Med.*, **94,** 361

234. Kimura, S. and Aoki, T. (1962). Functional activity of apocrine sweat gland in the goat. *Tohoku J. Exp. Med.*, **76**, 8

235. Allen, T. E. and Bligh, J. (1969). A comparative study of the temporal patterns of cutaneous water vapour loss from some domesticated mammals with epitrichial sweat glands. *Comp. Biochem. Physiol.*, **31**, 347

236. Bullard, R. W., Dill, D. B. and Yousef, M. K. (1970). Responses of the burro to desert heat stress. *J. Appl. Physiol.*, **29**, 159

237. Findlay, J. D. and Jenkinson, D. McE. (1964). Sweat gland function in the Ayrshire calf. *Res. Vet. Sci.*, **5**, 109

238. Findlay, J. D. and Robertshaw, D. (1965). The role of the sympatho-adrenal system in the control of sweating in the ox (*Bos taurus*). *J. Physiol. (London)*, **179**, 285

239. Otis, A. B. (1964). The work of breathing. In *Handbook of Physiology Section 3: Respiration*, Vol. 1, 463 (W. O. Fenn and H. Rahn, editors) (Washington, D. C. Amer. Physiol. Soc.)

240. McKerrow, C. B. and Otis, A. B. (1956). Oxygen cost of hyperventilation. *J. Appl. Physiol.*, **9**, 375

241. Baird, J. A., Hales, J. R. S. and Lang, W. J. (1973). Thermoregulatory responses to the injection of monoamines, acetylcholine and prostaglandins into a lateral cerebral ventricle of the echidna (*Tachyglossus aculeatus*). *J. Physiol. (London)* (in press)

5
Exercise and Thermoregulation

C. RICHARD TAYLOR

Harvard University

5.1   INTRODUCTION

During exercise animals increase the rate at which they consume energy and produce heat. Some of the energy is expended doing work against the external environment. Running, swimming or flying on the level all involve kinetic work and result in a change in velocity of the surrounding air or water. The kinetic work is dissipated as heat at a distance from the animal, as the air and water currents set in motion slow down. Climbing, flying upwards, lifting weights, etc. all require work against gravity. The gravitational work is stored as potential energy and is recovered when the animal or weight returns to the initial level.

Most of the energy expended during exercise, however, involves no work external to the animal. Instead it appears as heat which must be dissipated if the animal is to maintain a constant body temperature. The heat balance equation summarises this clearly:

$$\text{Heat production} = \text{Heat loss} \pm \text{heat storage} \pm \text{work}$$

Exercise comes in a multitude of forms and the optimal strategy for dealing with its increased heat production will differ from animal to animal and from one type of exercise to another. I should like to consider the magnitude of exercise heat loads, speculate as to the optimal strategies different animals might use for coping with them, and then consider what strategies, in fact, animals utilise. Finally, I would like to consider the extent to which control mechanisms for temperature regulation during exercise are different from those for temperature regulation in response to environmental heat loads. The scope of this paper does not enable me to be comprehensive, and unfortunately many interesting and important contributions to the physiology of temperature regulation during exercise have been omitted, particularly work on humans. I refer the reader to a number of excellent recent reviews[1-4].

5.2   MAGNITUDE OF EXERCISE HEAT LOADS

Perhaps the first question which comes to mind when discussing a heat load is, How large is it? For simplification, I should like to limit the consideration of magnitude to heat loads generated by mammals and birds while they move from one place to another. The amount of energy consumed and heat produced during locomotion will depend on the type, duration and speed of locomotion and the animal's size.

5.2.1   Heat produced by running on the level

What is the maximum amount of heat which a running animal might have to dissipate? Measurements of heat production of animals running at top speed do not exist. However, the magnitude of maximum running heat loads can be predicted if the top speed and weight of an animal are known. A convenient empirical relationship has been described recently relating energy cost of running to body size[5].

Oxygen consumption of a large number of running animals increases nearly linearly with increasing running speed (Figure 5.1a). This also appears to be the case for running man[6] where the linear relationship holds for both aerobic and anaerobic sources of energy[7]. It seems reasonable to assume that the linear relationship also applies for anaerobic sources of energy in other animals.

A second generalisation can be seen from looking at Figure 5.1a. The slope

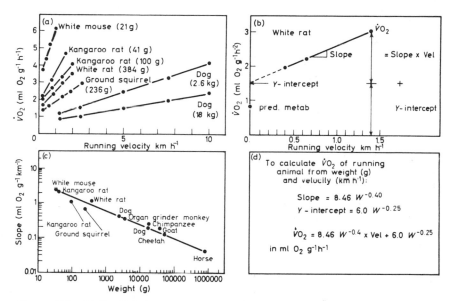

Figure 5.1   (a) Steady-state oxygen consumption of quadrupedal animals as a function of running velocity (Redrawn from Taylor et al[5]. by courtesy of Amer. J. Physiol.) (b) Steady-state oxygen consumption of the white rat as a function of running velocity (Redrawn from Taylor et al[5]. by courtesy of Amer. J. Physiol.) Oxygen consumption at any velocity can be calculated by adding (slope × velocity) to the y-intercept (oxygen consumption of the extrapolated zero running velocity). The y-intercept is greater than the observed resting metabolism or the standard metabolism predicted by Kleiber's equation[42]
(c) Slope of the relationship between steady-state oxygen consumption and running velocity plotted as a function of body weight on logarithmic coordinates (data from[5] and from unpublished observations in my laboratory on organ grinder monkey, chimpanzee, goat and cheetah).
(d) Calculation of oxygen consumption in running mammals from body weight and velocity

of the relationship between oxygen consumption and running velocity is steeper for small animals than for large animals. Thus, a small animal expends proportionately more energy per gram of body weight as it moves more quickly than a large animal. This slope is an important parameter. It is obtained by dividing the change in oxygen consumption by the change in velocity and its units are ml O_2 (g km)$^{-1}$, or the number of millilitres of oxygen expended in moving a one gram mass one kilometre. It is a constant for each animal since the relationship for each animal is linear.

It is possible to calculate the oxygen consumed by an animal running at any speed if one knows both the slope of the relationship between oxygen consumption and running speed and the extrapolated oxygen consumption at zero running velocity (y intercept). It is simply a matter of adding the product of the slope times the velocity to the y intercept as shown in Figure 5.1b.

Both the slope and the y intercept can be predicted reasonably well from body weight, for reasons which are unclear. If the slopes are plotted as a function of body weight on logarithmic coordinates, a nearly linear relationship is found (Figure 5.1c). A regression analysis of this relationship yields a simple equation for predicting the slope from body weight (slope $= 8.46$ $W^{-0.40}$) where the units of the slope are ml O_2 (g km)$^{-1}$ and W is body weight in grams. A mammal's resting metabolism can be calculated from body weight using the simple equation developed by Kleiber[42]: $M_{std} = 3.5$ $W^{-0.25}$ where M_{std} is standard metabolism in ml oxygen (g h)$^{-1}$ and W is the animal's weight in grams. The extrapolated zero running velocity is greater than the predicted standard metabolism. This is probably due to a postural effect, i.e. the energy cost of standing. The limbs of running animals can no longer be considered rigid members, requiring little energy for support. The y-intercept deviated from the predicted standard metabolism by a fairly consistent amount and is c. $1.7 \times M_{std}$. It is now possible to calculate the energy expenditure of an animal running simply from body weight and velocity. The equations are summarised in Figure 5.1d.

How much of the energy expended by running animals must be dissipated as heat? An animal running on level ground performs almost no external work, contrary to our intuitive conceptions. Frictional energy losses to the ground are slight. Work expended in overcoming air resistance is also negligible. Man, with his upright posture has perhaps the least streamlined body of any running mammal and expends the most energy in overcoming frictional resistance. Margaria has found that at top speed in a sprint, man expends only a few per cent of his total energy output overcoming the resistance of air[8]. Since almost no work is performed when an animal runs, almost all the energy expended will appear as heat which must be dissipated.

What is the maximum amount of heat produced by mammals running on level ground? Top speeds for animals can be found in the literature[9, 10]. I have calculated the heat loads which would be encountered by a variety of animals running at top speed by inserting these top speeds into the equations developed in Figure 5.1d. Maximum heat loads are plotted in two ways: the relative increase in metabolism at top speed over predicted resting metabolism as a function of log body weight (Figure 5.2a) and the amount of heat that would have to be lost per square centimetre of surface area when an animal runs at top speed as a function of log body weight (Figure 5.2b). Both plots yield a bell-shaped curve.

Small animals sprinting for a short distance (10–20 m) encounter heat loads *c*. 20 times the predicted resting metabolism. Intermediate sized animals (5–100 kg) sprinting at top speed increase their metabolism by 40–60 fold, while large animals such as horses, wild asses, elephants and rhinoceroses increase their metabolism by only 10–20 fold (Figure 5.2a). Plotting heat load per cm^2 surface area as a function of log body weight shows that during peak metabolism, small animals have a heat load of 30–60 cal cm^{-2}, intermediate sized animals 150–220 cal cm^{-2}, and large animals 60–120 cal cm^{-2}.

A third way to consider the magnitude of heat load is to compare the rate of heat produced by a unit mass of tissue. Each gram of tissue of a small animal has a higher metabolism than that of a larger mammal: the heat generated per gram by a 20 g mouse is more than 100-fold greater than that of a 5 000 000 g elephant, both at rest and while running.

5.2.2 Heat produced by running up and down hills

Running uphill requires work against gravity. Man must increase his metabolism markedly to maintain speed upon encountering even a slight incline. The mechanical work involved lifting one gram one vertical kilometre is 2.34 cal. Contrary to intuition, hard work decreases the maximum amount of heat which has to be dissipated during peak exertion. It is reasonable to assume that the peak metabolism is the same for level and uphill running. Thus the additional energy required by gravitational work simply slows the animal. The work is stored as potential energy and does not appear as heat. This is expressed in the heat balance equation:

$$\text{Heat loss} = \text{Heat produced} - \text{Heat stored} - \text{Work}$$

Another intuitively unreasonable consequence of this heat balance equation is that an animal encounters its most severe heat dissipation problems when running downhill. The potential energy stored running uphill is utilised running downhill in the acceleration of the limbs. Peak metabolism should be unchanged, thus the animal must dissipate both the peak metabolic heat produced and the heat produced as the potential energy is changed into kinetic energy and then to heat. In the heat balance equation the direction and thus the sign of the work changes (thus it is frequently referred to as negative work) (See Chapter 1):

$$\text{Heat loss} = \text{Heat produced} - \text{Heat stored} + \text{Work}$$

The relative importance of the work component in running up and down hills is greater in larger animals[11]. The amount of work to lift one gram one vertical kilometre is the same regardless of the size of the animal. Hill[12] assumes that the mechanical efficiency of muscles of different-sized animals is nearly the same. Thus, the same amount of energy should be expended in lifting one gram one vertical kilometre by animals regardless of their size. Energetic cost of level running in small animals is much greater than in large animals, thus, the relative increase in metabolism of small animals running

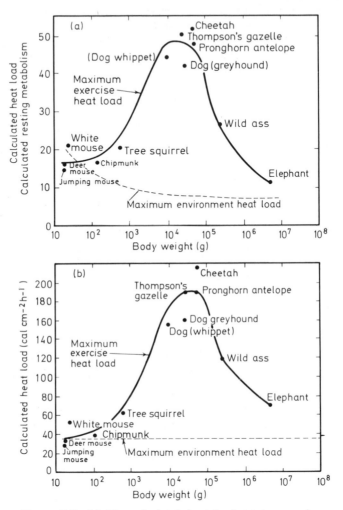

Figure 5.2 (a) The calculated heat loads at top running speeds (solid line) and the maximum environmental heat loads (dotted line) divided by predicted resting metabolism. Both are plotted as a function of log body weight. Top running speeds are those reported by Howell[9] and of Layne and Benton[10]. Oxygen consumption during running was calculated using the relationship of Taylor *et al*[5]. Resting oxygen consumption was calculated using Kleiber's equation[42]. Maximum environmental heat load was calculated for animals in a hot desert[22].

(b) Calculated heat loads at top running speeds and the maximum environmental heat loads per unit surface area. Both are plotted as a function of log body weight. Calculations are the the same as those in Figure 5.1a uphill at a given velocity will be less than in large animals. For example, energetic cost of level running of a 30 g mouse is about eight times as great as in a 17 500 g chimpanzee. Cost of lifting one gram one kilometre vertically was found to be similar. Therefore the increment in energy expenditure for mice to run uphill was about one-eighth that for chimpanzees. Because of the relatively small increase, a 30 g mouse could run vertically at a speed of 2 km h^{-1} with an increase in oxygen consumption of only $c.$ 25% over that for level running at the same velocity. In a 17 500 g chimpanzee this would require nearly a 200% increase in oxygen consumption and over a 600% increase would be required for a 1000 kg horse. In terms of heat balance the total efficiency of running up or down hill is very small for the mice and relatively greater for the larger animals. Thus, up and down hill running has little effect on the heat balance of small animals, but the work against gravity might significantly effect the heat balance of large animals.

5.2.3 Heat produced by flying

Birds fly faster, further, and at a lower energy cost than comparably-sized terrestrial animals can run[13, 14]. Flying birds, unlike running mammals, do not increase oxygen consumption linearly with speed. Instead, there is a speed at which oxygen consumption is minimal; if the bird flies either faster or slower, oxygen consumption will increase. This is true for the three birds where measurements are available: the budgerigar[15], the gull[16], and the crow[17]. A minimum cost of locomotion (in ml O_2 (g km)$^{-1}$) can be obtained by dividing oxygen consumption during flying by flying velocity. The minimum cost of flying, like the slope for running, is greater for smaller animals and changes in a predictable manner with body weight. This is true not only for flying birds, but also for flying insects[14].

Flying requires an animal to do work on its environment in overcoming the resistance of air. Direct measurements of the external work done are difficult to make, although Tucker[16] estimates that 20% of the energy expended by a flying animal goes into work overcoming the resistance of air. This being the case, only 80% of the energy consumed by a flying animal would appear as heat and then have to be dissipated.

The oxygen consumption for ascending flight at a given speed is higher than that for level or descending flight. Budgerigars, which are small 30–40 g birds, reach a peak oxygen consumption of about 35 ml O_2 (g h)$^{-1}$ ascending at a speed of 40 km h^{-1} or flying on the level at a speed of 48 km h^{-1}[15]. This is 12–14 times their predicted resting metabolism and would require a heat dissipation increase of $ca.$ 11-fold. When flying in turbulent air at speeds up to 33 km. h^{-1}, their oxygen consumptions were as high as 55 ml O_2 (g h)$^{-1}$, or $ca.$ 30 times resting level[18]. This would require a heat dissipation increase of $c.$ 24-fold.

5.2.4 Heat produced by swimming mammals

At the present time energetic measurements on truly aquatic swimming mammals such as porpoises, dolphins and seals are not available. Extrapolating data from fish, Schmidt–Nielsen[19] has calculated that a porpoise would increase its resting metabolism *ca.* 20-fold in swimming at 36 km h^{-1}. This assumes a 25% efficiency; thus only 75% of the energy consumed would appear as heat to be dissipated by the animal. Because of the high thermal conductivity of water, loss of the heat produced during swimming could be controlled easily by changing the peripheral blood flow[20]. There are a number of surface swimming mammals and birds, but these animals also either run or fly. Peak metabolism during the latter two forms of locomotion has already been discussed. I will also neglect aquatic swimming in this paper, since there is so little information available and a limited amount of space.

5.2.5　A comparison of the magnitude of exercise and environmental heat loads

What does an exercise heat load of 10–50 times resting metabolism mean in more familiar terms? One thinks of hot deserts as providing perhaps the most severe heat load on the face of the earth. How does a 50-fold exercise heat load compare with that imposed by a hot desert? Dill and his co-workers investigated the physiological problem of working in the heat[21]. They selected Boulder, Nevada for the site of their studies. In the summer air temperature reaches 48 °C consequently, during the construction of the Boulder Dam, many labourers suffered heat prostration. Dill and his co-workers took a donkey, a dog and a man on walks in the desert under these severe conditions. Since air temperature exceeded body temperature by about 10 °C, heat flowed into the animal from the environment and the only option for the heat dissipation was evaporative cooling. Thus, the environmental heat load could be obtained by measuring the weight loss due to evaporation. Using Dill's data, Knut Schmidt-Nielsen in his book *Desert Animals*[22], calculated that all three animals evaporated *ca.* 0.6 kg water (m^2 h)$^{-1}$ while walking in the desert. This would amount to a heat load *ca.* 14 times the standard metabolism for the 16 kg dog, 11 times that for the 79 kg man and seven times that for the 96 kg donkey. I have used the 0.6 kg (m^2.h)$^{-1}$ figure together with Benedict's equation for surface area (m^2 = 0.1 $W^{0.67}$, body weight, W in kg) to calculate the desert heat load for animals of different size. The calculations show that the maximum heat load due to a hot desert is 5–15 times the resting metabolic rate and decreases with increasing size of the animal.

In an important study, Virginia Finch measured the solar heat load on two African ungulates standing in the hot equatorial sun[23]. She found an environmental heat load *c.* 10 times the predicted resting metabolism. Thus, it seems reasonable to conclude that the magnitude of the maximum environmental and running heat loads are similar for small animals (less than 5 kg in weight). For intermediate size animals (5–200 kg), however, the maximum environmental heat load is only 1/10th the maximum heat load encountered while running. For larger animals (>200 kg) the magnitude of the two types of heat load is again similar.

5.3 MECHANISMS FOR DISSIPATING HEAT

5.3.1 Deferred heat dissipation—heat storage during peak metabolism

Heat storage is a viable strategy for dealing with the high heat production of sprinting, flying at high speeds or any form of exercise of short duration. About 0.82 cal are stored as the temperature of 1 g of tissue increases by 1 °C. If sprints are of short enough duration, body temperature could increase by an amount sufficient to store all of the heat produced without reaching lethal levels. Heat could then be dissipated when the animal stops and its heat production is low.

5.3.2 Evaporative cooling

Each gram of water which evaporates from an animal's surface carries with it *c.* 580 cal of heat. The heat of vaporisation varies with the temperature of the surface from which the evaporation occurs and the exact values have recently been the topic of some controversy[24, 25] (see Chapter 1).

Homeotherms utilise a number of mechanisms to increase evaporation in response to a heat load: small mammals spread saliva on their fur[26]; some birds and mammals increase respiratory evaporation by thermal panting; and many mammals, like man, sweat from the general body surface (see Chapter 4).

Evaporative cooling is not a viable strategy for dissipating the relatively large exercise heat loads of small animals. If a 30 g mouse used primarily evaporation to keep cool, it would lose water amounting to *ca.* 20% of its body weight each hour, and therefore would have to drink frequently to avoid dehydration.

Running enhances the efficiency of sweating as an evaporative cooling mechanism. The forced convection of air across the skin surface decreases the thickness of the boundary layer and increases the rate of evaporation from the wet skin. In order that evaporation from the skin should give a net loss of heat from an animal, skin temperature must be below core body temperature. A high peripheral blood flow is also required to carry the heat from the core of the body to the surface. The combination of these two requirements causes the animal to act as a heat sink and pick up large amounts of heat when air temperatures exceed skin temperature or when the animal stands in the sun. Dissipating this heat would require additional evaporative cooling. Most animals, however, avoid exercising in the heat.

Exercise might affect the ability of an animal to use panting as a mechanism for evaporative cooling. Large volumes of air are moved during thermal panting with a very small expenditure of energy. In the heat, both dogs[27] and birds[28] pant at a resonant frequency and thereby minimise the energy required to move the air. The changing positions of the internal organs and tensions of the intercostal muscles should result in a continuously changing resonant frequency during running or flight. It might be difficult therefore for an exercising animal to simultaneously adjust its respiratory rate within the constraints of this variable resonant frequency and still meet the increased demands for oxygen and regulated evaporative cooling.

5.3.3 Non-evaporative cooling

Ideally, animals that travel long distances or exercise for prolonged periods would dissipate most of their heat using non-evaporative mechanisms. Heat storage would eventually result in lethal body temperatures and evaporation would lead to severe dehydration.

Non-evaporative heat loss has been partitioned into its radiative and convective components for a number of resting animals[3, 23, 29], but data on running animals is limited to man[3]. I will lump the two components together and use the term conductance to compare non-evaporative heat loss of different animals while running. Conductance has a number of definitions in the literature. Here, I will use Tucker's definition of conductance for flying birds[16] since this is concerned only with non-evaporative heat loss and corrects for the work done against the environment:

Conductance
$(\text{cal cm}^{-2} \, {}^{\circ}\text{C}^{-1} \, \text{h}^{-1})$

$$= \frac{\begin{bmatrix} \text{Heat produced} \\ (\text{cal h}^{-1}) \end{bmatrix} - \begin{bmatrix} \text{Evap. heat loss} \\ (\text{cal h}^{-1}) \end{bmatrix} - \begin{bmatrix} \text{Heat stored} \\ (\text{cal h}^{-1}) \end{bmatrix} - \begin{bmatrix} \text{Work} \\ (\text{cal h}^{-1}) \end{bmatrix}}{\begin{bmatrix} \text{Surface area} \\ (\text{cm}^2) \end{bmatrix} \times \begin{bmatrix} T_{\text{body}} - T_{\text{air}} \\ ({}^{\circ}\text{C}) \quad ({}^{\circ}\text{C}) \end{bmatrix}}$$

Conductance defined in this way expresses the non-evaporative flow of heat across each cm^2 of surface for each ${}^{\circ}\text{C}$ gradient between core temperature and air temperature.

How does body size affect the magnitude of non-evaporative heat dissipation? The rate of non-evaporative heat loss is directly proportional to the surface area from which the heat can be dissipated. Small animals have relatively more surface area per calorie of heat produced than large animals, at least when resting. For example, a 20 g mouse at rest produces c. 2.16 cal cm^{-2}; less than half the 5.83 cal cm^{-2} produced by a 5 000 000 g elephant at rest. Thus, other parameters being equal, the mouse could lose twice the amount of its metabolic heat by non-evaporative means. At calculated peak metabolism the same 2:1 ratio holds for mouse and elephant (Figure 5.2b). The calculated peak metabolism of the intermediate sized sprinters, however, produces 60–70 times the amount of heat per square centimetre as a mouse, far too much to deal with by non-evaporative mechanisms. It is reasonable to look at non-evaporative heat-loss mechanisms as important means of dissipating exercise heat loads from small animals.

A high body temperature during exercise would increase non-evaporative heat loss. The rate of non-evaporative heat loss is approximately proportional to the temperature gradient over which the heat loss occurs. Thus for an animal running at an air temperature of 31 °C, a body temperature increase from 36 to 41 °C during exercise would double the rate of non-evaporative heat loss. A high temperature would be a more effective means of increasing non-evaporative heat loss from small animals, since the steeper gradient would operate over their relatively greater surface area.

Forced convection increases as animals run or fly. Most treadmill studies have neglected this fact and wind speed is seldom matched to tread speed. Forced convection decreases the thickness of the boundary layer surrounding an animal and thereby increases the gradient over which heat is lost by conduction from the skin surface to the air. The magnitude of the effect increases exponentially with increasing wind velocity. In Figure 5.3 this effect is

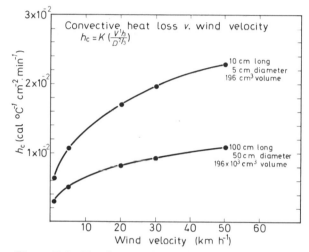

Figure 5.3 The increase in convective heat loss as a function of wind velocity for two cylinders with a ratio of length to diameter of 2 to 1 and weighing approximately 200 g and 200 kg, if their specific gravity was 1. Calculated from the equation of Porter and Gates[29]: $h_c = 6.17\ (V^{1/3}\ D^{2/3})$; where h_c equals convective heat loss (cal cm^{-2} °C^{-2} min^{-1}); $V =$ wind velocity in (cm s^{-1}); and D equals diameter of the cylinder (cm)

plotted for 200 g and 200 kg cylinders with a ratio of length:diameter of 2:1 using the Porter–Gates equations[29]. In both cases forced convection increases the rate of convective heat loss from the cylinder surface to the air by c. twofold as wind velocity increases from 0 to 5 km h^{-1}; by c. threefold as wind velocity increases from 0 to 30 km h^{-1}; and by c. 4.5-fold as wind velocity increases from 0 to 100 km h^{-1}. These results are similar to the analysis by Birkebak[30] who used data from Lentz and Hart[31] and Moote[32] on heat loss from pieces of fur heated on a guarded heat plate in a wind tunnel (see Chapter 1).

5.4 DEFERRED HEAT DISSIPATION—HEAT STORAGE DURING PEAK METABOLISM

5.4.1 A strategy for sprinters

The cheetah is the world's fastest terrestrial animal and has been reported to reach speeds of 110 km h^{-1} [9]. It is calculated that heat production would increase by 54-fold at this speed (Figure 5.2a). These high bursts of speed occur as the cheetah pursues its prey and are of very short duration. A chase is abandoned after several hundred yards if unsuccessful[33]. Usually an hour elapses before another attempt is made. This behaviour suggests that the cheetah may store heat during the chase, terminate pursuit when body temperature becomes too high and dissipate heat after stopping.

Running on a treadmill at 20°C with wind speed matched to tread speed, the cheetah stored most of the heat it produced while running. This was the case even at low speeds: seventy per cent of the heat produced during a

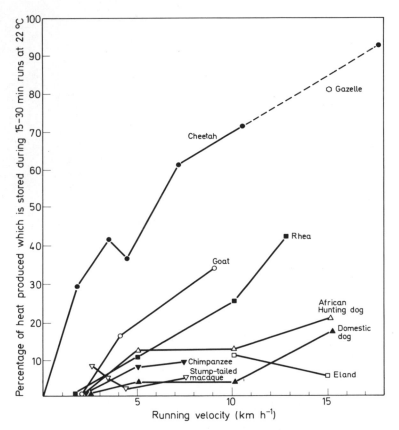

Figure 5.4 The percentage of the heat produced which is stored during 15–30 min runs at 22°C as a function of running velocity. Data were gathered from a variety of sources listed in the text of the paper

15 min run at 11 km h^{-1} was stored. This figure increased to >90% at 18 km h^{-1} (Figure 5.4).

Running at speeds of 110 km h^{-1}, rectal temperature of the cheetah would have to increase by c. 96 °C h^{-1} or 1.6 °C min^{-1} to store all of its calculated heat production. The cheetah's body temperature increased when they ran on a treadmill[34] the animals would not continue to run when their body temperatures reached a level between 40.5 and 41 °C. They would simply roll over on their back with their feet in the air and slide on the tread surface.

If, in nature, the cheetah also stops after its body temperature rises by 1.0–1.5 °C, the maximum distance which it could sprint would be <1 km which is about the distance which cheetahs are reported to pursue their prey in the wild and it seems possible that the duration of the cheetah's sprint is determined by the amount of heat which it can store before reaching a lethal body temperature.

This 'heat-storage strategy' may be common among intermediate-sized sprinters, whether they be birds or mammals. The rhea, an ostrich-like bird which lives in the South American pampas, ordinarily walks as it forages for food and sprints to avoid danger. Rheas were trained to run on treadmills where tread and wind speeds were matched. Their body temperatures increased as they ran at low velocities, the faster they ran, the greater the rate at which the body temperature increased. At higher air temperatures, or speeds exceeding 10 km h^{-1}, body temperature continued to rise until the animal appeared exhausted and stopped running[35].

5.4.2 Keeping a cool head while being chased

The cheetah's prey, the Thompson's gazelle, also runs at high speeds, reportedly reaching 90 km h^{-1}. Gazelles, like cheetahs, store most of the heat they produce when they sprint at high speeds[36]. Running around a small race track where speed was controlled by chasing them with a sack attached to the end of a long boom (instead of a cheetah), gazelles stored c. 80% of their calculated heat production at 15 km h^{-1}, at 25 km h^{-1}; and at 40 km h^{-1}. The magnitude of heat storage by cheetahs and gazelles was quite similar. Unlike the cheetah, however, the gazelles tolerate very high body temperatures, and are able to run further. The body temperature of the gazelle may increase by 6 °C during a run. How does the gazelle tolerate such high body temperatures? Probably the most temperature sensitive part of the body is the brain, where literally millions of bits of information must be processed and integrated at any instant of time. The gazelle uses an elegant mechanism to keep its brain cooler than the rest of the body during sprints. At the end of a 6 min run at 40 km h^{-1} carotid artery temperature exceeded brain temperature by 2.7 °C. How is this possible?

At the base of the skull in bovids there is an arrangement of blood vessels called the carotid rete. The brain is not supplied by an internal carotid artery, instead most of the blood passes to the brain via an external carotid artery. At the base of the skull this artery breaks up into thousands of small parallel arterials, the carotid rete. These reform before passing on to the brain. This rete lies within a venous pool in the cavernous sinus. The venous blood from the nasal mucosa drains into this venous pool. Thus, evaporation taking place from the nasal mucosa as the gazelle breathes cools the venous blood which returns to the cavernous sinus. This cool blood in turn cools the warm arterial blood on the way to the brain. The carotid rete is a counter-current heat exchanger which greatly enhances the efficiency of this heat exchange. Thus, the blood arriving at the brain can be considerably cooler than the blood leaving the heart.

This type of mechanism is not unique to gazelles. Direct measurements of it have been made on sheep[37] and goats[38]. More recently, there is evidence that dogs[39] and cats[40] may also utilise a similar type of selective cooling of the brain region. This certainly merits further investigation and must influence our thinking about hypothalamic thermostats.

5.4.3   Is heat storage important for all animals?

Neither small animals nor distance runners store large amounts of heat. Figure 5.4 shows clearly that heat storage accounts for a relatively small amount of the total heat produced by mice (unpublished observation), rats (unpublished observation), hunting dog[41], domestic dog[41] or the large African antelope, the eland[36]. Measurements are not available for animals at their peak speeds, and perhaps under these circumstances heat storage might be important. This matter merits further investigation.

5.5   EVAPORATIVE HEAT LOSS DURING EXERCISE

5.5.1   Small mammals

As a rule small mammals lack sweat glands on the general body surface, do not pant, and increase evaporative cooling in the heat only as an emergency mechanism when escape from the heat fails. Instead of developing means for increasing the rate of evaporation, they have adopted an ingenious mechanism which minimises evaporation as they breath. A temporal counter-current heat exchanger in the nose results in air being exhaled at temperatures below those of the inhaled air[43]. The water which evaporates to humidify the inhaled air before it arrives at the lung is recondensed on the surfaces of the nasal passages on exhalation.

Can this exchange be abolished to increase respiratory evaporation? During thermal panting, dogs abolish it by exhaling through the mouth[44]. During normal thermal panting air enters the dog's nose and leaves through the mouth, completely by-passing the exchanger. Another means of circumventing the exchange would be to increase the blood flow to the nasal mucosa. Thus, there are means to by-pass the exchanger. Are they utilised by running animals?

Measuring the small amounts of water evaporating from small mammals is a difficult task. In an extremely careful study, Raab and Schmidt-Nielsen[54] measured water loss from kangaroo rats, and white rats, as a function of running velocity at different air temperatures. They found that the nasal counter-current exchanger apparently still operates in running animals, and the amount of heat lost by evaporation could not account for more than 5–10% of the heat produced (Figure 5.5).

Wunder[45] reports a much higher evaporative heat loss from running chipmunks. He found that 53% of their heat production was lost by evaporation when they ran at 1.2 km h^{-1}. These results should be repeated and the mechanism should be elucidated. Perhaps the chipmunk exhales through its mouth, like the panting dog.

5.5.2   Animals that pant

A number of predators rely on chasing their prey for long distances and apparently win a contest of endurance. The tricoloured Cape hunting dog (*Lycaon pictus*) is known as an efficient hunter, relying on endurance rather than speed and tirelessly running down its prey. Some primitive men use a similar hunting strategy. Domestic dogs also run considerable distances. To run continuously for long periods requires an effective means of cooling to avoid lethal temperatures, however, the level at which the body temperature is regulated may differ during exercise and rest. At rest, both the hunting dog and domestic dog increase evaporation by panting. What happens when they run?

The hunting dog does not increase the percentage of heat loss through evaporation when it runs. It dissipates c. 25% of its total heat loss by evaporation both when resting and running (Figure 5.5). Domestic dogs, on the other hand, increase evaporation markedly as they run (Figure 5.5). At rest they lose c. 20% of their heat loss by evaporation. This percentage increases with increasing running speed and exceeds 50% at a running velocity of 15 km h^{-1}. In both animals most of the evaporation is from the respiratory tract and little comes from the skin surface[41]. The low evaporative loss from the African hunting dog might be considered an adaptation for increasing the distance it could pursue its prey. It could travel nearly twice as far as the domestic dog before having to stop for a drink. In the next section we will discuss the mechanisms by which the hunting dog is able to keep both evaporation and storage of heat at a low level.

The goat and cheetah also increase evaporation by panting in the heat. Both are able to increase evaporation by an amount sufficient to maintain their body temperature at 10°C below air temperature when air temperature is 50°C[34]. During exercise the goat increases evaporation in much the same manner as the domestic dog (Figure 5.5). The cheetah, however, does not utilise evaporative cooling when it runs. Instead it has a relatively lower water loss at higher speeds which probably reflects a greater tidal volume during each respiration, a consequent decrease in the proportion of dead space and a more complete extraction of oxygen from each litre of inspired air[46].

Flying birds also lose relatively less water for each millilitre of oxygen consumed during flight than at rest[15, 16, 47]. For example, evaporation from a resting gull accounts for c. 29% of the heat loss at air temperatures below 30°C. During flight only 18% of the heat loss is by evaporation. Since c. 20% of the metabolism goes into work, this 18% reflects an even greater decrease in water loss per litre of oxygen consumed. Bird lungs operate quite differently than those of mammals and I refer the reader who wishes to

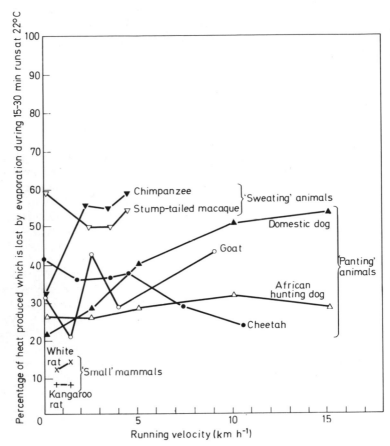

Figure 5.5 Percentage of heat produced which is lost by evaporation during 15–30 min runs at 22 °C. The data were compiled from sources listed in the text

pursue the mechanisms involved in respiratory evaporation in birds to Knut Schmidt-Nielsen's book *How Animals Work*[48].

5.5.3 Animals that sweat

Stump-tailed macaques[49] and chimpanzees (personal observations) sweat in the heat and while exercising. Evaporative heat loss from these two anthropoid primates was much higher during running than that observed in any of the panting animals. This reflects lower levels of heat storage and non-evaporative heat loss. Sweating, therefore, is an effective means of dissipating heat loads due to exercise, but it appears to require more water than panting.

5.6 NON-EVAPORATIVE HEAT LOSS DURING EXERCISE

5.6.1 Small mammals

Small animals lose most of their exercise heat load non-evaporatively (Figure 5.6). Conductance increases with increasing running speed both in white rats and kangaroo rats (Figure 5.7). The increase in conductance probably has two components: decreased amount of air trapped in fur and increased peripheral blood flow. Without further studies, it is not possible to evaluate the relative magnitude of the two effects.

5.6.2 Animals that pant and sweat

Except for the cheetah, animals that increase evaporative cooling by panting lose a greater percentage of heat loss by non-evaporative means than animals that sweat (Figure 5.6). When animals run, conductance increases by as much as five- to seven-fold over resting values (Figure 5.7). This increased conductance is found in all animals except the cheetah. Conductance reaches the highest levels in the African hunting dog and domestic dog, two long distance runners. Tucker has observed a similar increase in conductance in flying gulls (5.8 × rest)[16] and budgerigars (5.0 × rest)[15]. The increase can be explained by the forced convection during running and flying and increased peripheral blood flow.

5.7 INDEPENDENT CONTROL MECHANISMS FOR EXERCISE AND HEAT LOADS?

An enormous amount of effort has been expended investigating the mechanisms controlling man's body temperature during exercise, yet the situation remains unresolved. Predictive models for thermoregulation have been devised for man at rest, but incorporating data from exercise into these models has proved difficult[50]. The demands placed on the thermoregulatory systems by exercise and environmental heat loads are often quite different, as are the optimal physiological strategies for dealing with them. I should like to offer some speculations about why the task of understanding temperature-control mechanisms during exercise has proved difficult. Even though these ideas are somewhat wild, and may prove to be totally incorrect, perhaps they will stimulate some thought and, hopefully, some experimental investigations. I should like to suggest that the mechanisms for maintaining a constant body temperature in the heat have evolved independently of those for maintaining a constant body temperature during exercise. If this is the case, one would expect to find various degrees of overlap of control, ranging from complete separation to identical systems. Is there any evidence for this?

5.7.1 Horses and donkeys

Evans and Smith[51] concluded that the sweat glands of the horse are controlled by increases in plasma adrenalin together with changes in blood flow to the sweat glands. Circulating adrenalin increases during exercise, thus, this

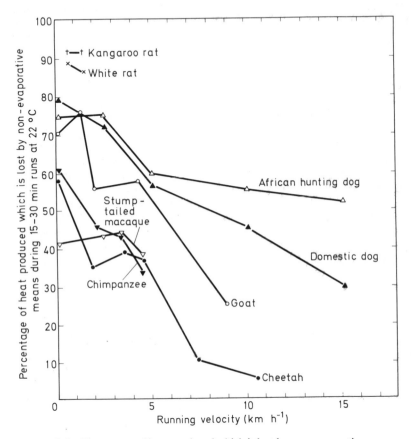

Figure 5.6 Percentage of heat produced which is lost by nonevaporative means during 15–30 min runs at 22 °C. Data are from sources listed in the text

hormonal mechanism of control might be suitable for controlling exercise heat loads. If the rate of excretion of adrenalin is proportional to heat production, this would give a precise means of regulating heat loss in relation to heat production.

The horse, and the closely related donkey, also sweat in response to heat, a situation where there is no increase in plasma adrenalin. Jenkinson and Blackburn[52] described a network of nerves around the sweat glands of the horse. It was these two facts that led David Robertshaw and me[53] to look at the control of sweating in the donkey during heat exposure and to compare this with control of exercise-induced sweating. We found that we could abolish heat-induced sweating on one side of the face by cutting the sympathetic nerves supplying the sweat glands. This same donkey, however, would sweat at about the same rate from both sides of the face after exercise. To investigate this further we abolished the release of circulating adrenalin

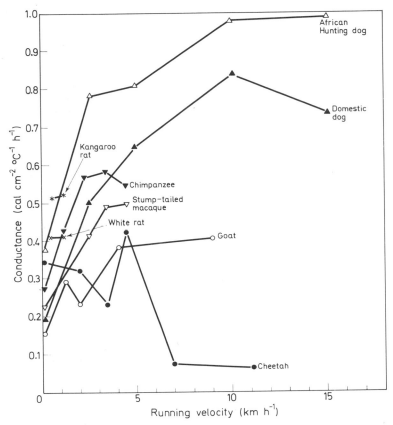

Figure 5.7 Conductance (see definition on page 172 of text) as a function of running velocity. Data is from sources listed in the text

during exercise by surgically denervating both adrenal medullas. After recovering from surgery, the donkey still sweated in response to heat on the innervated side of the face. During running, however, there was no sweating on the denervated side. We did find exercise induced sweating on the innervated side. It occurred later, however, and at higher body temperatures than in the earlier experiments. Heat-induced and exercise-induced sweating in the donkey and horse, therefore, appear to have different elements in their control (see Chapter 4, Figure 4.1).

5.7.2 Primates

The thermal sweat glands of anthropoid primates, including man, are controlled by cholinergic neurones during heat exposure. During exercise, however, circulating adrenalin also appears to play an important role in controlling sweating. Robertshaw, Taylor and Mazzia[49] studied the stump-tailed macaque (*macaca speciosa*), an anthropoid primate, which was found to control sweating in a manner similar to humans. During exercise macaques can sweat at a rate 50% higher than the maximum rate achieved during heat exposure alone. The release of adrenalin by the adrenal medulla appears to be responsible for the high rate of sweating during exercise. Blocking the release of adrenalin (using the same techniques as used in the donkey experiments) abolished the increased sweating which was observed with exercise. The increment could be restored by giving infusions of adrenalin to the denervated animals. Thus, the rate of sweating during exercise is modified and perhaps geared to heat production by the increased rate of secretion of adrenalin.

5.7.3 Kangaroos

T. J. Dawson of the University of New South Wales in Australia (personal communication) has recently made some fascinating observations on evaporative cooling mechanisms in the red kangaroo. Preliminary experiments indicate a complete separation of evaporative mechanisms for dissipating exercise and environmental heat loads: they pant in the heat and sweat during exercise. It would be interesting to know if the sweating is mediated entirely by circulating adrenalin. If future experiments confirm these preliminary findings, a strong case could be made that the heat-loss mechanisms for dealing with exercise and environmental heat loads evolved separately.

References

1. Bligh, J. and Moore R. (editors) (1972). *Essays on Temperature Regulation*, (Amsterdam: North Holland Publishing Company)
2. Hammel, H. T. (1968). Regulation of internal body temperature. *Ann. Rev. Physiol.*, **30**, 641
3. Nielsen, B. (1969). Thermoregulation in rest and exercise. *Acta. Physiol. Scand. Suppl.*, **323**, 1
4. Whittow, G. C. (editor). (1971). *Comparative Physiology of Thermoregulation. Volume 2, Mammals.* (New York: Academic Press)
5. Taylor, C. R., Schmidt-Nielsen, K. and Raab, J. L. (1970). Scaling of energetic cost of running to body size in mammals. *Amer. J. Physiol.*, **219**, 1104
6. Margaria, R., Cerretelli, P., Aghemo, P. and Sassi, G. (1963). Energy cost of running. *J. Appl. Physiol.*, **18**, 367
7. Margaria, R., Cerretelli, P., diPrampero, P. E., Massari, C. and Torelli, G. (1963). Kinetics and mechanism of oxygen debt contraction in man. *J. Appl. Physiol.*, **18**, 371
8. Margaria, R. (1968). *Int. Z. Angew. Physiol. Einschl. Arbeits Physiol.* **25**, 339
9. Howell, A. B. (1944). *Speed in Animals.* (Chicago, Illinois: Chicago University Press)
10. Layne, J. N. and Benton, A. H. (1954). Some speeds of small mammals. *J. Mammal.*, **35**, 103

11. Taylor, C. R., Caldwell, S. L. and Rowntree, V. J. (1972). Running up and down hills: Some consequences of size. *Science*, **178**, 1096
12. Hill, A. V. (1950). The dimensions of animals and their muscular dynamics. *Sci. Progr.* **38**, 209
13. Tucker, V. A. (1971). Flight energetics in birds. *Amer. Zool.*, **11**, 115
14. Tucker, V. A. (1970). Energetic cost of locomotion in animals. *Comp. Biochem. Physiol.*, **31**, 841
15. Tucker, V. A. (1968). Respiratory exchange and evaporative water loss in the flying Budgerigar. *J. Exp. Biol.*, **48**, 67
16. Tucker, V. A. (1972). Metabolism during flight in the laughing gull, *Larus atricilla*. *Amer. J. Physiol.*, **222**, 237
17. Bernstein, M. H., Thomas, S. P. and Schmidt-Nielsen, K. (1972). As the crow flies: Energy cost of locomotion. *Fed. Proc.* **31**, 325, 1972.
18. Tucker, V. A. (1966). Oxygen consumption of a flying bird. *Science*, **154**, 150
19. Schmidt-Nielsen, K. (1972). Locomotion: Energy cost of swimming, flying and running. *Science*, **177**, 222
20. Scholander, P. F. (1957). The wonderful net. *Sci. Amer.* **196**, 96
21. Dill, D. B. (1938). *Life, heat and altitude Physiological effects of hot climates and great heights.* (Cambridge, Massachusetts: Harvard University Press)
22. Schmidt-Nielsen, K. (1964). *Desert Animals. Physiological Problems of Heat and Water.* (New York: Oxford University Press)
23. Finch, V. A. (1972). Thermoregulation and heat balance of the East African eland and hartebeest. *Amer. J. Physiol.*, **222**, 1374
24. Mitchell, D., Wyndham, C. H., Atkins, A. R., Vermeullen, A. J., Hofmeyer, H. S., Strydom, N. B. and Hodgson, T. (1968). Direct measurements of thermal responses of nude resting man in dry environments. *Arch. Ges. Physiol.*, **303**, 324
25. Wenger, C. B. (1972). Heat of evaporation of sweat: thermodynamic considerations. *J. Appl. Physiol.*, **32**, 456
26. Hainsworth, F. R. and Stricker, E. M. (1970). Salivary cooling by rats in the heat. In *Physiological and Behavioral Temperature Regulation.* (J. D. Hardy, A. P. Gagge and J. A. J. Stolwijk, editors) (Springfield, Illinois: C. C. Thomas Publ.)
27. Crawford, E. C., Jr. (1962). Mechanical aspects of panting in dogs. *J. Appl. Physiol.*, **17**, 249
28. Crawford, E. C., Jr. and Kampe, G. (1971). Resonant panting in pigeons. *Comp. Biochem. Physiol.*, **40A**, 549
29. Porter, W. P. and Gates, D. M. (1969). Thermodynamic equilibria of animals with environment. *Ecol. Monog.*, **39**, 227
30. Birkebak, R. C. (1966). Heat transfer in biological systems. In *International Review of General and Experimental Zoology*, Vol. 2., (W. J. L. Felts and R. J. Harrison, editors) (New York: Academic Press)
31. Lentz, C. P. and Hart, J. S. (1960). *Can. J. Zool.*, **38**, 679
32. Moote, I. (1955) *Textile Res.*, **25**, 832
33. Schaller, G. B. (1969). Hunting behaviour of the cheetah in the Serengeti National Park, Tanzania. *E. Afr. Wildl. J.*, **6**, 95
34. Taylor, C. R. and Rowntree, V. J. (1973). Temperature regulation and heat balance in running cheetahs: A strategy for sprinters? *Amer. J. Physiol.*, **224**, 848
35. Taylor, C. R., Dmi'el, R., Fedak, M. and Schmidt-Nielsen, K. (1971). Energetic cost of running and heat balance in a large bird, the rhea. *Amer. J. Physiol.*, **221**, 597
36. Taylor, C. R. and Lyman, C. P. (1972). Heat storage in running antelopes: Independence of brain and body temperature. *Amer. J. Physiol.*, **222**, 114
37. Baker, M. A. and Hayward, J. N. (1968). The influence of nasal mucosa and the carotid rete upon hypothalamic temperature in sheep. *J. Physiol. (London)*, **198**, 561
38. Taylor, C. R. (1966). The vascularity and possible thermoregulatory function of the horns in goats. *Physiol. Zool.*, **29**, 127
39. Magilton, J. H. and Swift, C. S. (1969). Response to veins draining the nose to alar-fold temperature changes in the dog. *J. Appl. Physiol.*, **27**, 18
40. Baker, M. A. (1972). Influence of the carotid rete on brain temperature in cats exposed to hot environments. *J. Physiol. (London)* **220**, 711
41. Taylor, C. R., Schmidt-Nielsen, K., Dmi'el, R. and Fedak, M. (1971). Effect of hyper-thermia on heat balance during running in the African hunting dog. *Amer. J. Physiol.*, **220**, 823

42. Kleiber, M. (1961). *The Fire of Life. An Introduction to Animal Energetics.* (New York: Wiley and Sons)
43. Schmidt-Nielsen, K., Hainsworth, F. R. and Murrish, D. E. (1970). Counter-current heat exchange in the respiratory passages: Effect on water and heat balance. *Resp. Physiol.*, **9**, 263
44. Schmidt-Nielsen, K., Bretz, W. L. and Taylor, C. R. (1970). Panting in dogs: Unidirectional air flow over evaporative surfaces. *Science*, **169**, 1102
45. Wunder, B. A. (1970). Energetics of running activity in Merriam's chipmunk, *Eutamias merriami. Comp. Biochem. Physiol.*, **33**, 821
46. Taylor, C. R. (1969). Metabolism, respiratory changes and water balance of an antelope, the eland. *Amer. J. Physiol.*, **217**, 317
47. Hart, J. S. and Roy, O. Z. (1967). Temperature regulation during flight in pigeons. *Amer. J. Physiol.*, **213**, 1311
48. Schmidt-Nielsen, K. (1972). *How Animals Work.* (London: Cambridge University Press)
49. Robertshaw, D., Taylor, C. R. and Mazzia, L. M. Sweating in primates: Role of secretion of the adrenal medulla during exercise. *Amer. J. Physiology*, **224**, 678
50. Mitchell, D., Atkins, A. R. and Wyndham, C. H. (1972). Mathematical and physical models of thermoregulation. In *Essays on Temperature Regulation.* (J. Bligh and R. Moore, editors) (Amsterdam: North Holland Publishing Co.)
51. Evans, C. L. and Smith, D. F. G. (1956). Sweating responses in the horse. *Proc. Physiol. Soc. B*, **145**, 61
52. Jenkinson, D. M. and Blackburn, P. S. (1968). The distribution of nerves, monoamine oxidase and cholinesterase in the skin of the horse. *Res. vet. Sci.*, **9**, 165
53. Robertshaw, D. and Taylor, C. R. (1969). Sweat gland function of the donkey (*Equus asinus*). *J. Physiol.*, **205**, 79
54. Raab, J. L. and Schmidt-Nielsen, K. (1972). Effect of running on water balance of the kangaroo rat. *Amer. J. Physiol.*, **222**, 1230
55. Blatt, C. M., Taylor, C. R. and Habal, M. B. (1972). Thermal panting in dogs: The lateral nasal gland, a source of water for evaporative cooling. *Science*, **177**, 804

6
Physiological Adaptations to the Desert Environment

A. BORUT* AND A. SHKOLNIK†
* The Hebrew University, Jerusalem
† Tel-Aviv University, Tel-Aviv

6.1 INTRODUCTION

Of all terrestrial habitats the desert is the most extreme and the basic provision of the basic needs of animals living there confronts them with the most acute problems.

The geological history of most existing deserts began at the Miocene period, simultaneously with the adaptive radiation of birds and mammals. Prior to this arthropods, molluscs and reptiles had colonised a variety of land habitats and were thus able to adjust to life in the desert much earlier. However, the history of the fauna of any desert is a complicated subject and tracing the evolutionary pathways of different animal groups towards their present representation in the desert still remains speculative.

Environmental constituents are by no means the only direct factors pertinent to the emergence of a physiological adaptive pattern of an animal. Any single characteristic in this pattern may be related to either one or a combination of the three following aspects:

1. Body size,
2. Phylogeny,
3. Specific adjustment to the animal's present habitat.

While assessing the contribution of each of these aspects to the emergence of a particular physiological mechanism is rarely possible[1], cumulative comparative information in respect of certain animal groups facilitates the approach to this subject. A few pertinent examples could, perhaps, illustrate the point, to wit:

(a) Recovery of water in respiratory passages is widely acknowledged as an advantage for desert life; however, in birds and rodents this characteristic is found to be closely related to body size and has not specifically evolved under desert conditions[2].

(b) Aestivation contributes to energy and water conservation in the desert and forms part of the adaptive pattern of some desert rodents, yet desert-dwelling ground squirrels (Sciuridae) have inherited this characteristic from their cold adapted hibernating relatives[3].

(c) Examples of the specific effect of the habitat are more difficult to cite since only few comparisons of the physiology of desert-dwelling species to their non-desert close relatives have been carried out. Some of the investigators[4] who adopted this approach in their studies of the North American Cricetid genus *Peromyscus* ended up by only emphasising the significance of the group pattern. A convincing example is shown in the comparison between *Gazella thomsoni* and the desert penetrating *G. grantii*, both from East Africa[5, 150]. When dehydrated and exposed to high ambient temperature (45 °C) the latter species is able to raise its body temperature to 46.5 °C v. 42.5 °C in *G. thomsoni*, thereby improving the ability to cope with the impact of desert conditions.

The more efficient the physiological capacity of an animal the more versatile becomes its exploitation of the habitat in its extreme conditions.

Among all physiological characteristics of animals only those that appear to be of survival advantage in the desert, will be considered here as an adaptation to life in this habitat. These adaptations centre mainly around the management of an efficient and economic water balance and a tolerable energy budget under conditions of high ambient temperatures, intense radiation, and scarcity of water and food.

Behavioural adaptation complements and strengthens physiological adaptability and in a way compensates for the inaptitude of an animals' physiology by shielding it against climatic hardship. This enables the animal to thrive in the desert by circumventing its hostile conditions. With decreasing body size behavioural adaptation plays a more prominent role[6]. However, as this review will be focused on physiological mechanisms only, behavioural aspects will not be dealt with. (See Chapter 7.)

The literature covered by this review extends mainly over the period from 1964 onwards, with no claim to exhaustiveness. We consider the year 1964 to be significant in the history of desert research in view of the comprehensive reviews on desert life published then. Of these the most prominent is the book by Schmidt-Nielsen[6]. Others by various authors are included in the Handbook of Physiology[7] and among the more recent ones there are the reviews by Edney[8], Dawson and Bartholomew[9], Bartholomew and Dawson[10], Mayhew[11] and Serventy[12].

6.2 ADAPTATIONS RELATING TO CONSERVATION OF WATER NOT NEEDED FOR COOLING

6.2.1 Restricting water loss through the integument

Life on land is associated with the organism's aptitude to save water to prevent desiccation. In the desert, where the air saturation deficit with water vapours exceeds all other land habitats, the water-proofing of the integument becomes a vital necessity and a major feature in the adaptive pattern of desert

Table 6.1 **Transpiration in arthropods from various habitats measured in dry air at temperatures between 20°C and 30°C. The values are given as $\mu g\ cm^{-2}\ h^{-1}\ mmHg^{-1}$ and may be converted to $cm\ s^{-1}$ by multiplying by 2.90×10^{-4}** (From Edney[8], by courtesy of *Science*)

Species	Habitat	Transpiration
Isopod crustaceans		
Porcellio scaber	Hygric	110
Venezillio arizonicus	Xeric	32
Hemilepistus reaumuri	Xeric	23
Insects		
Calliphora erythrocephala	Mesic	51
Blatta orientalis	Mesic	48
Glossina palpalis adults	Mesic	12
Glossina morsitans pupae	Xeric	0.3
Tenebrio molitor larvae	Xeric	5
Tenebrio molitor pupae	Xeric	1
Thermobia domestica adults	Xeric	15
Myriapods		
Lithobius sp.	Hygric	270
Glomeris marginata	Hygric	200
Arachnids		
Pandinus imperator	Mesic	82
Androctonus australis	Xeric	0.8
Galeodes arabs	Xeric	6.6
Ixodes ricinus	Mesic	60
Ornithodorus moubata	Xeric	4.0

animals. Because of the volume/surface ratio its role is much more significant in small animals.

Arthropods—A high degree of water-proofing was found in insects, and since the early studies of Ramsey[13], Beament[14] and Wigglesworth[15], this was attributed to the epicuticle. Edney[8] demonstrated that transpiration rates in arthropods from xeric environments are much lower than in mesic species. Studies on arachnids[16,17] support this finding. (Table 6.1.)

The rate of cuticular transpiration is proportional to the saturation deficit of the air and the wind speed. It is largely independent of prevailing temperatures, but at a certain point, the transition temperature, evaporation rises abruptly.

Water loss through the cuticle is restricted owing to a closely packed and organised polar layer of lipid molecules; the transition phenomenon ensues as a result of disorganisation and disorientation of these molecules caused by elevated temperature[18]. Transition temperatures are generally higher in desert species than in the non-desert ones. Beament[19] and Loveridge[20] determined a transition temperature of 48 °C in desert orthopterans (*Schistocerea gregaria* and *Locusta migratoria*) as compared to 30 °C found in non-desert species (*Periplaneta* sp.). A transition temperature of 50 °C was found in tenebrionid desert beetles.

Edney[8] suggested that arthropods with high transition temperatures have also a low cuticular transpiration. Such relations were indeed shown in three species of tenebrionid beetles studied by Ahearn[21] who also proved that species active in the autumn had a lower transition temperature than that found in the summer-active species.

The significance of the epicuticle in the water conservation of isopods is not yet clear. A relatively high rate of evaporation is found in these animals and this is reflected in their behavioural pattern in the desert[8,204].

Landsnails—They are the only invertebrates that accompany arthropods in certain desert areas. The role of the integument in conserving water was recently assessed in the desert snail *Sphincterochila boissieri*[22,23] (Hellicellidae). This snail, abundant in the desert of North Africa and the Middle East, aestivates in the barren soil fully exposed to the impact of the desert all summer long. The daily water loss measured in these animals in nature during the summer amounted to only 0.034% of their total body water. Considering that the water content of the snail may exceed 80% of its body, the small daily loss explains the ability of these molluscs to survive even through several years of continuous drought.

Machin[24] compared structure and rates of water loss through water filled shells of the Hellicellid land snails, *Helix aspera* from mild mesic areas, *Otala lactea* from dry mesic conditions and *Sphinterochila boissieri*. He found in still air at 22 °C a daily loss of 1.3 mg/animal through the shell of the first species (mean surface area 17.40 ± 2.35 cm²); 1.14 mg from the second species (mean surface area 15.77 ± 0.41 cm²) and only 0.26 mg through the thick shell of the third desert species (surface area 8.33 ± 0.28 cm²). Yom-Tov[22] also confirms the high degree of water-proofing in the desert snails which exceeds even that of the insect cuticle. Machin[25], however, concludes that, rather than physiological adaptation it is the thickness, size and proportion that endow these shells with their ability to reduce water loss.

Amphibians—Evaporation in amphibians, even xerophilous ones (certain toads and frogs) is not altered by the presence of their skin[26,27]. The ability to penetrate into desert areas, although to a limited extent only, which is found in certain species, depends mainly on appropriate behaviour. One species (*Chiromantis xeramplina*) from Rhodesia was reported to possess an extremely restricted cutaneous evaporation[27].

Reptiles—The classical concept that reptilians' skin is impermeable to water prevailed until recent years. In 1964, after examining data available at that time, Schmidt-Nielsen suggested that cutaneous evaporation in reptiles may be greater than was considered likely[6]. When partitioning cutaneous evaporation from pulmonary loss and measuring its rate directly, it was found indeed to contribute the greatest part of the total evaporation. At 23 °C the cutaneous loss measured in a variety of reptiles[28] amounted to 66–87% of the total evaporation. At temperatures above 40 °C respiratory loss as measured in the desert Iguanid *Sauromalus obesus*, exceeded the cutaneous loss. A correlation could be established between the rate of cutaneous loss and the availability of water in the environment. However, while drawing such conclusions one should not overlook differences existing among taxonomic groups, which may sometimes overshadow those due to the ecological background. This was claimed by Dmi'el[29] to be the case in his comparison of cutaneous evaporation in mesic and desert colubrid and viperid snakes.

Birds—Since sweat glands are absent in birds' skin, it was generally assumed that in this group cutaneous evaporation is negligible. In recent years, however, it has been demonstrated that in many birds 50% or more of the total evaporation—when measured at 30 °C and 35 °C, occurs just through this avenue[30]. So far no correlation has been found between the degree of water-proofing of birds' skins and the habitat. An exception—according to present knowledge—is the Ostrich in whom a very low cutaneous evaporation was demonstrated, amounting to less than 2% of the total evaporation at 40 °C ambient temperature[31].

Mammals—Mammals which depend on sweating for evaporative cooling may lose a tremendous amount of water through their skin. The ability of the skin to restrict water loss when evaporation is not called for has not been assessed in sweating mammals in the desert. In non-sweating mammals, like rodents, evaporation through the skin may be very low. In the desert-dwelling Heteromyid *Dipodomys merriami* this may not exceed 16% of the total evaporation[32] and when the animal is on dry diet, may be even negligible[33]. Such may also be the case in other desert rodents; yet in *Peromyscus maniculatus sonorensis*, a North American Cricetid inhabiting desert mountains, cutaneous evaporation accounted for about 46% of the total, similar to values found in white rats[32,109].

In the desert diurnal *Acomys russatus* a cutaneous loss as high as 70% of the total evaporation was measured at 30 °C[34].

6.2.2 Minimising the amount of water lost with electrolyte and nitrogenous waste excretion

The contribution of excretory organs to survival in the desert lies in their ability to help the organism to conserve its body water. This may be achieved by eliminating the end products of the nitrogenous metabolism, as well as an excess of electrolytes ingested with food and drinking water, in a minimum volume of fluid. Furthermore, excreting electrolytes in a concentrated solution could make possible the usage of salty water, juicy desert plants etc. as food and water sources.

An intriguing correlation between the nature of the nitrogenous end product and the availability of water in the organism's environment (particularly in its embryonic stages), has long ago been pointed out. Very often this correlation is cited as an example of evolution at a physiological level[35]. Members of animal groups that excrete purine compounds, such as uric acid, guanine and xanthine, may be considered as pre-adapted to life in a xeric environment. Purines are non-toxic almost non-soluble compounds; they may be eliminated in a crystallised form almost without waste of water. Land snails, insects, lizards and snakes as well as birds all excrete uric acid. Insects also excrete guanine and xanthine and so do arachnids. Isopods, although penetrating into the desert, excrete ammonia as the main end product of their nitrogenous metabolism[36]. Excretion of ammonia is typical of an aquatic habitat and most isopods are indeed found in water or humid environments. Land isopods maintain this feature typical of their entire group even in the desert.

In desert snails, sealed in their calcareous shell during prolonged aestivation, uric acid forms a sediment in their body. Voidance of the stored excreta takes place on the rare rainy days when the snails become active. Recently, however, ammonia was detected diffusing from the land snail of the Californian desert *Otala* (Helix) *lactea*. The ammonia nitrogen eliminated by this species was found to be only 5% of the total nitrogen excreted by the active snail, but accounted for 30% of the nitrogen excretion in the aestivating ones. The role that elimination of ammonia may play in the deposition of calcium carbonate in the shell of the snail, is intriguing but requires further clarification[35,37].

In ureatelic animals the elimination of both urea and electrolytes demands its toll in the form of water lost as urine. The capacity of the kidney to produce a concentrated urine, relative to the concentration of the plasma, determines its contribution to the water economy of the organism. Mammals possess the capacity to form the most concentrated urine. The spatial organisation of the renal nephrons is held responsible for this ability by providing a structural basis for a countercurrent multiplier. The tubular segments of the nephrons, known as Henle's loops, which function in this concentrating mechanism extend along the entire width of the renal medulla and reach the tip of the papilla. Their relative length determines among other factors the concentrating capacity of the particular kidney. Sperber[38] pointed to the significance of the 'relative medullary thickness' in the ability to concentrate urine and to colonise dry habitats. The functional meaning of these relations are further discussed and clarified by Schmidt-Nielsen and O'Dell[39] and reviewed by Berliner and Bennett[40].

A quantitative evaluation of the kidney's contribution to the water economy of a desert mammal was first presented by Schmidt-Nielsen and Schmidt-Nielsen in 1951[33] in comparing the kangaroo-rat (Heteromyidae) to the laboratory rat. They demonstrated that Heteromyid desert rodents may concentrate their urine up to about 15 times their plasma concentration. Urea, however, is concentrated up to 400 times. Later investigators provided data supporting this finding and a further few desert rodents of different families were found capable of concentrating urine to about 25 times their plasma values, with a urea concentration capability of 800 times[41]. Thus it appears that desert rodents possess the most efficient mammalian kidney[42]. Along with this ability, the relative medullary thickness in desert rodents is the highest and the renal papilla often projects into the ureter.

The ability of primitive non-desert Heteromyids (*Liomys salvani* and *L. irroratus*) to produce urine about as concentrated as in their famous relative of the desert, may point to the possibility that this outstanding 'desert adaptation' could have evolved in this family before they encountered desert conditions[43].

This may also be the case with other mammalian families represented in the desert. Further comparative studies would be required to elucidate this point.

The renal capacity of desert carnivores has not been studied. The high urea concentration as found in the cats urine (2300 mosmol) may indicate the importance of the kidney in the water economy of this group[6].

Urine concentration in large desert herbivorous mammals is not as high as in the small ones. The urine urea may be very low consistent with the low protein content in their diet and the re-use of urea by their intestinal micro-organisms[44].

Desert inhabiting members of other mammalian groups probably also surpass their non-desert relatives in their ability to produce a more concentrated urine. This is evident in 'primitive' mammalian groups like hedgehogs (Erinaceidae). Maximal urine concentration in the European hedgehog (*Erinaceus europaeus*) was found to be 2900 mosmol, while a hedgehog living in the deserts of North Africa and the Middle East, *Hemiechinus auritus*, can produce urine as concentrated as 5900 mosmol. The length of their renal papillae differ accordingly (Yacobi and Shkolnik, personal communication).

The role of the kidney in the water economy of desert marsupials is generally similar to that found in placental mammals. The kidney is adapted in its structure to the animal's habitat[212]. Maximal concentration reported in the literature for marsupials comes from the small desert carnivorous mulgara (*Dasycercus cristicauda*) and amounts to 4000 mosmol. In herbivorous xeric a kangaroos urine concentration of up to 2700 mosmol was reported[27]. The ability to concentrate electrolytes in the urine also helps to conserve water. This applies to purinotelic as well as to ureatelic land organisms. In purinotelic animals, however, the urine excreted with the faecal material and the final concentration of the excreta is accomplished extrarenally (cloaca and hindgut). This process in desert animals will be discussed under the appropriate heading. In mammals, excess of electrolytes in the plasma is dealt with by the concentrating mechanism of their kidney. Desert rodents with long renal papillae reveal the highest known electrolyte concentrating ability, 1500–2000 mequiv.l^{-1} are common in many desert rodents[39]. Higher concentrations are known: In *Notomys cervinus* (Muridae) 2190 mequiv.l^{-1} was found[41] and in *Acomys russatus* even 3000 mequiv.l^{-1} [34]. A very high electrolyte concentration of over 2000 mequiv.l^{-1} was also reported in the marsupial *Macropus eugenii* (Tammar wallaby)[212].

Desert ungulates are less able to achieve a high urinary electrolyte concentration. Much more potassium is excreted and sometimes very little sodium in comparison with rodents. This may reflect the composition of their food[45,46].

Among the invertebrates only in insects is the osmolarity of the excreta higher than that of blood (haemolymph). Among insects the ratio of urine and faeces to haemolymph concentration is highest in desert species. In the desert locust *Schistocerca gregaria* a ratio of 2 was demonstrated by Phillips[47], and in tenebrionid beetles, a group very conspicuous in the desert, a ratio of up to 10 was found by Ramsay[48]. The Malpighian tubules along with the rectal segment of the hindgut comprise the excretory mechanism of the insects. Iso- or hypotonic urine is voided from the Malpighian tubules into the rectum. Epithelial wall thickenings known as rectal papillae withdraw water from the content of the hindgut, urine and egesta. The explanation for the 'uphill' withdrawal of water is based on the model suggested by Diamond and Bossert[207], which assumes a two membrane three compartmental mechanism located in the papilial epithelium. Water in the insect's rectum follows an active electrolyte transport into the extensive intercellular spaces within the rectal papillae. Solutes are returned from the intercellular spaces to the cells across the basal surface and water moves to the haemolymph propelled by hydrostatic pressure. Recycling of solutes brings about a continuous osmotic flow. Organic macromolecules are found in the rectal papillar cells and intercellular spaces. They too may contribute to the general concentration and may influence the flow of water and solutes through the cells and intercellular spaces[49]. In *Tenebrio* as well as in other coleopteran and lapidopteran insects a structure known as acryptonephridial complex was described by Ramsay[48]. This complex is comprised of segments of Malpighian tubules running close to the rectum. Grimstone et al.[50] have demonstrated that potassium (K^+) is transported from the haemolymph into the perirectal Malpighian tubules against a very large electrochemical gradient, and a concentration of 5400 mosmol is built up in the tubules lumen. This could be instrumental in the establishment of a steeper absorption gradient across the rectum[49].

Gut, cloaca and salt glands—In reptiles and birds these play a major role in conserving water by way of reabsorbing fluid from the excreta. Schmidt-Nielsen et al.[51] suggested that sodium and the accompanying water may be absorbed from the cloaca and, in certain reptiles and birds the salt could subsequently be eliminated by their salt glands. Active sodium (Na^+) transport from the cloaca was demonstrated in both reptiles[52-54] and in birds[55]. Skadhauge[56] also showed that the water moves from the cloaca up into the large intestine where water and ions are being absorbed. Withdrawal of water in this case may take place as suggested by the two-layer model mentioned previously[57]. The nitrogenous end product, excreted as uric acid and urates contribute only little to the cloacal osmotic concentration.

In the desert iguana (*Dipsosaurus dorsalis*) colloid osmotic pressure across the cloaca was found to be sufficient to account for the fluid reabsorption from the cloaca[208]. The higher level of plasma albumins found in semi-desert and desert reptiles[59] may bear some relevance to this mechanism. The efficient exploitation of the inherent capacity to excrete uric acid thus conserving water, is greatly dependent on the presence of salt glands. These glands, first discovered in marine birds and reptiles[60] represent an adaptation not only to marine existence, they also help in conserving water in uricotelic desert reptiles and birds. Furthermore, by excreting electrolytes in a hypertonic solution, salt glands become integrated in the process of water and salt reabsorption from the cloaca and the consequent concentration of the voided uric acid[51]. Following the discovery of active salt glands in the desert iguana (*Dipsosaurus dorsalis*) and *Uromatix aegyptius* (Agamidae) such glands were found in many desert lizards and their function and contribution to electrolyte and water balance was studied by many investigators. In the desert iguana it was studied by Minnich[61] and by Templeton *et al.*[62]. Grenot[63] investigated the water and electrolyte metabolism of the Saharian herbivorous agamid lizard *Uromastix acantinurus* and evaluated the role of the salt glands in this animal. Duvdevani[176] presented similar information on four species of small insectivorous lizards of the Genus *Acanthodactylus* inhabiting areas of different aridity in Israel. Duvdevani further demonstrated that in the lizards he studied shortage of water enhanced the activity of salt glands.

Electrolytes are generally eliminated through the nares of the desert lizards in a crystallised form. Murrish and Schmidt-Nielsen[58] described the process of crystallisation in the desert iguana. The hypertonic aqueous solution secreted by the salt glands of the lizard accumulates in a depression located within the nasal passages and humidifies the air inhaled over it. As water evaporates, the salt crystallises.

In birds nasal salt glands were, so far, found in the desert dwelling ostrich (*Struthio camelus*) and the desert partridge (*Ammoperdix heyi*)[51]. Cade and Greenwald[65] described salt glands in 21 species of falconiform birds few of which thrive under extreme desert conditions. These authors worked out the quantitative contribution of the salt glands to the water and salt regulation in a small Accipiter. Up to now we have no comprehensive water balance studies in birds or reptiles which would enable us to assess the difference in the capabilities and contribution of salt glands in desert *v.* non-desert animals. Neither do we have a quantitative comparison of water and salt balance in a desert reptile or bird with or without salt glands.

Faecal water loss—The amount of water lost in faeces depends on the organism's state of hydration, hence on the amount of water in the food, the availability of drinking water and the rate of loss to the environment. In most land animals the faeces may contain 50–70% water when the animals are adequately supplied with drinking water. In grazing cows it may exceed 80%.

The excrement of arthropods, reptiles and birds contain egesta as well as 'urine'. To a certain extent the same mechanisms are involved in withdrawing water from both, before these are expelled (see above). In faecal pellets of xeric insects 75% water may generally be found in humid conditions; this may drop to 35% in dry air[66].

Desert locusts which usually excrete pellets containing 70–76% water can also excrete pellets with only 4% water[67].

In faeces of desert lizards 50–60% water was found. When the faeces were separated from urine in three species of insectivorous desert lizards (Genus *Acanthodactylus*), it was revealed that the faecal water loss amounted to 6–23% of the total water loss and greatly exceeded the urinary loss (2–6 times more)[176]. Mendelssohn, Duvdevani and Dmi'el (personal communication), measured water content in faecal pellets (separated from urine) of the desert herbivorous lizard *Uromastix aegyptius*. When fully hydrated (fed on fresh lettuce) 50% water was found, but only 26% when the animal was fed dry straw.

Faecal water loss in the Colubrid desert snake *Spalerosophis cliffordi*, at 30 °C 22% relative humidity, amounted to over 8% of the total water loss[68].

Droppings of birds contain an average of 75–80% water, but when there is a water shortage much dryer excrements are expelled. The zebra finch (*Taeniopygia castanotis*), an Australian passerine and the black-throated sparrow (*Amphispiza bilineata*) from the North American desert, both void droppings containing 80% water. When water supply is restricted, faecal moisture drops to 65% and 57% respectively[69,70]. In Stark's lark (*Spizocorys starki*) from the Namib desert a drop in moisture was shown from 75% to 51%[71]. A similar drop (from 75–80% to 60%) was also found in the Australian xeric budgerigar (*Melopsittacus undulatus*)[69]. According to Serventy[12] 'the percentage of moisture in droppings of the Bourke Parrot of the desert was much less than in similar parrots from mesic and humid parts of Australia'.

Water lost by mammals in their faecal pellets may amount to 45% of their total water loss, as was found in a dehydrated Hereford steer under simulated desert conditions[77]. In desert adapted mammals, the camel and the kangaroo-rat, it may be as low as 0.5%[33,73], but in the majority of desert mammals studied, faecal water loss amounted to 10–20% of the total water loss.

Minimum moisture was found in the faeces of desert dwelling mammals. In camel, donkey, merino sheep, the Beduin goat and kangaroo-rat it may drop to 42%[33,45,73,75,76].

In non-desert mammals, several of which are taxonomically close to some of the above mentioned, minimum faecal water content is much higher[46,73,76,77].

Although the mechanism of water withdrawal from the digestive tract has aroused much interest, little is known about the control of this process or the ability to increase its efficiency when water availability is reduced. When it is realised that even in desert species water lost via this avenue may exceed 20% of the total water loss, much more attention should be paid to the study of this problem.

6.2.3 Minimising respiratory water loss

Respiratory air comes into contact with the thin, moist membranes serving as gas exchange surfaces in all land dwelling animals. In the course of ventilation of these surfaces water evaporation becomes unavoidable. The actual amount of water lost by the animal depends, of course on the magnitude of its metabolism and on the absolute water content of the inspiratory air. In the dry air of the desert this loss is of special importance.

In endothermic animals expiratory air is, most of the time, expelled at higher than ambient temperatures and has a large water-vapour carrying capacity. In addition, their ventilation rate is more intense than in other groups and proportionally higher in small-bodied endotherms.

A reduction in the respiratory water loss takes place if the expired air is exhaled at a temperature lower than body temperature, thus containing less water when saturated. Expiration of air at a lower than body temperature was first described by Jackson and Schmidt-Nielsen[78] in rodents, but to a certain extent, the findings are probably true for any animal with relatively narrow and moist respiratory passages. In rodents the vascular nasal conchae constitute a water and heat counter-current exchange mechanism, whereby inspired air is warmed and moistened by evaporation and heat exchanged with the nasal mucosa. On expiration, the saturated out-going air cools because of lower mucosa temperature due to evaporation on inspiration. As a result, water is condensed and deposited on the mucosa and heat of condensation is recovered. The deposited water serves as a source of evaporation in the next cycle. This countercurrent mechanism with a temporal separation serves both water and heat recovery[79]. The magnitude of water recovery depends mainly on ambient conditions, the cooler and/or drier the air, the larger the cooling effect on the mucosal membranes and the greater the water recovery[80]. However, calculation from a simulated model of exchange in the nasal passages of the kangaroo-rat showed that over a range of ambient temperatures 10 °C– 36 °C and relative humidities 0–100% the predicted nasal vapour recovery was always between 66 and 77%[81]. It should be emphasised that this is not an adaptation peculiar to desert rodents; the same phenomenon was observed in the laboratory rat[79]. The mechanism is primarily a heat exchange and conservation device important in low ambient temperatures. A similar method of water recovery prevails in small birds, although their shorter nasal passages decrease its efficiency[80].

Reptiles profit much less from this mechanism. Their nasal passages are too short and too wide to allow for an efficient heat exchange and their body temperatures, on many occasions, do not deviate considerably from that of the surrounding air. However, in all cases where the reptile's body temperature increases above the ambient air by basking or by contact with warm substrates (thigmothermy), water conservation is possible and actually has been found[2]. In the desert iguana (*Dipsosaurus dorsalis*), when its body temperature is elevated to 42 °C while the ambient temperature is 30 °C, 31% less water is lost through the nose compared to a lizard with body temperature equal to the ambient temperature. Again, this is not particular to desert reptiles although such basking situations are quite common in diurnal desert reptiles.

The efficiency of the nose water exchanger diminishes with increasing body size. As nasal passages widen, a decreasing proportion of inspiratory air comes into contact with the nasal mucosa. In a bird the size of a duck exhaled air temperature is appreciably higher than that of a wren under the same ambient conditions. We also know that in man, at moderate ambient temperatures, the expired air is close to body temperature[2]. Even so, there are quite a few desert mammals of intermediate size and long snouts, in whom the magnitude of this effect would be worth studying.

In land *insects* the occlusive spiracles of the tracheal respiratory system are very important in cutting down respiratory water loss. This was proved by demonstrating a direct relationship between evaporation and differential spiracular closure in the tsetse fly (*Glossina*)[82]. The cyclic outbursts of CO_2 described in some insects may also participate in cutting down water loss through spiracular control[83]. At rest about 25% of the evaporative water loss is spiracular. This was found in the tsetse fly[82] and in the desert locust (*Schistocerca*)[84]. Efficient water saving is also conspicuous in active insects. During flight the oxygen uptake of a tsetse fly increases by 22 times over the resting value, whereas its evaporation increases by only six times[82]. Weis-Fogh found that the extra water lost by the desert locust during flight in dry air was so small that it could be completely replaced by the additionally generated metabolic water[8].

Isopods still retain pleopods (gill-like appendages) as respiratory organs, though the more xeric ones have branched invaginations extending into the pleopods (pseudotrachea). However, no data on respiratory water loss is available for desert species of isopods[8,204].

6.3 ADAPTATIONS IN HEAT PRODUCTION AND HEAT DISSIPATION

6.3.1 Heat production

In all animals the rate of resting metabolism depends on body temperature and, like most biological processes, obeys the Van't Hoff law. This relationship is quantitatively expressed as Q_{10}, i.e. the ratio of the rate of oxygen consumption at a particular temperature to that at a temperature 10 °C lower. In a hot environment it is only logical to expect modification of the heat generating physiological processes which would tend to help the animal to cope with the environmental heat load.

In *reptiles*, behaviourally established rather than environmentally imposed body temperatures appear to have been a major factor in evolution[85]. Accordingly reptiles have variable preferred activity temperatures, the limits of which differ with the reptile species. They are also not the same for all biological functions of the animal; digestion and territorial defence may be carried out at a temperature not equal to that prevailing in respect of other activities. Behavioural thermoregulation is quite complex and involves a whole set of physiological adjustments. Comprehensive literature has accumulated over the years on subjects pertaining to the basic way a reptile functions. This information, gained by using desert lizards as experimental animals, was recently summarised[11,86].

The standard (resting) metabolism of lizards compared to that of mammals is very low. The metabolic ratio of mammal to lizard of equivalent body weight, both at 37 °C may, at times, amount to 6.7 when compared with *Dipsosaurus dorsalis* of 69 g weight, and to 2.3 when compared with *Sceloporus occidentalis* of 16 g[86]. This low metabolic rate may be advantageous to life at high ambient temperatures as was suggested by Schmidt-Nielsen and Dawson[87] and Dawson[85].

The relationship between the standard (resting) metabolic rate and body weight in reptiles has been worked out by comparing a variety of reptiles, all of them at a body temperature of 30 °C[88] or at 37 °C[86], the latter being quite close to the activity temperature of most thermophilic* desert lizards. In a few well known desert lizards, such as *Dipsosaurus dorsalis* and *Crotaphytus*

---

* Thermophily is defined by a mean body temperature above 36 °C in active lizards—most diurnal desert lizards are thermophilic.

collaris, metabolic rates lower than expected in accordance with their body weight were revealed, they were at 37 °C, one-quarter or one-third lower. However, others, e.g. different *Uta* species do not behave so, thus no clear-cut ecological correlations are possible.

Recently, four species of the small insectivorous lacertid genus *Acanthodactylus*, all thermophilic and living in biotopes of increasing aridity, were studied by Duvdevani and Borut[64]. When their resting metabolism was compared, it was found that the species which lives in the most arid habitat, *A. boskianus*, (7.8 g body weight) at 37 °C, deviates maximally (57%) from its expected metabolism. However, this is by no means the lowest found, small iguanids may go much lower. In a non-thermophilic, desert dwelling iguanid of 1 g body weight, Snyder[89] found a metabolic rate less than 16% of that expected at 30 °C. According to the author, this is instrumental in cutting down evaporative water loss.

With accumulating knowledge it becomes increasingly clear that Scholander's conclusions[90-93] according to which basal metabolic rate in *birds and mammals* is non-adaptive to climatic conditions, are not valid for many desert endotherms.

During the long periods when the animal is at rest, presumably at ambient temperatures prevailing within its thermoneutral zone*, reduced metabolism cuts down heat production and thereby saves water otherwise needed for its dissipation when ambient temperatures are high. It also saves food. Furthermore, it may help small mammals resting in humid subterranean shelters where high humidity makes heat dissipation by evaporation difficult[94]. Reducing metabolism may be of special significance in small birds and mammals where heat production—compared to body weight—is large[95].

Another way of conserving water and food at high ambient temperatures while at rest, can be achieved when the thermoneutral zone of an animal shifts or extends to higher ambient temperatures. Both modifications in heat production are quite commonly used together, the reduction as well as the displacement.

In *birds* it is not easy to correlate modifications in basal heat production to the ecological demands of the desert. Some recent evaluations of the relationship between body weight and basal metabolism indicate interordinal differences[96,97]. Passerine birds (order Passeriformes) have an appreciably higher metabolic rate per unit weight than birds of comparable body size belonging to other orders. Considering that the great majority of desert birds are active during the day and do not make use of cool and relatively moist shelters, the failure to demonstrate widespread metabolic adaptations seems surprising. It should, however, be remembered that heat production in flight imposes a very large heat load demanding means of fast dissipation (see Chapter 5). Such a load overshadows the environmental stress and this may explain the similarity in heat production and heat dissipation evidenced even in experiments carefully designed to find out differences due to desert life. Calder and Schmidt-Nielsen[98] carried out such an experiment by comparing the reactions of a bird exposed to extreme desert conditions, the Californian roadrunner (*Geococcyx californicus*) with those of the rock dove (*Columba*

---

* A thermoneutral zone comprises the range of ambient temperatures within which the metabolic rate is constant and minimal and wherein the basal or resting metabolism is measured.

livia) both of approximately the same body weight. Their conclusions support and corroborate the earlier views that the physiological capacity of thermoregulation in desert birds is very similar to that of non-desert dwellers[98,100].

However, low metabolic rates are found in desert dwelling goatsuckers (*Caprimulgiformes*) and owls (*Strigiformes*). Goatsuckers commonly roost during the day and also nest exposed directly to the sun, thus being subject at times to appreciable heat loads. Their metabolic rate was found to be in a range between 39% and 65% of the rate expected in accordance with their body weight, using the equation of King and Farner[99]. At high ambient temperatures goatsuckers were found to have a low metabolic rate, a comparatively small increase in body temperature and low evaporation rates[97,211]. The low metabolism is obviously associated with the exceptional powers of thermoregulation that those birds possess.

Lasiewski and Seymour[101] have lucidly demonstrated the significance of low metabolism in the desert inhabiting poorwill (*Phalaenoptilus nuttalli, Caprimulgiformes*). (Figure 6.1). Compared to three xeric birds of approximately equal body weight, representing three different orders, the low evaporation of the poorwill is outstanding; its body temperature is also kept lower, yet it dissipates at high ambient temperatures a higher portion of the heat generated.

Very low basal metabolic values were also revealed in some small American desert owls (*Strigiformes*)[102]. Carefully collected comparable data on non-desert relatives of the *Caprimulgiformes* and *Strigiformes* are needed so as to decide whether those characteristics evolved specifically as a response to a hot xeric environment or were determined at the ordinal level. Accumulating findings in respect of low basal metabolism in other xeric birds would also be pertinent. The Inca dove (*Scardafella inca*) has a low metabolism when compared with other Columbiformes[103] (see Figure 6.1). Low basal metabolism was also reported in the Californian quail (*Loportyx californicus*)[104].

It is worth drawing attention to the fact that in certain avian groups the emergence of a modification in the basal metabolism may be surprisingly fast. Although house sparrows (*Passer domesticus*) were spreading in the U.S. only about a century ago, those settled in hot-humid surroundings like Houston, Texas, have a lower heat production than the sparrows from colder environments such as Michigan or Colorado[105].

In *marsupials* the relationship between body weight and basal metabolism parallels that of higher eutherian groups, but is about 30% lower. The information is based on observations of marsupials ranging from mouselike creatures of 9 g weight up to 54 kg weighing macropods[106] and including conspicuous members of the Australian desert fauna. This 'pre-adaptation' to desert life is also shared by some groups of lower eutherians such as insectivores[107]. Moreover, *hedgehogs* (Erinaceidae–Insectivora) present a good example of reduction in the basal metabolic level associated with life in the desert. The European hedgehog (*Erinaceus europaeus*) has, in common with marsupials and other primitive eutherians, a low body temperature, around 34 °C, and a weight-specific basal metabolism, 70% that of advanced eutherians. However, if we 'correct' his metabolic level to a theoretical body temperature of 38 °C typical for advanced mammals, by assuming a Q_{10} of 2.3, the hedgehog will closely approximate to the 'normal' mammalian values. Metabolism measured in a desert hedgehog (*Paraechinus aethiopicus*) amounted to only

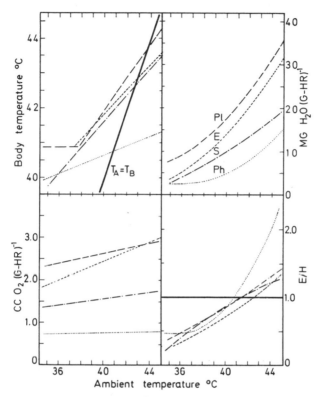

Figure 6.1 Comparison of respiratory and thermoregulatory data at high ambient temperatures in four birds of hot habitats. The birds belong to four different orders but have approximately the same body weight ≈ 40 g. Measurements were carried out under identical conditions and show the relations between body temperature (upper left), evaporative water loss (upper right), oxygen consumption (lower left) and the ratio of heat loss by evaporation to heat produced (lower right) and ambient temperature. Data is presented as regression lines:
1. African weaverbird (*Ploceus cucullatus*—Passeriformes)—long dashed lines.
2. Chinese painted quail (*Excalfactoria chinensis*—Galliformes)—short dashed lines
3. Inca dove (*Scardafella inca*—Columbiformes)—dash dot lines.
4. Poorwill (*Phalaenoptilus nuttali*—Caprimulgiformes)—dotted lines.
(From Lasiewski and Seymour[101], courtesy of *Physiol. Zool.*)

half that of the European hedgehog. Thermoneutrality in the desert species was reached at an ambient temperature some 3 °C higher[108].

Hart[109] pooled and compared data on heat production and dissipation in 22 hot-arid desert *rodents* and 52 non-desert species. These rodents were studied by many investigators who used different techniques and kept their animals in different 'basal' conditions and different acclimations prior to the experiments. In spite of all this he found that in hot-arid and desert rodents the basal metabolic level was 10% lower than that expected in relation to their body weight, according to the Brody–Proctor equation[110]. Metabolism in the 52 non-desert species averaged about 10% above the expected. The lower critical point (lowest ambient temperature of the thermoneutral zone) of 19 desert species averaged 30.0 °C ±0.7 °C, i.e. 3 °C higher than the 28 non-desert species. No difference was found in the average span of the thermoneutral zone, which was apparently due to the difficulties in correctly measuring the upper end point of the zone. At high ambient temperatures evaporation and cooling are impeded by high relative humidities. Many of the previous measurements of metabolism at high ambient temperatures were carried out at high humidities, due to limitations in the experimental set up. The problems inherent in such measurements are fully discussed by Lasiewski *et al.*[111]. In addition to the peculiarities in the metabolic pattern of desert rodents, as demonstrated above, group patterns emerge when enough data is available to compare desert species with their non-desert relatives.

In the family Heteromyidae comprising the 'classical' desert kangaroo-rat (*Dipodomys merriami*) adaptations involving heat production may have been evolved before specialising for desert life. The primitive non-desert genus *Liomys* also shows the typical narrow thermoneutral zone that most investigators found in the genus *Dipodomys*, as well as an equally low basal metabolic rate[43,109].

The diurnal desert ground squirrels (*Sciuridae*) of the genus *Citellus* (*sensu lato*) have, when compared to other desert rodents, a rather wide thermoneutral zone of about 10 °C. According to present information a wide thermoneutral zone is found also in ground squirrels from colder habitats[112-115], however, reduction in the basal metabolic rate is not apparent in all desert ground squirrels[10,116].

In the North American cricetid group a correlation between low heat production and aridity was found by McNab and Morrison[117] while studying different species of the genus *Peromyscus*, representing a variety of ecological backgrounds. No such adaptability of metabolism was found within species in this genus. Hayward[4] comparing five subspecies of *P. maniculatus* from different environments including high desert, concluded that basal metabolic rate appears to play an insignificant role in the climatic adaptation and distribution of those mice. His measurements indicate that selection of suitable microclimates—and other behavioural adaptations as nest building, huddling etc.—enables this species to spread over its wide ecological range[118].

Information about other families, such as old-world desert murids or gerbillides is too meagre to assess group patterns. It certainly seems plausible that in Muridae lowered basal metabolism may develop in response to life in deserts. This was found both within the genus *Notomys* in Australia[94] and the genus *Acomys* of the Middle East[34].

Still less information is available about metabolism in desert Lagomorphs. Jack rabbits, non-burrowing hares (genus *Lepus*) from the American deserts show no reduction in their basal metabolism[119,120]. Is this the pattern of all rabbits and hares?

Compared with the number of small wild mammals examined, information available about the big ones is rather scant and for good reasons. A kick from a big one is much worse than a bite from a small one. To this has to be added the less trivial fact that facilities needed for experiments with small animals are much less costly to acquire.

Evaporative cooling processes are more economical in large- than small-bodied mammals therefore water conserving changes in heat production occur usually only under condition of water restriction.

In camels dehydrated to 77% of their original body weight, measured metabolism, when corrected to an equivalent body temperature of fully hydrated camels, decreased by the same amount. This correction is necessary since the body temperature of a dehydrated camel may vary by as much as 7 °C[121].

Taylor reports a decrease of 15% in the basal metabolic rate of six species of wild bovids when their water uptake was restricted and they were exposed to 40 °C. He did not find any reduction in the metabolism of the waterbuck (*Kobus defassa*) which is limited in its distribution to places near water[122]. That changes in the respiratory pattern of big herbivores are important to their survival in arid habitats, and not only by virtue of lowering heat production, becomes evident from the findings of Taylor and Lyman[123] on the eland (*Taurotragus oryx*) of 200–1000 kg body weight. The eland has a high basal metabolic rate 30% more than the expected according to Kleiber[95]. In addition, the eland has a high thermal conductivity, narrow thermoneutral zone and a lower critical point at 22 °C. These animals browse in the cool hours of the day. According to the authors their increased metabolism at ambient temperatures below thermoneutrality brings about their greater uptake of fresh acacia leaves, thereby augmenting fluid gain.

In domestic breeds of various bovids reduction of metabolism is known to occur upon water depletion[210], but in breeds selected and especially developed for life in hot environments, a lowering of the metabolic rate is quite common even when water is available. The zebu cattle, sheep[125] and the Beduin goat from extreme deserts in the Middle East may serve as examples. Basal metabolism measured in Beduin goats was 30% less than predicted and the lower critical point was about 26 °C when compared to a mountain goat of Mediterranean breed which maintained a 'normal' metabolism even at an ambient temperature of 10 °C[76].

A Q_{10} *value* of 2–3 for an alteration in metabolism is common in all animals, ectothermic as well as endothermic; these alterations paralleling the hypo- or hyperthermic changes occurring in the animals. Moderation in the magnitude of this effect can, under conditions of heat load, decrease the heat generated by metabolism and spare cooling effects and evaporation of water. In the same way an increase in this effect at low ambient temperatures can accelerate the rate of warming of an ectotherm to preferred body temperature. Such an effect is well known in lizards[85,86].

Schmidt-Nielsen[6] stated that lower Q_{10} values in *reptiles* would result in an ability to tolerate higher temperatures, on account of a smaller oxygen demand and biochemical reactions relatively independent of temperature. Quite commonly Q_{10} values in lizards change abruptly and diminish at high ambient temperatures (*Amphibolurus*, Varanidae). In others Q_{10} decreases gradually over the whole temperature range (*Crotaphytus*, Iguanidae). Usually the values do not drop below two[86]. Dawson[85] who searched for a correlation between thermophily and low metabolic Q_{10} values of lizards failed to establish such correlation and attributed this to differences in techniques and methods of data analysis. When, following Dawson's comments, a comparison was made between four species of the genus *Acanthodactylus* (Lacertidae), the most widespread and desert adapted species, *A. boskianus*, was found to have a Q_{10} value of only 1.4 over the span of 35–42.5 °C. *A. boskianus* is an extremely successful small desert lizard as is obvious from its dispersal throughout deserts in the Near East and North Africa. It adjusts within 5 min to the substrate temperature. A low Q_{10} value allows him thus a relatively constant metabolism in spite of differences in substrate temperatures so typical between shade and sun in the desert[64].

Further information on small active desert lizards should help in establishing whether this is a general or common pattern.

A normal Q_{10} of 2.4 was, however, found in a small non-thermophilic desert lizard, *Xantusia vigilis*, Iguanidae[89].

In *birds*, the increase in metabolism due to higher body temperature does not seem to be great. Lasiewski and Seymour[101] who measured metabolism in four xeric bird species at high ambient temperatures, assumed the Q_{10} effect for metabolism to be about 2. However, they questioned the validity of this value for birds in general.

In *rodents* body temperature usually increases within the thermoneutral zone. The relevant data has been collected and presented by Hart[109]. It shows that in most rodents this occurs within a span of about only 2 °C difference in body temperature. (*Dipodomys*, *Peromyscus*, *Meriones*). In one group of rodents, members of the ground squirrel group (Sciuridae) considerable changes in body temperature were found without concomitant increase in metabolism. This allows for more heat storage in the body and curtails the contribution of the endogenous heat production in hyperthermy typical of all small bodied animals. This feature helps in establishing diurnal activity patterns in members of this group. Most outstanding in this respect is the antelope ground squirrel, *Citellus* (*Ammospermophilus*) *leucurus*. Its body temperature increases over a span of 6 °C, (up to 42 °C) with almost no augmented metabolism. Since the body weight of this ground squirrel is no more than 100 g the heat storage capacity is used up in desert summer in the course of a short burst of outside activity. The animal thereupon retires to underground burrows scattered in its territory where it dissipates the excess heat by contact with the cooler ground[109,113].

The mechanism allowing such independence of metabolism in endothermic animals is well worth investigating. Present explanations range from shunting of blood or decrease in respiration of non-vital organs[109] to extreme decrease n muscular tonus. The latter phenomenon and a simultaneous anomalous decline in metabolic rate was found in a rock hyrax (*Heterohyrax brucei*) at ambient temperature above 35 °C[126].

No modification in the Q_{10} value of metabolism in big ungulates has been detected so far. In dehydrated camels, whose body temperatures may fluctuate daily by up to 7 °C, it averaged 2.1[121]. In zebu cattle an increase in metabolism was found to parallel an increase in body temperature. The magnitude of the metabolic increase could be accounted for by assuming a Q_{10} values of two[128]. It therefore, appears that in this case increasing body temperature for the purpose of heat storage demands a metabolic price (see Section 6.3.3.). To 'counter' this ungulates 'evolved' rapidly changing values of respiratory frequency. Even for an animal which does not rely on panting to dissipate heat—like camels—the Q_{10} value of respiratory frequency is 11 over the same temperature range where a Q_{10} of 2.1 was calculated for metabolism[121]. The intense response of respiratory frequency to body temperature works both ways: At night and in the early morning when body temperature of ungulates subject to fluctuations is low, inspirations are slow and deep and a greater part of the alveolar volume is ventilated. As a consequence higher extraction percentage of oxygen is achieved, and relatively less ventilation is needed for a given metabolic level, whereby less water is evaporated. At high body temperatures when respiratory frequency increases, by far exceeding the augmentation in metabolism, oxygen extraction is lowered and a higher relative amount of water evaporated enhancing cooling efficiency. This has been found in the eland (*Taurotragus oryx*) but could be true for any mammal with the same thermal relations[127].

With additional respiratory dead spaces (frontal sinuses) becoming functional under heat load, the ratio of dead space to alveolar volume increases. As a result the amount of water evaporated per unit volume of oxygen consumed is further augmented and a build-up of alkalosis is avoided. Such a pattern was described by Taylor et al.[128] in the wildebeest (*Connochaetes taurinus*).

In contrast to all the above findings in ungulates, no similar increase in respiratory frequency was recorded in rodents at high ambient temperatures[109].

6.3.2 Torpor

Far-reaching adaptations in metabolism facilitating survival in the desert are phenomena generally grouped under the term dormancy. Common to all these phenomena is the cessation of activity by an animal usually hidden in a sheltered place so as to save energy and water, and to avoid exposure to unfavourable conditions when these prevail.

In *insects* the quiescent period takes place in any developmental stage typical to the species. A functional classification of the many types of dormancy found in insects was recently attempted by Mansingh[129]. These dormancies may be due to lower than optimal temperatures (hibernation), higher than optimal temperatures (aestivation), or else to hygric or nutritional causes (athermopause). The development of the dormant period ranges through stages, beginning with quiescence due to slight and short-term adversity of weather and finally going over into a diapause. This last form is the most highly evolved dormancy which overcomes cyclic, long-term and extreme environmental conditions. Diapause ensues before any exogenous environmental influence and is maintained irrespective of the environment, it therefore synchronises the active stages with suitable environmental conditions of temperature and food availability. In regions of arid summer, characterised by lack of moisture and food, survival of many insects depends on summer dormancy[130,214].

Prolonged dormancy is known in desert *snails*. It lasts over most of the year, sometimes even continues over a few years of drought. During this time the snail is sealed in its shell by a highly impermeable epiphragm, its metabolism and loss of water is very low (see Section 6.2.1).

The main factor triggering the arousal of the snail is moisture. Overall activity of populations of desert snails is observed only on rainy days[22,23].

Some desert *reptiles* have fixed seasonal cycles wherein they cease feeding and remain dormant and inactive during the winter independent of the temperatures they are kept in (*Phrynosoma m'calli*); others can be maintained in activity in the laboratory the whole year round (*Dipsosaurus dorsalis*)[11].

For dormancy in reptiles exhibiting physiological changes independent of changes in body temperature, Mayhew[11] coined the term 'Brumation'. According to Mayhew, present evidence points to control of brumation by photoperiod. In some cases reduced food supply was suspected to trigger this state.

In several species of endotherms a drop in body temperature to levels quite close to that of the environment occurs owing to a periodic lowering of metabolism. Among desert *mammals* this is best investigated in *rodents* and therefore these will be dealt with first.

The drop in body temperature and the quiescence associated with it when the animal is within its burrow, helps it to avoid excessive environmental stress and to stretch limited resources. Implied in this is the fact that the animal can increase its metabolism and raise its body temperature back to normal values of about 37 °C.

This drop and the consequent rise in metabolism occurs sometimes for several hours daily, during any period of the year, this stage being classified as daily torpor or else it may imply longer periods and be confined to certain seasons—summer (aestivation) or winter (hibernation). With accumulating knowledge of this feature it becomes increasingly hard to draw a physiological distinction between any of the above described situations.

All types of torpor blend into one another in related rodents including the xeric ones, with a wide range of interspecific responses[131]. Some hibernate, some aestivate, some do both, others are in a state of daily torpor the year round or only seasonally; during other seasons they enter a prolonged state of torpor[132,133].

Among the first to draw attention to the similarity of hibernation and aestivation were Bartholomew and Hudson[134]. It has recently been shown[135] that entrance into and arousal from even a daily torpor cycle is qualitatively similar to that of deep hibernation. It involves similar changes in heart rate before and during cooling, irregular apnea etc. On the other hand, rodents in long hibernation were found to warm up and wake completely every 5–14 days, and produce and void urine[131,136,137].

Rodents of a body weight below 165 g probably have also to wake up to consume, during a long hibernation period, food which they had hoarded.

This was extrapolated theoretically because of the exceedingly large amount of fat the rodents would otherwise need to survive the whole hibernation period[137].

How much energy do the various forms of torpor spare? Tucker[138] calculated that during a 10 h torpor cycle at an ambient temperature of 15 °C, *Perognathus californicus* utilises only 19% of the energy needed to maintain the body at a normal body temperature level. Three quarters of that amount is needed just for the re-warming, so presumably in desert rodents with higher microclimatic temperatures the energy saving might be greater. Even in deep, long-term hibernation the overall metabolic rate is no less than $\frac{1}{5}-\frac{1}{10}$ of that of a normally warm animal, as 90% of the energy is expanded in the periodic awakening of the animal, as for example in *Citellus*[137].

With regard to the importance of saving water during torpor, the question is not so clear. Most desert mice, when normally active in the laboratory under simulated burrow conditions (high relative humidity), are in positive water balance without having to drink. Fisher and Manery[137] found that metabolically generated water accumulates in the hibernating, mountain dwelling *Citellus lateralis*, owing to sparse evaporation in the moist burrow. They presented evidence for stepwise reductions in body weight during hibernation, which are due to the necessary urinations. (It should be noted that 1 g of fat generates metabolically 1.08 g of water). So, although desert rodents in torpor might generate less metabolic water by utilising stored food instead of fat, and evaporate more due to warmer and drier burrows, the possibility of water excess still exists.

Another point which corroborates the conclusion that torpor—especially in its short term episodes like daily cycles—is primarily an energy conserving device, appears in the way in which torpor ensues. Long-term hibernation is governed by inborn circannian cycles of growth, hibernation, reproduction etc. Only the timing of the different phases may be influenced by temperature or other environmental factors[131,136,139]. This is understandable since a long preparatory period of fattening and/or food hoarding is necessary. Modifications of such set patterns, usually concurring with its shortening, allow for more influence by extraneous factors. Finally, the daily torpor cycle, when carefully investigated, appears to be a response to one factor: food deprivation or curtailment. This torpor, i.e. in response to food scarcity, at least in laboratory experiments, was induced at different ambient temperatures even close to thermoneutrality. Tucker[133] established in *Perognathus californicus* (Heteromyidae) a precise relationship between the length of the daily torpor cycle and the amount of food presented to the mouse. Attempts to induce torpor in desert mice by water shortage were much less convincing[132]. The short-term torpor is more common among xeric and desert rodents. It may correlate with acute food shortage which is liable to occur at any season in the desert.

The lowering of body temperature during torpor does not involve complete relaxation of temperature regulation or sensing mechanisms[116]. Body temperatures in torpor may follow quite closely that of the environment, within 1 or 2 °C. However, as ambient temperature decreases a 'critical' body temperature is reached. At body temperatures lower than this, the spontaneous re-warming of the animal is difficult. In many torpid animals, as this temperature is being approached warming efforts become evident and the temperature difference between body and surrounding increases. Many torpid rodents also re-warm and wake up when the critical body temperature is reached. Now those rodents which aestivate or are in short-term torpor have higher critical body temperatures, ranging between 15 °C and 10 °C, as against that close to freezing in deep hibernators[132]. According to this author higher critical body temperature may be geared to the higher minimal microenvironmental temperatures encountered in the burrow.

The last point that will be discussed here is: Did torpor develop in response to food scarcity or other external factors in desert surroundings?

Deep hibernation is known in only 5 main groups of rodents out of a total of 14 or 15 groups. All those groups have representatives in the desert. When examined, the types of torpor found in the desert dwellers generally appear to be a modification of the rigid circannian pattern of hibernation developed in response to cold habitats, in more boreal, non-desert members of the group. In the desert dwellers the fixed rhythm has less and less control as the animals evolve in a 'homeothermic' direction. As a result shorter periods of facultative torpor, daily torpor, or abandonment of this faculty altogether, are found in desert rodents. These modifications probably evolved in adaptation to more arid conditions with the drying out of desert regions from the miocene period onwards[3,136].

The groups concerned are: Dipodoidea, Heteromyidae, Cricetidae, Muscardinidae, Sciuridae.

'Development' of torpor in desert rodents in the direction described above can proceed even within the confines of a single genus. This was demonstrated in the ground squirrels of the genus *Citellus* (sensu lato) of the family Sciuridae[136]. Northern species fall into obligatory hibernation with a precise circannian rhythm. Some of the desert species still enter into obligatory torpor in response to external stimuli (*C. mohavensis*), some have no obligatory phase (*C. tereticaudus*), while some do not show any kind of torpor at all (*C.-Ammospermophilus-leucurus*).

The genus *Citellus* is comparatively well known because it serves as a favourite experimental animal in investigations on hibernation. As biological knowledge expands, more such examples might emerge.

The more advanced groups evolved from cricetid stock, such as the gerbillids and murids, did not develop a faculty for torpor[3]. These groups are well represented in the old world deserts. Here they may show hypothermia, a drop in body temperature at low ambient temperatures, without the ability to rewarm unless by extraneous heat. Such a case was described by Shkolnik and Borut[34] in *Acomys russatus* (Muridae).

Bats also penetrate into the desert. Their roosting in caves in this environment assures them a more favourable microclimate. Quite commonly body temperatures of resting bats drop, and many theories have been advanced as to the way such adaptive dormancy was developed. Recent views[140,141] hold that a daily type of torpor was evolved—or retained—from a more primitive and less precise type of thermoregulation in tropical insectivorous bats. This was necessary in order to overcome possible variations in the amount of flying insects. Cases of such variations were reported even in the tropics. The ability of insectivorous bats to colonise more temperate (or arid?) zones was, therefore, a pre-adaptation and only later did they evolve 'physiological mechanisms appropriate to prolonged hibernation or more precise thermo-regulation[141].

Hibernating bats lose $\frac{1}{3}-\frac{1}{2}$ less water by evaporation than active bats, when compared at ambient temperatures of 30 °C. However, even this amount is much greater than in rodents. Bats may cluster together to retard evaporation. At any rate the caves to roost in are selected for the temperatures prevalent in them rather than for their relative humidities[137].

No special capacity for water conservation was found in desert dwelling bats (Reference cited in Dwyer[141]); so in this group too torpor appears to be primarily a means to conserve energy resources.

Body temperature variations from moderate nightly hypothermia to deep torpor were found in several orders of *birds*. This information was thoroughly discussed and summarised by Dawson and Hudson[97]. Seasonal torpor—or what may correspond to hibernation in mammals—was up to now described only in the order Caprimulgiformes (goatsuckers). Most members of this order examined are desert dwellers of the U.S. and Australia. Their exceptionally low metabolism and efficient cooling ability have been mentioned before. However, here too, this kind of torpor seems to evolve in response to times of scarcity of flying insects; especially as the time of goatsuckers activity is typically short—they fly at dusk and before dawn. Torpor in goatsuckers is induced by prior starvation. It was found to occur also in the European goatsucker (*Caprimulgus europaeus*) even at high and constant ambient temperatures[97,142-145].

In the European goatsucker torpor at low ambient temperatures and body temperature below 10 °C lasts no longer than one day. Conversely, the U.S. desert inhabiting poorwill (*Phalaenoptilus nutalli*) was kept in the laboratory dormant for more than a month, also at a body temperature below 10 °C. It re-warmed, however, and awoke every 4 days and activated its kidneys[145].

Accordingly, the basic physiological mechanism seems to be similar, at least in these two birds, and the torpor is probably not a result of adaptation to desert life.

6.3.3 Hyperthermy and heat storage

Many endotherms increase their body temperature when subjected to high ambient temperatures. A higher, regulated body temperature preserves, as long as possible, the direction of heat flow away from the body by keeping the animal hyperthermic to the environment. When eventually the ambient temperature exceeds that of the body, the highest possible body temperature is attained. This cuts down heat flow into the body. As a result of such adjustments water needed for evaporative cooling is economised. In the same way regulated, elevated body temperature is commonly used to facilitate loss of heat in exercising endotherms. While the body temperature of an endotherm increases, heat is stored in the body in direct proportion to its mass multiplied by its specific heat. If the mass of the body is large the amount of heat stored is substantial. This also saves a considerable amount of cooling water, the contribution of such heat storage to the water balance of camels in shortage of drinking water, was first fully elucidated by Schmidt-Nielsen[6].

In *birds* controlled hyperthermia is considered a cornerstone of adjustment to high ambient temperatures[97]. Elevations of 4 °C in body temperature are frequently tolerated. Only large birds, heavier than 100 g, can remain cooler by 1 °C–3 °C for 1–4 h, at ambient temperatures of 44 °C–46 °C; smaller ones approach the ambient temperature closely (see Figure 6.1).

Ostriches (*Struthio camelus*) which weigh about 100 kg maintain a stable body temperature around 40 °C even when exposed for some time to 50 °C. Their evaporative mechanism is so efficient that even in most extreme ambient temperatures, almost no increase in their basal metabolism becomes evident. In dehydrated birds, which lost 14% of their body weight, fluctuations in body temperature set in and evaporation decreased. Increases up to 4 °C in body temperature were measured at high ambient temperatures[31,146].

Among small *mammals* the state is best known in rodents. While generally their body temperatures increase in high ambient temperatures, certain taxonomic trends in its regulation seem to emerge[109]. In the Heteromyidae, for example, the limited powers of evaporation force body temperature to rise parallel to the mounting ambient temperature. This results in limited ability to withstand ambient temperatures above 34 °C.

Hyperthermy and heat storage in ground squirrels (Sciuridae) was dealt with in more detail in Section 6.3.1, under 'Q_{10} effect'.

Body temperature changes are of cardinal importance in many hot climate and desert ungulates. They occur both in small bodied gazelles (12–26 kg weight) and in large bodied bovids like the eland (*Taurotragus oryx*), the zebu cattle and others weighing up to one ton. The extent of changing body temperatures is fully revealed under the influence of extreme ambient temperatures. The advantage of this change to the animal may be appreciated when cyclic fluctuations of ambient temperatures take place during a normal desert summer day—real or simulated. Occurrence and magnitude of body temperature fluctuations are also often dependent on dehydration.

The different 'ways' by which fluctuations in body temperature are 'used' by different sized bovids, were demonstrated by Taylor[5,147,148] in experiments simulating desert conditions. In large-bodied bovids heat storage is regularly practised. An extreme example is provided by the eland (*Taurotragus oryx*) 150–1000 kg body weight. Its body temperature may be as low as 32.8 °C after 12 h at 22 °C, it slowly warms up to almost 40 °C when exposed for 12 h to ambient 40 °C. Not much change was found between well-watered and water restricted eland, although a sizeable reduction was evident in the evaporative water loss.

In small bodied bovids, the gazelles (*G. thomsonii* and *G. granti*) high body temperature fluctuations were recorded under water restriction. With free water available the gazelles pant and evaporate enough water to keep body temperatures within less than a 2 °C variation, even when ambient temperature reaches 45 °C; whereas upon water restriction they increase their body temperature and depend on hyperthermy to regulate it and to restrict water loss. Body temperatures of up to 46.5 °C could be maintained by *G. granti* for up to 6 h without any ill effect, a feature pertinent to the gazelle's penetration into the arid desert of East Africa. Under the same conditions of ambient temperature up to 45 °C, *G. thomsonii*, which does not penetrate desert areas, could increase its body temperature only to 42 °C.

Heat storage in gazelles is important while they are running, most of the heat they generate being stored. The stored heat is dissipated when they rest. Being 'sprinters', the amount of heat they can store determines the length of time they can run[150]. (See Chapter 5).

The oryx (*Oryx beisa*), 70–300 kg, is a desert bovid of intermediate size which exploits both a change in heat storage and hyperthermy. Upon water restriction hyperthermy in the oryx reaches the same magnitude as in *G. granti*. Apparently hyperthermy has evolved in response to desert environment since the oryx's close relative, the wildebeest (*Connochaetes taurinus*), with about the same body weight, does not increase its body temperature above 41.5 °C and does not rely on hyperthermy[147,148]. Neither does the guanaco (*Lama guanicoe*) a non-desert relative of the camel (60 kg body weight) show any hyperthermy, even when dehydrated and exposed to 45 °C[149].

The high body temperatures measured during hyperthermy in desert inhabiting bovids such as *G. granti* and the oryx (*Oryx beisa*) has focused attention on devices to cool the blood reaching the brain. Differences in blood temperature in the carotid artery point to the possibility that the carotid rete mirabile is a heat exchanger. Venous blood, cooled in the nasal passages, draws the heat off the arterial blood[5,150] (see Chapter 5). The presence of devices for maintaining temperature gradients between head and body may be phylogenetically 'old'. They are known in reptiles[86,151]. A gecko was described by the latter authors as capable of cooling the blood supply to its head.

6.3.4 Effects of radiation

Most of the physiological studies on desert animals were carried out in climatic chambers and metabolic cages. Desert conditions in these devices were simulated by high temperatures and low relative humidities. As radiation is more difficult to simulate, effects of solar radiation were generally overlooked. Recently, however, several investigators have assessed the quantitative impact of this factor and the ways desert animals cope with it while 'trying' to regulate their body temperature.

In desert areas, radiation measured on a flat surface exposed to the sun amounts to 1.2–1.6 cal cm^{-2} min^{-1} [152,159]. A considerable part of this energy is re-radiated to the atmosphere. The integument of an animal, especially the colour of its fur and its surface greatly affect the magnitude of reflection of the solar radiation. Edney[159] found in the Namib desert the reflection from the dorsal half of the tenebrionid beetle, *Onymacris rugatipennis*, to be 38% of the incident radiation. In *Onymacris brincki*, a beetle with white elytra, reflection amounted to 79%. A high degree of reflectivity, well over 90% of the incident radiant energy was measured in the desert land-snail *Sphincterochila boissieri*[22,23]. In the brownly striped land snail *Helicella seetzeni*, cohabiting the same area, Yom-Tov measured a 10% lower reflectivity[22].

The significance of surface colour of reptiles in relation to radiant energy was broadly discussed by Norris[154]. Heppner[155] has shown that blackened birds when exposed to the sun, absorb 3.1 cal min^{-1} more than the original white birds of the same species. Dawson and Brown[156] found that the total reflectance to solar radiation of the pale hip fur of the red kangaroo

(*Megaleia rufa*) amounts to less than in the dark grey-brown euro (*Macropus robustus*). Finch[157] has pointed out the significance of reflectance of radiant energy in wild East African ungulates and concluded that because of this reflectance, the total absorption of potential energy in the eland and the hartebeest (*Alcelaphus buscelaphus*) is reduced to considerably less than 50%.

Porter and Gates[158] have integrated the radiant energy in a model for an overall energy budget of an animal, and this has facilitated the evaluation of the role radiant energy plays in an animal.

When exposed to the sun, radiation is the single greatest factor in an animal's thermal balance. Under mild radiation loads, when a tenebrionid desert beetle maintains its body temperature constant, the contribution of radiation to its heat balance amounts to 0.170 cal cm^{-2} min^{-1} compared to 0.003 cal cm^{-2} min^{-1} gained from metabolism.

The relative importance of solar radiation in big animals was demonstrated by Finch[157] in a study on the energy budget of East African bovids in outdoor conditions. She has proved that evaporative thermoregulatory responses, both cutaneous and respiratory, vary in relation to skin temperature and cutaneous evaporation under simulated conditions in climatic chambers, may be double that of an animal exposed to solar radiation.

Besides colour which reflects the incident radiation, as mentioned before, other characteristics of the integument, such as the relative size of its surface, its thermal conductance as well as the shape of the body, affect the impact of the sun's radiation. Of prime importance in this respect are behavioural adaptations, especially those adjusting the angle of the animal's body to the sun's rays and managing economically the duration of exposure. Edney[159] found that exposing a tenebrionid beetle for 15 min to the full impact of the Namib desert sun, will cause a 10 °C elevation of its body temperature. However, the free moving beetle will maintain its body temperature constant by taking advantage of shaded areas. Shades cast by desert scrub and rocks are not only characterised by much lower radiation fluxes than in the exposed areas, but also by a soil surface temperature lower by over 30 °C[152].

The clear desert skies, its dry air and the high albedo of the soil may in the end make a net sum of radiation over an open surface in the desert lower than in non-desert regions of the same latitude. In the evening and mornings the values of such net radiation in the desert may even be negative[152]. When such conditions prevail, the black colour of an animal may be advantageous in exploiting sun radiation for the purpose of warming up; endothermic desert animals may thus save a considerable amount of metabolic energy. Hamilton and Heppner[160] and Heppner[155] observed in black-dyed zebra finches (*Taeniopygia castanotis*) an economy in metabolism exceeding by 23% that in undyed birds under equal conditions of exposure to artificial sun radiation at 10 °C.

6.3.5 Aspects of heat dissipation (thermal conductance)

The Newtonian model of heat loss is extensively used to illustrate the relations between parameters important in body temperature regulation of birds and mammals. These parameters are: heat production, heat loss and temperature gradients between the animal and its environment. Its establishment in zoological thought and its importance in studying adaptation to various thermal surroundings is due to Scholander's work[90-93]. Heat loss from an inactive homeotherm below thermoneutrality—as presented in the Newtonian model—is determined by the temperature difference between the animal and its environment times a constant which depends on the body shape, size and surface characteristics. This constant is defined as the animal's thermal conductance. Its reciprocal, insulation (also coined by Scholander) represents the body's resistance to heat loss[161].

Thermal conductance is an overall expression of heat loss. It comprises heat lost through avenues of evaporation as well as conduction, convection and radiation.

In an endothermic animal, which is in a thermal steady state, heat loss equals heat gain. Since endogenous heat production is weight-dependent[95,96,110] it follows that conductance and insulation are also weight-dependent[90,209]. The equations relating conductance to body weight show no significant difference between birds and mammals[161].

Scholander et al.[90] emphasised the importance of thermal conductance (or insulation) in thermoregulatory adaptation of endotherms to arctic and tropic environments. It remains to be seen if there are any discernible adaptations in the thermal conductance to hot and arid desert conditions. Figures available for comparison are almost exclusively derived from studies on small birds and small mammals (mostly rodents). The reason for this is the limited availability of body temperature measurements combined with measurements of metabolism, which is essential for calculations in line with the Newtonian heat loss model.

In birds no general trend is evident in adaptation to desert conditions. Birds from tropics or hot deserts seem to have relatively high conductivity values (low insulation). The information, however, is based on too few samples. Within the goatsuckers (Caprimulgiformes) only small deviations from values expected according to body weight are found in the poorwill (*Phalaenoptilus nuttali*) and nighthawk (*Chordeiles minor*). Some small desert owls have low conductance[162,209]. In arid zone or desert rodents no different overall trend was found when their conductance was compared to non-desert forms[109]. Desert species of the genus *Peromyscus* (Cricetidae) have lower conductance than non-desert ones, to compensate for lower metabolism[117,163]. Other desert rodents may have similar, higher or no different values from their non-desert relatives[109,161].

In evaluating apparent differences in conductance, the possibility of changes due to seasonal acclimatisation have to be considered. Acclimatisation in contrast to acclimation, usually alters the animal's insulation and can account for much of the variability between species observed[109].

In desert animals it is the conductance at high ambient temperatures which is of interest, particularly at the high end of the thermoneutral zone and above. Unfortunately, here information is very fragmentary. In addition a considerable proportion of heat loss at high ambient temperatures is due to evaporation. Therefore, information has to take into account and compare both evaporation and 'dry', non-evaporative heat loss. Data on small rodents was compiled by Hart[109]. Within the thermoneutral zone non-evaporative heat loss generally increases more than the evaporative heat loss. No notable difference has been found between desert and mesic animals. Most rodents have a low capacity to dispense their metabolic heat by evaporation at the upper end of the thermoneutral zone. Thus high values of 'dry' thermal conductance are of prime importance to their heat balance. A notable exception are the diurnal ground squirrels, who have a very high capacity of evaporative cooling.

In Jack-rabbits (*Lepus alleni*) non-evaporative thermal conductance increases when ambient temperature approaches body temperature. When the former exceeds the latter, conductance drops abruptly to its minimal level thus cutting down heat flow into the body. This is particularly important in animals with extensive surface areas (big ears etc.)[119,120]. Most regrettably no information is available about patterns of non-evaporative cooling in other mammals. In birds no decrease in conductivity was detected under similar conditions[97].

In recent years several investigators explored and further elaborated the relationship of parameters within Newton's law of cooling as applied to birds and mammals. One of their aims was to arrive at a better characterisation of ecological correlations in basal metabolism, minimal conductance and the resulting body temperature[162,163].

The dangers inherent in excessive manipulation of the Newtonian model are clearly outlined by Calder and King[164]. In addition, information concerning thermoregulatory patterns in desert animals, tabulated and used by McNab[163] and Yarbrough[162] is based on too few different species. Comparative information is, in most cases, missing as regards their non-desert close relatives. All this rather detracts from the usefulness of their conclusions.

6.4 ADAPTATIONS IN WATER METABOLISM

6.4.1 Sources, depletion and replenishment

A great deal of research and investigation has been devoted to ways and devices for water conservation in desert animals, less concern has been focused on mechanisms, abilities and patterns of water gain.

Plain drinking when water is available, is observed in many desert animals. However, as water in the desert is scanty and occurs only sporadically, the ability to tolerate long periods of water restriction and to withstand a high degree of dehydration constitutes for many animals a vital problem of adaptation. Imbibing high volumes of water to replenish the loss rapidly is equally essential to desert dwellers and so is the ability to utilise brackish water and fluids available as plant sap.

Certain animals are able to balance their water economy without ever drinking free water. This ability was fully discussed and convincingly proved by Schmidt-Nielsen[6]. It is now generally known that in many animals an economic use and efficiently reduced loss of water may be balanced by water preformed in their food plus water gained by its oxidation. Desert animals, especially small ones, often achieve such balance by merely taking advantage of favourable shelters and by appropriate behaviour. Pertinent to this aspect is the extensive nocturnal activity of desert animals of all groups. Nocturnal activity not only helps to avoid the hazards of diurnal desert conditions it also favours the gain of water by granivorous animals and those who 'graze' on dead plant material. Taylor[72] has shown that such food, after it has been equilibrated with air at 17 °C and 85% relative humidity, may contain 72 g water/100 g of dry matter. Large daily temperature fluctuations are typical of most desert areas, and are associated with increase in the humidification of the air during the night. Such conditions may prevail all the year round.

Most *desert arthropods* utilise free water when this is sporadically available. Observations on insects drinking are well documented in literature[67]. The tenebrionid beetle *Adesmia*, abundant in the Negev desert of Israel, is often seen on cool mornings imbibing small drops of dew condensed on the numerous flint slabs[165]. Many desert arthropods may gain water from damp surfaces. Isopods do it by oral and anal drinking[8]. Lycosid spiders were found to suck water from soil capillaries even against a pressure of 600 mmHg[166]. *Ocnera*, a tenebrionid beetle from the Negev forages at night and when the air approaches the dew point it squeezes water from hygroscopic porous straw, which is very dry during the day[165,167]. Information on arthropods being able to draw water directly from unsaturated air is recently accumulating.

Absorption of water by desert organisms from subsaturated air had long ago attracted the attention of both plant and animal physiologists. Since the early thirties when Buxton[168] demonstrated this capability in Tenebrio larvae, it has been found to exist in several arthropods living at various degrees of air humidity[18,169,170].

Edney[171] studied the ability to absorb water vapour from subsaturated air in the *Arenivaga* sp. that inhabit desert sand dunes in South California. He also investigated the well known cockroaches *Blata orientalis* and *Periplaneta americana*, both taxonomically close to *Arenivaga* (Dictyoptera, Blatoidea). The ability to take up water from air was found to exist in the nymph and in wingless females (males are winged) of *Arenivaga* only, and not in the two other non-desert roaches. At air humidities of 82.5% over a temperature range from 10–30°C dehydrated *Arenivaga* took up water from air until their body weight prior to desiccation was regained, presumably replenishing all the water lost.

Beatment[18] and Noble-Nesbitt[170] have shown that the desiccated firebrat, *Thermobia domestica* (Thysanura), gained water even at relative humidities of 63%. A desert thysanuran from the Namib (*Ctenolepisma terebrans*) absorbed water from air even at humidities below 50%[153]. (Figure 6.2).

The mechanism behind the driving force for water absorption from the air is still unknown. Beament[18,169] and others have suggested a model in which epicuticular pores and lipids participate in this mechanism and account for a more rapid inward movement of water. Beament's model postulates a lipid barrier over the surface of water, composed of microcapillaries which open outwards through the cuticle. This barrier, complete during transpiration, becomes disrupted when water absorption takes place and a meniscus is being formed, pulled down by inner 'suction forces' that withdraw water from the capillaries. Edney[171] found that the energy expenditure involved in absorption is very small compared to the insects' metabolic rate. The absorption of 6 mg water in one day by a 100 mg *Arenivaga* involves the expenditure of only 0.036 cal.

When water is extremely restricted, insects are reported to withstand a depletion of body water from a level of 75% of their fat-free total weight to as low as 60%[172]. Edney[171] found in the desert cockroach *Arenivaga*, in the course of one week, a loss equal to 30% its original weight. He also discovered that, while being dehydrated, the insect continued to regulate efficiently its osmotic pressure, elevated from 433 mequiv.l^{-1} in the normal to only 452 mequiv.l^{-1} in the dehydrated (616 mequiv.l^{-1} was the expected number in the absence of regulation). Edney[8] concludes, however, that 'desert species differ

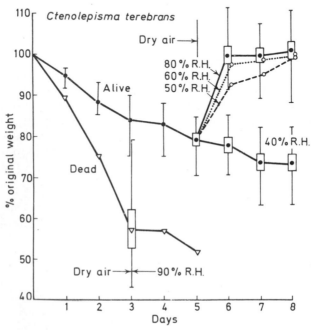

Figure 6.2 Changes in weight (presumed water) in the desert thysanuran *Ctenolepisma terebrans*. Dead insects lose water faster than living ones, and the latter gain water in 50% relative humidity or above after dehydration. Means and limits are shown, and the height of the rectangles, where included, represents 1 standard error each side of the mean (From Edney[153], by courtesy of *Physiol. Zool.*)

from other species of insects far more with respect to transpiration than with respect to tolerance of low body water content'.

The prolonged survival, up to 6 years, of *land snails* in museum collections is widely documented in malacological literature. It was previously mentioned that Schmidt-Nielsen *et al.*[23] have measured in desert snails exposed in their natural habitat a water loss of 0.5 mg per one summer day per snail. They state that 'a 4 g specimen contains about 1400 mg water and since the water loss during the cooler part of the year probably is reduced, several years should elapse before critical levels of water loss would be reached'. As a matter of fact, water content of these snails was maintained in about 80% of the snails' soft tissue all the year round. Simultaneously with the catabolic process that gradually reduce the total mass of the dormant snail, metabolic water is continuously generated in the sealed snail, thus contributing to the maintenance of a stable weight/water ratio. The arousal of desert snails occurs on rainy days or on nights abundant in dew. Along with the food then consumed (soil-surface algae and lichens) the snails take into their gut water-soaked mud thereby replenishing their food and water content.

Desert reptiles too may drink water when available; some were observed to lick water from plants[173,174]. Snakes are able, even in extreme deserts, to maintain a balanced water economy on the water gained with their food[29,175]. Many carnivorous lizards may do the same[176]. Nevertheless, an ant-eating Agamid from Australia, *Amphibolurus ornatus*, was found to face severe water shortage during a period of drought. Two varieties, differing in their physiological response to dry conditions have been distinguished in a local population of this species[177]. One, described as 'slow growers' retained sodium ions in the extracellular fluid which was consequently expanded in volume by withdrawal of water from the cells. Thus, an osmotic equilibrium between the two compartments was maintained, although hypernatremia was built up to a level of 300 mequiv.l^{-1}. This storage of electrolytes helps to conserve water by saving the fluids otherwise used in excretion. The other variety of the species, the 'fast growers' lose weight during the dry season and are apparently dehydrated. Losses of up to 45% of the original body weight were found in the field. However, with losses of up to 25% body weight, extracellular volume was maintained, most of the loss therefore being sustained by the cells. Following rain, plasma concentration and volume were restored within 10 h in both varieties.

Tolerance of substantial elevations in extracellular ion concentrations enables also other lizards to exercise this type of water conservation in periods of water shortage (e.g. *Tachisaurus rugosus*)[27]. In a way this electrolyte storage is reminiscent of the heat storage practised by mammals and birds.

A high capability to withstand dehydration was equally recorded in the desert turtle, *Gopherus agassizi*, which can also tolerate a large increase in plasma concentration[178]. This species can live for years without drinking, but if water becomes available, it can increase, by 41–43% its body weight by drinking water. Storage of water may contribute, in certain reptiles, to the ability to withstand dehydration. The bladder of the above-mentioned American desert turtle[178] and that of the desert turtle from Egypt, *Testudo leithii*[179] were assumed to play such a role. Norris and Dawson[180] found in three species of the lizard *Sauromalus* storage of water in accessory lymph spaces extending along the lateral abdominal fold to the head region.

Being diurnal animals of small body size that hardly exploit favourable shelters, it is surprising that many *birds* are found independent of drinking water. Apparently this is achieved by an economic loss. Only few species in the desert are rigidly restricted to the vicinity of water points; many—even when occasionally observed drinking—can manage on the water gained with their food.

Oxidative water was found to compensate for only part of the water loss. Even in the Australian zebra finch (*Taenyopygia castanotis*)[181] and in the

African scaly weaver (*Sporopipes squamifrons*)[182], both granivorous birds highly adapted to life in desert, oxidative water amounted to only half of the evaporative water loss. The addition of quantities of preformed water, as found in certain desert succulent plant parts or in bodies of prey (mainly insects and vertebrates) may balance the water economy of many species[70,183].

Birds of various families that never or only rarely drink, were systematically recorded in Africa[184-186] and in Australia[187].

Few seed-eating species are restricted in the desert to the vicinity of water, be it a well, hole or cistern, and they drink frequently. Columbiformes, pigeons and sand-grouses may fly great distances to drink. The latter are famous for their bizarre manner in which males carry water to their young over distances of 25–30 km[188] (Mendelssohn, personal communication). Many other birds will drink intermittently. Dawson and Bartholomew[9], in summarising data of *ad lib.* drinking of a variety of birds, have pointed out that desert dwelling species are notably more economic in their drinking habits. The ability to cope with a strenuous shortage of water is important in desert birds and often may be put to test. Losses of body weight during dehydration amounting to 30–50 % of the initial weight, as well as a rapid replenishment of this loss, are reported by MacMillen and Trost[103], and by Dawson and Bartholomew[9].

Unfortunately, only little is known on body fluid distribution during dehydration and rehydration in birds. The same is true for the ionic and osmotic regulation under such circumstances[189].

Drinking balances the water economy by adding the volume required beyond that obtained from the food and metabolism. Yet many *mammals*— as we have seen also in representatives of other animal groups—thrive in the desert without drinking. This enigmatic ability was first explained by Schmidt-Nielsen and Schmidt-Nielsen[190] in the kangaroo-rat (*Dipodomys merriami*) and their approach to the problem was followed by many investigators. Most small desert rodents and carnivores do not drink regularly, several seed-eating rodents do not utilise water even when available. Few rodents that never drink may be active during the day but these species are abundantly supplied with water by either eating halophytic juicy plants (*Psammomys obesus*— Gerbillidae), or land snails (*Acomys russatus*—Muridae), or being omnivorous (*Citellus leucurus*—Sciuridae)[39,113,191].

During the dry season most large mammals should have access to water at least periodically. Taylor[77] assessed the water requirements of some East African ungulates (Bovidae) and found under simulated desert conditions that the minimal daily water drinking volume needed to balance the water output of many of these animals ranged from 3.0–3.5 l/100 kg of the animal's body weight. Nevertheless, the eland, oryx (*Oryx beisa*) and a species of gazelle (*G. granti*) were found capable of surviving in dry areas without having to drink. The eland takes advantage of the acacia trees scattered in his natural habitat, which provide him with shady shelter during the heat of the day, and the edible leaves of the acacia are not only of high nutritional value, they also contain 58 % water. By calculating the weight of acacia leaves that a browsing eland will consume during a day to meet its metabolic demands, Taylor and Lyman[123] found that 4.0 lH_2O/100 kg of the eland's body weight can be gained. This equals the amount of fluid needed by the eland to survive without direct drinking.

The oryx and the gazelle in the arid areas of East Africa feed on dry grass that contains during the day only 1 % of preformed water, but by grazing at night when these plants contain 30% of water, the oryx and the gazelle as well as the eland can be independent of drinking water[72].

When exposed to high temperature and dry air, mammals lose water rapidly and become dehydrated. The degree of dehydration is generally evaluated as a percental loss of body weight. Such an evaluation may reflect the extent of water depletion only if the duration of dehydration was short, which can be achieved by exposure to acute dehydrating conditions. A prolonged water deprivation may reduce the animal's food intake bringing about a loss in its dry weight simultaneously with the loss of water. By measuring directly the water content of the animal during dehydration by the use of an appropriate marker, the exact degree of dehydration can be assessed.

When deprived of water and exposed to conditions at 37 °C and 15–20% relative humidity, the gerbill *Meriones crassus* (Gerbillidae) and the Spiny mouse *Acomys cahirinus* (Muridae), both desert species, were shown to withstand a loss of water amounting to 7% and 12.8% of their body weight respectively. The laboratory rat withstood an even greater loss of water up to 18.6% of body weight, and moreover at a much faster rate[192].

A loss of 30% body weight during water deprivation was reported for many desert ungulates, including the camel[73]; donkey[45]; merino sheep[75]; and goats[76]. Most ungulates studied lose their appetite when the drop in their body weight exceeded 25% of their initial weight. The only exception were the goats from Sinai which continued eating even at a loss of 30% weight. In these ruminants it was also determined that the loss of body weight approximately equalled that of water.

When water is lost to the environment during exposure to high temperatures and dry air, the volume of the blood is affected before the fluids in the other body compartments. Since the amount of water lost can, within a short time, exceed the plasma volume, maintaining the volume of the circulating fluid becomes vital. It can be achieved either by a rapid water exchange between the different compartments to make an even distribution of the loss possible, or by maintaining the relative volume of the blood at the expense of other compartments.

In the laboratory rat[192,193], the donkey[74], merino sheep[75] and goats[76] water is lost from the blood as well as from the other compartments. In these animals, as has been shown in rats and desert goats a high level of normal body water content will be of great advantage during prolonged periods of dehydration. Only in the camel[73] and the spiny mouse[192] has an ability to maintain a relatively high, almost unchanged blood volume in face of severe dehydration been found so far. Mechanisms controlling the plasma proteins and thereby the oncotic pressure of the blood[6] as well as the permeability of blood capillaries[194] contribute to this ability.

Animals in the desert not only drink intermittently, but may be forced to spend only as little time as possible near water points either due to lurking carnivores, to competition or to the temporary nature of the source. A drinking capacity that would enable them to replenish considerable water losses within a short time is therefore greatly advantageous.

Dehydrated jerboas (*Jaculus jaculus*—Dipodidae) have been observed to take in within a few minutes a volume of water equal to 4–5% of their body weight; spiny mice (*Acomys russatus*) imbibe water up to 9.26%, and *A. cahirinus* up to 11.3% of their body weight[6]. The drinking capacity of merino sheep in Australia amounts to volumes corresponding to 15% of their body weight. The camel, a 'master drinker' can imbibe within 10 min over 100 l which equal about 30% his body weight[6,73] and the donkey is almost as good a drinker as the camel and even a faster one. A desert goat dehydrated to 70% its initial body weight replenished the entire loss within 2 min[76].

6.4.2 Drinking salt solutions

Water available in the desert is often to a varying degree saline. Yet, during the dry season it may constitute an indispensable source for drinking. The sap of many succulent desert plants which contain considerable amounts of fluid and may be utilised by some animals as a water substitute, is generally highly saline. The ability to gain water from salt solutions depends on the animal's ability to expel the ingested electrolytes in a solution more concentrated than that imbibed, hence on the capacity of the excretory organs. This ability was recorded in many desert vertebrates.

The Agamid desert *lizard Uromastix* obtains considerable amounts of water from highly saline desert plants. The desert iguana, *Dipsosaurus dorsalis*, ingests during the summer vegetation containing 50% water and found to be very rich in potassium. Templeton *et al.*[62] demonstrated that by secretion through a salt gland of a fluid with a very high potassium content and by cloacal elimination of potassium urates, an electrolyte and water balance can be achieved.

In many *birds and mammals* the ability to utilise salt solutions has been actually assessed by their ability to maintain their body weight on a dry diet with NaCl solutions of varying concentrations as the only drinking source. Through such a procedure some rodents may give up drinking altogether, and even when exposed to 30 °C and 30% relative humidity will balance their water economy on the fluid gained with their food (dry barley)[6,34]. In these cases a high protein diet will drive the animal into a negative water balance thus making it reveal its potency of utilising salt solutions.

While the majority of terristrial birds tested are found to be unable to maintain their body weight on solutions of a greater than 300 mM NaCl (approx. 50% sea water), many desert species as for instance the black-throated sparrow (*Amphispiza bilineata*) can subsist on more concentrated solutions. Some species even match the ability of salt-marsh and coast-dwelling birds, that can drink solutions as concentrated as sea water[12,189].

When comparing the Bobwhite (*Colinus virginianus*), the Californian (*Lophortyx californicus*) and Gambel's quails (*Lophortyx gambelli*), McNabb[195] demonstrated a positive correlation between their ability to effectively utilise sodium chloride solutions and the degree of water shortage in the typical habitat of each species. None of the species mentioned possesses active salt glands at adolescence. Their ability to secrete the salt must therefore depend mainly on renal and cloacal mechanisms. In the kidney of the salt marsh race of the Savannah sparrow (*Passerculus sandwichensis beldingi*), a sea-water

Table 6.2 **Kidney structure and concentrating capacity in relation to the ability to drink salt solutions in rodents from different families and habitats in Israel** (A. Shkolnik, personal communication)

	Body weight g	Family	Habitat	Relative medullary thickness*	Maximal concentration of NaCl solution utilised M l^{-1}	Mean maximal urine concentration mosmol l^{-1}
Apodemus mystacinus	36.4	Muridae	mesic	6.4	0.4	2950
Acomys cahirinus	36.6	Muridae	†	8.3	0.5	2050
Acomys cahirinus	32.6	Muridae	‡	9.9	0.8	3933
Acomys russatus	52.8	Muridae	desert	11.4	1.0	7850
Meriones tristrami	51.7	Gerbillidae	†	8.2	1.3	5650
Meriones crassus	67.1	Gerbillidae	desert	10.3	1.5	6950
Mesocricetus auratus	59.3	Cricetidae	dry-cold	8.6	0.6	2775

* According to Sperber: see Schmidt-Nielsen and O'Dell[9]
† Population from Galilee, mesic conditions
‡ Population from Sinai, extreme desert

drinking bird, large numbers of nephrons with loops of Henle are indeed found[196].

The question whether desert mammals can drink sea water was first asked by Adolph[197] and positively answered for the kangaroo-rat (*Dipodomys merriami*)[190]. Since then an impressive ability to utilise salt solutions was demonstrated in many mammalian groups.

The Tammar wallaby, a semi-xeric marsupial was found capable of drinking sea water[212]. Hedgehogs use fluids of electrolyte concentration equivalent to 0.7 M NaCl (Yacobi and Shkolnik, 1972, personal communication) and desert rodents are able to utilise solutions exceeding twice the concentration of sea water. Maximal concentration of salt solutions utilised for drinking by various rodents are presented in Table 6.2.

The correlation to the structure (relative medullary thickness) and concentrating ability of the kidney is evident.

Besides the water conserving desert mammals, salt-marsh and coast-dwelling mammals have also been found capable of subsisting on high salt solutions for drinking[198,199].

6.4.3   Total water exchange with the environment

The overall kinetics of the entire exchangeable water pool, i.e. the total water turnover in desert animals has been assessed mainly in mammals. The techniques used in this assessment involved labelling the animal's body water by an appropriate tracer, usually tritiated water. The rate at which the tracer decays in samples of body fluids indicates the rate at which water is exchanged with the environment.

In *mammals* of different size it was found that the turnover of body water is exponentially related to weight. To make possible a comparison of water turnover in various animals Richmond *et al.*[200] suggest weight $^{0.80}$ as a likely function in freely drinking animals; Macfarlane[124] prefers to use weight $^{0.82}$.

Water turnover has been found to vary with environmental conditions that affect water expenditure and reflect the physiological adaptation of the animal. As the techniques for measuring water turnover can easily be applied in field studies this method is very useful to gain information on the overall water economy of animals freely ranging in their natural habitat, as well as assessing the impact of lactation on it.

While studying a variety of ungulates from different environments, Macfarlane *et al.*[201] concluded that 'survival time without water during snmmer in hot desert conditions is inversely proportional to water turnover'. A similar relation between water turnover and survival time without drinking was established in desert *dasyurid marsupials*[213]. However, animals occupying the same habitat differ greatly in the rates of their water turnover[201,205,206].

In their investigation of animals from different environments—arctic to arid subtropics—Macfarlane *et al.*[201] concluded that in every environment there was a different hierarchy in the animals' water turnover. They have also pointed out that metabolic rate follows the hierarchy established for survival, for water dependence and water turnover.

Few measurements of total water exchange have been applied to studies of *reptiles* and birds. Minnich and Shoemaker[202] found in the desert iguana (*Dipsosaurus dorsalis*) that lizards from irrigated areas that contain natural dense vegetation, exchange water at much higher rates than those from areas of sparse natural vegetation. These rates also tallied with the rates of weight gain in the lizards. Water turnover in the desert iguana thus reflects the rigid coupling of water and food intake in non-drinking animals.

The use of the tritiated water technique to determine body water kinetics in desert *birds* was first reported by Ohmart *et al.*[203]. In captive roadrunners (*Geococcyx californianus*) under simulated desert conditions (no drinking and controlled ambient temperatures of 30–32 °C) the rate of water turnover was considerably lower than that measured in roadrunners kept at low ambient temperatures (8 °C) and having water *ad lib*. Ohmart *et al.* also suggests that the regression coefficient for the equation expressing the relationship between water exchange and body weight is much lower in birds (0.69) than in mammals.

Finally it should be said that in understanding an animal's existence in the desert it should be remembered that the ability of an animal to thrive in this habitat depends on a multitude of factors. Physiological factors are only part of these and so is the interplay with behavioural adaptation. The power of an animal to compete with other species for the natural resources and its aptitude to avoid predation, are also of prime importance. The relative role each factor plays in the survival of an animal in the desert varies in different groups and even species.

References

1. Brower, J. E. and Cade, T. J. (1966). Ecology and physiology of *Napaeozapus insignis* (Miller) and other woodland mice. *Ecology*, **47**, 46
2. Schmidt-Nielsen, K. (1972). *How Animals Work*, (Cambridge: Cambridge University Press)
3. Cade, T. J. (1964). Evolution of torpidity in rodents. *Ann. Acad. Sci. Fenn., Ser. A.* IV. **71**, 77
4. Hayward, J. S. (1965). Metabolic rate and its temperature-adaptive significance in six geographic races of *Peromyscus*. *Can. J. Zool.*, **43**, 309
5. Taylor, C. R. (1972). The desert gazelle: a paradox resolved. *Symp. Zool. Soc. London*, **31**, 215
6. Schmidt-Nielsen, K. (1964). *Desert animals: Physiological Problems of Heat and Water*, (London: Oxford University Press)
7. Dill, D. B. (editor) (1964). *Adaptation to the Environment. Handbook of Physiology, Section 4* (Washington: Amer. Physiol. Soc.)
8. Edney, E. B. (1967). Water balance in desert arthropods. *Science*, **156**, 1059
9. Dawson, W. R. and Bartholomew, G. A. (1968). Temperature regulation and water economy of desert birds. *Desert Biology*, Vol. 1, 357–394 (G. W. Brown, Jr., editor) (New York and London: Academic Press)
10. Bartholomew, G. A. and Dawson, W. R. (1968). Temperature regulation in desert mammals. *Desert Biology*, Vol. I, 395–421 (G. W. Brown, Jr., editor) (New York and London: Academic Press)
11. Mayhew, W. W. (1968). Biology of desert amphibians and reptiles. *Desert Biology*, Vol. 1, 195–356 (G. W. Brown, Jr., editor) (New York and London: Academic Press)
12. Serventy, D. L. (1971). Biology of desert birds. *Avian Biology*, Vol. 1, 287–339 (D. S. Farner, J. R. King and K. C. Parkes, editors) (New York and London: Academic Press)
13. Ramsay, J. A. (1935). Methods of measuring the evaporation of water from animals. *J. Exp. Biol.*, **12**, 355

14. Beament, J. W. L. (1945). The cuticular lipoids of insects. *J. Exp. Biol.*, **21**, 115
15. Wigglesworth, V. B. (1945). Transpiration through the cuticule of insects. *J. Exp. Biol.*, **21**, 97
16. Cloudsley-Thompson, J. L. (1961). Some aspects of the physiology and behaviour of Galeodes arabs. *Entomol. Exp. Appl.*, **4**, 257
17. Hadley, N. F. (1970). Water relations of the desert scorpion, *Hadrurus arizonensis*. *J. Exp. Biol.*, **53**, 547
18. Beament, J. W. L. (1964). The active transport and passive movement of water in insects. *Adv. Ins. Physiol.*, **2**, 67
19. Beament, J. W. L. (1959). The water proofing mechanism of arthropods. *J. Exp. Biol.*, **36**, 391
20. Loveridge, J. P. (1968). The control of water loss in *Locusta migratoria migratoroides* R. and F. I. cuticular water loss. *J. Exp. Biol.*, **49**, 1
21. Ahearn, G. A. (1970). The control of water loss in desert tenebrionid beetles. *J. Exp. Biol.*, **53**, 573
22. Yom-Tov, Y. (1970). Investigations in the ecology and survival of two snails in the Negev desert. *Ph.D. Thesis*, Tel-Aviv University (Hebrew)
23. Schmidt-Nielsen, K., Taylor, C. R. and Shkolnik, A. (1971). Desert snails: problems of heat, water and food. *J. Exp. Biol.*, **55**, 385
24. Machin, J. (1967). Structural adaptation for reducing water loss in three species of terrestrial snails. *J. Zool. London*, **152**, 55
25. Machin, J. (1968). The permeability of the epiphragm of terrestrial snails to water vapor. *Biol. Bull*, **134**, 87
26. Adolph, E. F. (1933). Exchanges of water in the frog. *Biol., Rev.*, **8**, 224
27. Bentley, P. J. (1971). *Endocrines and Osmoregulation* (Berlin, Heidelberg and New York: Springer verlag)
28. Bentley, P. J. and Schmidt-Nielsen, K. (1966). Cutaneous water loss in reptiles. *Science*, **151**, 1547
29. Dmi'el, R. (1972). Effects of activity and temperature on metabolism and water loss in snakes. *Amer. J. Physiol.*, **223**, 510
30. Lasiewski, R. C., Bernstein, M. H. and Ohmart, R. D. (1971). Cutaneous water loss in the roadrunner and poor-will. *Condor*, **73**, 470
31. Schmidt-Nielsen, K., Kanwisher, J., Lasiewski, R. C., Cohn, J. E. and Bretz, W. L. (1969). Temperature regulation and respiration in the ostrich. *Condor*, **71**, 341
32. Chew, R. M. (1965). Water metabolism of mammals. *Physiological Mammalogy*, Vol. II, 43–178 (M. V. Mayer and R. G. Van Gelder, editors) (New York and London: Academic Press)
33. Schmidt-Nielsen, B. and Schmidt-Nielsen, K. (1951). A complete account of the water metabolism in kangaroo rats and an experimental verification. *J. Cell. Comp. Physiol.*, **38**, 165
34. Shkolnik, A. and Borut, A. (1969). Temperature and water relations in two species of spiny mice (*Acomys*). *J. Mamm.*, **50**, 245
35. Campbell, J. W., Drotman, R. B., McDonald, J. A. and Tramell, P. R. (1972). Nitrogen metabolism in terrestrial invertebrates. *Nitrogen Metabolism and the Environment*, 1–54 (J. W. Campbell and L. Goldstein, editors) (London and New York: Academic Press)
36. Dresel, I. B. and Moyle, V. (1950). Nitrogeneous excretion of isopods and amphipods. *J. Exp. Biol.*, **27**, 210
37. Speeg, K. V. and Campbell, J. W. (1968). Formation and volatilization of ammonia gas by terrestrial snails. *Amer. J. Physiol.*, **214**, 1392
38. Sperber, I. (1944). Studies on the mammalian kidney. *Zool. Bidr. Upps.*, **22**, 249
39. Schmidt-Nielsen, B. and O'Dell, R. (1961). Structure and concentrating mechanism in the mammalian kidney. *Amer. J. Physiol.*, **200**, 1119
40. Berliner, R. W. and Bennett, C. M. (1967). Concentration of urine in the mammalian kidney. *Amer. J. Med.*, **42**, 777
41. MacMillen, R. E. and Lee, A. K. (1967). Australian desert mice: independence of exogenous water. *Science*, **158**, 383
42. Dantzler, W. H. (1970). Kidney function in desert vertebrates. *Hormones and the Environment*, 157–190 (G. K. Benson, and J. G. Phillips, editors) (Cambridge: Cambridge University Press)

43. Hudson, J. W. and Rummel, J. A. (1966). Water metabolism and temperature regulation of the primitive heteromyids, *Liomys salvani* and *Liomys irroratus. Ecology,* **47,** 345

44. Houpt, T. R. (1970). Urea and the ruminant: Movement of endogenous urea nitrogen into the rumen. *Urea and the Kidney,* 105–111 (B. Schmidt-Nielsen and D. W. S. Kerr, editors) (Amsterdam: Excrepta Medica Foundation)

45. Maloiy, G. M. O. (1970). Water economy of the somali donkey. *Amer. J. Physiol.,* **219,** 1522

46. Maloiy, G. M. O. and Hopcraft, D. (1971). Thermoregulation and water relations of two East African antelopes: the hartebeest and impala. *Comp. Biochem. Physiol.,* **38A,** 525

47. Phillips, J. E. (1964). Rectal absorption in the desert locust, *Schistocerca gregaria* Forskal. I. Water. *J. Exp. Biol.,* **41,** 15

48. Ramsay, J. A. (1964). The rectal complex of the mealworm, *Tenebrio molitor* L. (Coleoptera, Tenebrionidae). *Phil. Trans. Roy. Soc. London, Ser. B.,* **248,** 279

49. Wall, B. J. (1971). Local osmotic gradients in the rectal pads of an insect. *Fed. Proc.,* **30,** 42

50. Grimstone, A. V., Mullinger, A. M. and Ramsay, J. A. (1968). Further studies on the rectal complex of the mealworm *Tenebrio molitor* L. (Coleoptera, Tenebriondae). *Phil. Trans. Roy. Soc. (London), Ser. B.,* **253,** 343

51. Schmidt-Nielsen, K., Borut, A., Lee, P. and Crawford, E. C. (1963). Nasal salt excretion and possible function of the cloaca in water conservation. *Science,* **142,** 1300

52. Bentley, P. J. and Schmidt-Nielsen, K. (1965). Permeability to water and sodium of the crocodilian Caiman sclerops. *J. Cell. Comp. Physiol.,* **66,** 303

53. Junqueira, L. C. U., Malnic, G. and Monge, C. (1966). Reabsorptive function of the ophidian cloaca and large intestine. *Physiol. Zool.,* **39,** 151

54. Braysher, M. and Green, B. (1970). Absorption of water and electrolytes from the cloaca of an Australian lizard, *Varanus gouldii* (Gray). *Comp. Biochem. Physiol.,* **35,** 607

55. Skadhauge, E. (1967). *In vivo* perfusion studies of the cloacal water and electrolyte resorption in the fowl (*Gallus domesticus*). *Comp. Biochem. Physiol.,* **23,** 483

56. Skadhauge, E. (1968). The cloacal storage of urine in the rooster. *Comp. Biochem. Physiol.,* **24,** 7

57. Bindsler, N. and Skadhauge, E. (1971). Sodium chloride absorption and solute-linked water flow across the epithelium of the coprodeum and large intestine in the normal and dehydrated fowl (*Gallus domesticus*). *In vivo* perfusion studies. *J. Physiol.,* **216,** 753

58. Murrish, D. E. and Schmidt-Nielsen, K. (1970). Exhaled air temperature and water conservation in lizards. *Resp. Physiol.,* **10,** 151

59. Khalil, F. and Abdel-Messeih, G. (1963). Tissue constituents of reptiles in relation to their mode of life. III. Nitrogen content and serum proteins. *Comp. Biochem. Physiol.,* **9,** 75

60. Schmidt-Nielsen, K., Jorgensen, C. B. and Osaki, H. (1958). Extrarenal salt excretion in birds. *Amer. J. Physiol.,* **193,** 101

61. Minnich, J. E. (1970). Water and electrolyte balance of the desert iguana, *Dipsosaurus dorsalis,* in its natural habitat. *Comp. Biochem. Physiol.,* **35,** 921

62. Templeton, J. R., Murrish, D. E., Randall, E. M. and Mugaas, J. N. (1972). Salt and water balance in the desert iguana, *Dipsosaurus dorsalis.* I, The effect of dehydration, rehydration and full hydration. *Z. Vergl. Physiol.,* **76,** 245

63. Grenot, C. (1968). Sur l'excertion nasale des sels chez le lézard saharien: *Uromastix acanthinurus. C.R. Acad. Sc.* (Paris), **266,** 1871

64. Duvdevani, I. and Borut, A. (1973). Oxygen consumption and total evaporative water loss in four species of fringed-toed lizards, *Acanthodactylus* (Lacertidae). *Copeia,* in press

65. Cade, T. J. and Greenwald, L. (1966). Nasal salt secretion in falconiform birds. *Condor,* **68,** 338

66. Bursell, E. (1960). Loss of water by excretion and defecation in the tsetse flies. *J. Exp. Biol.,* **37,** 689

67. Uvarov, B. (1966). *Grasshoppers and Locusts, Vol. 1,* (Cambridge: Cambridge University Press)

68. Dmi'el, R. and Zilber, B. (1971). Water balance in a desert snake. *Copeia*, 754
69. Cade, T. J. (1964). Water and salt balance in granivorous birds. *Thirst*, 237–254 (M. J. Wayner, editor) (New York: McMillan)
70. Smyth, M. and Bartholomew, G. A. (1966). The water economy of the Black throated sparrow and the rock wren. *Condor*, **68**, 447
71. Willoughby, E. J. (1968). Water economy of the Stark's lark and grey-backed finch-lark from the Namib desert of South Africa. *Comp. Biochem. Physiol.*, **27**, 723
72. Taylor, R. C. (1968). Hygroscopic food; a source of water for desert antelopes. *Nature (London)*, **219**, 181
73. Schmidt-Nielsen, B., Schmidt-Nielsen, K., Houpt, T. R. and Jarnum, S. A. (1956). Water balance of the camel. *Amer. J. Physiol.*, **185**, 185
74. Maloiy, G. M. O. and Boarer, E. D. H. (1970). Response of the Somali donkey to dehydration: hematological changes. *Amer. J. Physiol.*, **221**, 37
75. Macfarlane, W. V. (1964). Terrestrial animals in dry heat: ungulates. *Adaptation to the Environment. Handbook of Physiology, Section 4*, 509–539 (D. B. Dill, editor) (Washington: Amer. Physiol. Soc.)
76. Shkolnik, A., Borut, A. and Choshniak, J. (1972). Water economy of the beduin goat. *Symp. Zool. Soc. London*, **31**, 229
77. Taylor, R. C. (1968). The minimum water requirements of some East African bovids. *Symp. Zool. Soc. London*, **21**, 195
78. Jackson, D. C. and Schmidt-Nielsen, K. (1964). Countercurrent heat exchange in the respiratory passages. *Proc. Natn. Acad. Sci. USA*, **51**, 1192
79. Schmidt-Nielsen, K. (1969). The neglected interface: the biology of water as a liquid gas system. *Quart. Rev. Biophys.*, **2**, 283
80. Schmidt-Nielsen, K., Hainsworth, F. R. and Murrish, D. E. (1970). Counter current heat exchange in the respiratory passages: effect on water and heat balance. *Resp. Physiol.*, **9**, 263
81. Collins, J. C., Pilkington, T. C. and Schmidt-Nielsen, K. (1971). A model of respiratory heat transfer in a small mammal. *Biophys. J.*, **11**, 886
82. Bursell, E. (1964). Humidity. *The Physiology of Insecta*, Vol. 1, 323–361 (M. Rockstein, editor) (New York: Academic Press)
83. Buck, J. (1962). Some physical aspects of insect respiration. *Ann. Rev. Entomol.*, **7**, 27
84. Church, N. S. (1960). Heat loss and the body temperature of flying insects. I. Heat loss by evaporation of water from the body. *J. Exp. Biol.*, **37**, 171
85. Dawson, W. R. (1967). Interspecific variation in physiological responses of lizards to temperature. *Lizard Ecology*, 230–257 (W. W. Milstead, editor) (Columbia: U. of Missouri Press)
86. Templeton, J. R. (1970). Reptiles. *Comparative Physiology of Thermoregulation*, Vol. 1. 204–249 (G. C. Whittow, editor) (New York: Academic Press)
87. Schmidt-Nielsen, K. and Dawson, W. R. (1964). Terrestrial animals in dry heat: desert reptiles, *Adaptation to the Environment, Handbook of Physiology, Section 4*, 467–481 (D. B. Dill, editor) (Washington: Amer. Physiol. Soc.)
88. Bartholomew, G. A. and Tucker, V. A. (1964). Size, body temperature, thermal conductance, oxygen consumption, and heart rate in Australian varanid lizards. *Physiol. Zool.*, **37**, 341
89. Snyder, G. K. (1971). Adaptive value of a reduced respiratory metabolism in a lizard. A unique case. *Resp. Physiol.*, **13**, 90
90. Scholander, P. F., Walters, V., Hock, R. and Irving, L. (1950). Body insulation of some arctic and tropical mammals and birds. *Biol. Bull.*, **99**, 225
91. Scholander, P. F., Hock, R., Walters, V., Johnson, F. and Irving, L. (1950). Heat regulation in some arctic and tropical mammals and birds. *Biol. Bull.*, **99**, 237
92. Scholander, P. F., Hock, R., Walters, V. and Irving, L. (1950). Adaptations to cold in arctic and tropical mammals and birds in relation to body temperature, insulation, and basal metabolic rate. *Biol. Bull.*, **99**, 259
93. Scholander, P. F. (1955). Evolution of climatic adaptations in homeotherms. *Evolution*, **9**, 15
94. MacMillen, R. E. and Lee, A. K. (1970). Energy metabolism and pulmocutaneous water loss of Australian hopping mice. *Comp. Biochem. Physiol.*, **35**, 355
95. Kleiber, M. (1961). *The Fire of Life: An Introduction to Animal Energetics*, (New York: Wiley)

96. Lasiewski, R. C. and Dawson, W. R. (1967). A re-examination of the relation between standard metabolic rate and body weight in birds. *Condor*, **69**, 13
97. Dawson, W. R. and Hudson, J. W. (1970). Birds. *Comparative Physiology of Thermoregulation*, Vol. I, 223–310 (G. C. Whittow, editor) (New York and London: Academic Press)
98. Calder, W. A. and Schmidt-Nielsen, K. (1967). Temperature regulation and evaporation in the pigeon and the roadrunner. *Amer. J. Physiol.*, **213**, 883 •
99. King, J. R. and Farner, D. S. (1961). Energy metabolism, thermoregulation and body temperature. *Biology and Comparative Physiology of Birds*, Vol. 2, 215–288 (A. Marshall, editor) (New York: Academic Press)
100. Bartholomew, G. A. and Cade, T. J. (1963). The water economy of land birds. *Auk*, **80**, 504
101. Lasiewski, R. C. and Seymour, R. S. (1972). Thermoregulatory responses to heat stress in four species of birds weighing approximately 40 grams. *Physiol. Zool.*, **45**, 106
102. Ligon, J. D. (1969). Some aspects of temperature relations in small owls. *Auk*, **86**, 458
103. MacMillen, R. E. and Trost, C. H. (1967). Thermoregulation and water loss in the Inca dove. *Comp. Biochem. Physiol.*, **20**, 263
104. Brush, A. H. (1965). Energetics, temperature regulation and circulation in resting, active and defeathered California quail, *Lophortyx californicus*. *Comp. Biochem. Physiol.*, **15**, 399
105. Hudson, J. W. and Kimzey, S. L. (1966). Temperature regulation and metabolic rhythms in populations of the house sparrow, *Passer domesticus*. *Comp. Biochem. Physiol.*, **17**, 203
106. Dawson, T. J. and Hulbert, A. J. (1970). Standard metabolism, body temperature, and surface areas of Australian marsupials. *Amer. J. Physiol.*, **218**, 1233
107. Dawson, T. J. (1972). Primitive mammals and patterns in the evolution of thermoregulation. *Essays on Temperature Regulation*, 1–18 (J. Bligh and R. E. Moore, editors) (Amsterdam–London: North Holland)
108. Shkolnik, A. (1972). Personal communication
109. Hart, J. S. (1971). Rodents. *Comparative Physiology of Thermoregulation*, Vol. II, 1–149 (G. C. Whittow, editor) (New York and London: Academic Press)
110. Brody, S. (1945). *Bioenergetics and Growth*, (New York: Reinhold)
111. Lasiewski, R. C., Acosta, A. L. and Bernstein, M. H. (1966). Evaporative water loss in birds. I. Characteristics of the open flow method of determination, and their relation to estimates of thermoregulatory ability. *Comp. Biochem. Physiol.*, **19**, 445
112. Hock, R. J. (1960). Seasonal variations in physiologic functions of Arctic ground squirrels and black bears. *Bull. Mus. Comp. Zool.* (*Harvard*), **124**, 155
113. Hudson, J. W. (1962). The role of water in the biology of the antelope ground squirrel, *Citellus leucurus*. *Univ. Calif. Publ. Zool.*, **64**, 1
114. Hudson, J. W. (1964). Temperature regulation in the round-tailed ground squirrel, *Citellus tereticaudus*. *Ann. Acad. Sci. Fenn.*, Ser. A., IV, **71**, 219
115. Yousef, M. K. and Bradley, W. G. (1971). Physiological and ecological studies on *Citellus lateralis*. *Comp. Biochem. Physiol.*, **39A**, 671
116. Hudson, J. W. (1967). Variations in the pattern of torpidity of small homeotherms. *Proc. III Int. Symp. Mammal. Hiber.*, 30–46 (Edinburgh and London: Oliver and Boyd
117. McNab, B. K. and Morrison, P. (1963). Body temperature and metabolism in subspecies of *Peromyscus* from arid and mesic environments. *Ecol. Monogr.*, **33**, 63
118. Hayward, J. S. (1965). Microclimate temperature and its adaptive significance in six geographic races of *Peromyscus*. *Can. J. Zool.*, **43**, 341
119. Schmidt-Nielsen, K., Dawson, T. J., Hammel, H. T., Hinds, D. and Jackson, D. C. (1965). The jack rabbit—a study in its desert survival. *Hvalradets Skrifter Norske Videnskaps Acad.* (*Oslo*), **48**, 125
120. Dawson, T. J. and Schmidt-Nielsen, K. (1966). Effect of thermal conductance on water economy in the antelope jack rabbit, *Lepus alleni*. *J. Cellular Physiol.*, **67**, 463
121. Schmidt-Nielsen, K., Crawford, E. C. Jr., Newsome, A. E., Rawson, K. S. and Hammel, H. T. (1967). Metabolic rate of camels: effect of body temperature and dehydration. *Amer. J. Physiol.*, **212**, 341
122. Taylor, C. R., Spinage, C. A. and Lyman, C. P. (1969). Water relations of the waterbuck, an East African antelope. *Amer. J. Physiol.*, **217**, 630

123. Taylor, C. R. and Lyman, C. P. (1967). A comparative study of the environmental physiology of an East African antelope, the eland, and the Hereford steer. *Physiol. Zoöl.*, **40**, 280

124. Macfarlane, W. V. (1965). Water metabolism of desert ruminants. *Studies in Physiology*, 191–199 (D. R. Curtis and A. K. McIntyre, editors) (New York: Springer Verlag)

125. Macfarlane, W. V. (1968). Adaptation of ruminants to tropics and deserts. *Adaptation of Domestic Animals*, 164–182 (E. S. E. Hafez, editor) (Philadelphia: Lea and Febiger)

126. Bartholomew, G. A. and Rainy, M. (1971). Regulation of body temperature in the rock hyrax, *Heterohyrax brucei. J. Mammal.*, **52**, 81

127. Taylor, C. R. (1969). Metabolism, respiratory changes, and water balance of an antelope, the eland. *Amer. J. Physiol.*, **217**, 317

128. Taylor, C. R., Robertshaw, D. and Hofmann, R. (1969). Thermal panting: a comparison of wildebeest and zebu cattle. *Amer. J. Physiol.*, **217**, 907

129. Mansingh, A. (1971). Physiological classification of dormancies in insects. *Can. Ent.*, **103**, 983

130. Lees, A. D. (1955). *The Physiology of Diapause in Arthropods.* (*Cambridge Univ. Press*)

131. Pengelley, E. T. (1967). The relation of external conditions to the onset and termination of hibernation and estivation. *Proc. III Int. Symp. Mammal. Hiber*, 1–29 (Edinburgh and London: Oliver and Boyd)

132. MacMillen, R. E. (1965). Aestivation in the cactus mouse, *Peromyscus eremicus. Comp. Biochem. Physiol.*, **16**, 227

133. Tucker, V. A. (1966). Diurnal torpor and its relation to food consumption and weight changes in the California pocket mouse, *Perognathus californicus. Ecology*, **47**, 245

134. Bartholomew, G. A. and Hudson, J. W. (1960). Aestivation in the Mohave ground squirrel, *Citellus mohavensis. Bull. Mus. Comp. Zool. (Harvard)*, **124**, 193

135. Wang, L. C. H. and Hudson, J. W. (1970). Some physiological aspects of temperature regulation in the normothermic and torpid hispid pocket mouse, *Perognathus hispidus. Comp. Biochem. Physiol.*, **32**, 275

136. Pengelley, E. T. and Kelly, K. H. (1966). A circannian rhythm in hibernating species of the genus *Citellus* with observations on their physiological evolution. *Comp. Biochem. Physiol.*, **19**, 603

137. Fisher, K. C. and Manery, J. F. (1967). Water and electrolyte metabolism in heterotherms. *Proc. III Int. Symp. Mammal. Hiber.*, 235–279 (Edinburgh and London: Oliver and Boyd)

138. Tucker, V. A. (1965). The relation between the torpor cycle and heat exchange in the California pocket mouse, *Perognathus californicus. J. Cell. and Comp. Physiol.*, **65**, 405

139. Armitage, K. B. and Shulenberger, E. (1972). Evidence for circannual metabolic cycle in *Citellus tridecemlineatus*, a hibernator. *Comp. Biochem. Physiol.*, **42A**, 667

140. McNab, B. K. (1969). The economics of temperature regulation in neotropical bats. *Comp. Biochem. Physiol.*, **31**, 227

141. Dwyer, P. D. (1971). Temperature regulation and cave-dwelling in bats: an evolutionary perspective. *Mammalia*, **35**, 424

142. Peiponen, V. A. (1965). On hypothermia and torpidity in the nightjar (*Caprimulgus europaeus L.*). *Ann. Acad. Sci. Fenn. Ser. A.* IV., **87**, 1

143. Peiponen, V. A. (1966). The diurnal heterothermy of the nightjar. *Ann. Acad. Sci. Fenn. Ser. A.* IV., **101**, 1

144. Dawson, W. R. and Fisher, C. D. (1969). Responses to temperature by the spotted nightjar (*Eurostopodus guttatus*). *Condor*, **71**, 49

145. Ligon, J. D. (1970). Still more responses of the poor-will to low temperatures. *Condor*, **72**, 496

146. Crawford, E. C. Jr. and Schmidt-Nielsen, K. (1967). Temperature regulation and evaporative cooling in the ostrich. *Amer. J. Physiol.*, **212**, 347

147. Taylor, C. R. (1970). Strategies of temperature regulation: effect on evaporation in East African ungulates. *Amer. J. Physiol.*, **219**, 1131

148. Taylor, C. R. (1970). Dehydration and heat: effects on temperature regulation of East African ungulates. *Amer. J. Physiol.*, **219**, 1136

149. Rosenmann, M. A. and Morrison, P. (1963). Physiological response to heat and dehydration in the guanaco. *Physiol. Zool.*, **36**, 45

150. Taylor, R. C. and Lyman, C. P. (1972). Heat storage in running antelopes: independence of brain and body temperatures. *Amer. J. Physiol.*, **222**, 114
151. Webb, G. J. W., Johnson, C. R. and Firth, B. T. (1972). Head-body temperature difference in lizards. *Physiol. Zool.*, **45**, 130
152. Hadley, N. F. (1970). Micrometeorology and energy exchange in two desert arthropods. *Ecology*, **51**, 434
153. Edney, E. B. (1971). Some aspects of water balance in tenebrionid beetles and a thysanuran from the Namib desert of Southern Africa. *Physiol. Zool.*, **44**, 61
154. Norris, K. S. (1967). Color adaptation in desert reptiles and its thermal relationships. *Symposium on Lizard Ecology*, 162–229 (W. Milstead, editor) (Columbia: U. of Missouri Press)
155. Heppner, F. H. (1970). The metabolic significance of differential absorption of radiant energy by black and white birds. *Condor*, **72**, 50
156. Dawson, T. J. and Brown, G. M. (1970). A comparison of the insulative and reflective properties of the fur of desert kangaroos. *Comp. Biochem. Physiol.*, **37**, 23
157. Finch, V. A. (1972). Thermoregulation and heat balance of the East African eland and hartebeest. *Amer. J. Physiol.*, **222**, 1374
158. Porter, W. P. and Gates, D. M. (1969). Thermodynamic equilibria of animals with environment. *Ecol. Monographs*, **39**, 227
159. Edney, E. B. (1971). The body temperature of tenebrionid beetles in the Namib desert of Southern Africa. *J. Exp. Biol.*, **55**, 253
160. Hamilton, W. J. and Heppner, F. H. (1967). Radiant solar energy and function of black homeotherm pigmentation: a hypothesis. *Science*, **155**, 196
161. Herreid, C. F. II and Kessel, B. (1967). Thermal conductance in birds and mammals. *Comp. Biochem. Physiol.*, **21**, 405
162. Yarbrough, C. G. (1971). The influence of distribution and ecology on the thermoregulation of small birds. *Comp. Biochem. Physiol.*, **39A**, 235
163. McNab, B. K. (1970). Body weight and the energetics of temperature regulation. *J. Exp. Biol.*, **53**, 329
164. Calder, W. A. and King, J. R. (1972). Body weight and the energetics of temperature regulation: a re-examination. *J. Exp. Biol.*, **56**, 775
165. Broza, M. (1972). Personal communication
166. Parry, D. A. (1954). On the drinking of soil capillary water by spiders. *J. Exp. Biol.*, **31**, 218
167. Bodenheimer, F. S. (1953). Problems of animal ecology and physiology in deserts. *Desert Research*—Proc. Int. Symp., Jerusalem, Israel
168. Buxton, P. A. (1930). Evaporation from the mealworm (*Tenebrio, Coleoptera*) and atmospheric humidity. *Proc. R. Soc.*, **B106**, 560
169. Beament, J. W. L. (1965). The active transport of water: evidence, model and mechanisms. *Symp. Soc. Exp. Biol.*, **19**, 273
170. Noble-Nesbitt, J. (1969). Water balance in the firebrat, *Thermobia domestica* (Packard). Exchanges of water with the atmosphere. *J. Exp. Biol.*, **50**, 745
171. Edney, E. B. (1966). Absorption of water vapour from unsaturated air by *Arenivaga* sp. (Polyphagidae, Dictyoptera). *Comp. Biochem. Physiol.*, **19**, 387
172. Rockstein, M. (editor) (1964). *The Physiology of Insecta*, Vol. 1 (New York and London: Academic Press)
173. Mayhew, W. W. (1963). Biology of the granite spiny lizard, *Sceloporus orcutti*, *Amer. Mid. Nat.*, **69**, 310
174. Meyer, D. E. (1966). Drinking habits in the earless lizard, *Holbrookia maculata*, and in two species of horned lizards (*Phrynosoma*). *Copeia*, 126
175. Mendelssohn, H. (1963). On the biology of the venomous snakes of Israel. *Israel. J. Zool.*, **12**, 143
176. Duvdevani, I. (1971). The water and electrolyte metabolism in lizards of the genus *Acanthodactylus* Wiegmann 1834 (Lacertidae). *Ph.D. Thesis*, Hebrew University of Jerusalem (in Hebrew)
177. Bradshaw, S. D. (1970). Seasonal changes in the water and electrolyte metabolism of Amphibolorus lizard in the field. *Comp. Biochem. Physiol.*, **36**, 689
178. Dantzler, W. H. and Schmidt-Nielsen, B. (1966). Excretion in fresh water turtle (*Pseudemys scripta*) and desert tortoise *Gopherus agassizii*. *Amer. J. Physiol.*, **210**, 198

179. Hassan, R. M. (1966). Nitrogenous excretion in reptiles with special reference to the purine end metabolites. *M.Sc. Thesis*, Cairo Univ., Egypt
180. Norris, K. S. and Dawson, W. R. (1964). Observations on the water economy and electrolyte excretion of chuckwallas (*Lacertilia, Sauromalus*) *Copeia*, 638
181. Cade, T. J., Tobin, C. A. and Gold, A. (1965). Water economy and metabolism of two estrildine finches. *Physiol. Zool.*, **38,** 9
182. Cade, T. J. (1965). Survival of the scaly-feathered finch (*Sporopipes squamiffrons*) without drinking water. *Ostrich*, **36,** 131
183. Immelman, K. and Immelman, G. (1968). Zur Fortpflanzungs biologie einige Vögel in der Namib. *Bonn. Zool. Beitr.*, **19,** 329
184. Irwin, M. P. S. (1956). Notes on the drinking habits of birds in semi-desertic Bechuanaland. *Bull. Brit. Ornithol. Club*, **76,** 99
185. Winterbottom, J. M. (1963). Notes from Namaqualand and Bushmanland. *Ostrich*, **34,** 156
186. Willoughby, E. J. and Cade, T. J. (1967). Drinking habits of birds in the Central Namib desert of South West Africa. *Sci. Pap. Namib Desert Res. Sta. No.* **31,** 1
187. Fisher, C. D., Lindgren, E. and Dawson, W. R. (1972). Drinking patterns and behavior of Australian desert birds in relation to their ecology and abundance. *Condor*, **74,** 111
188. Cade, T. J. and MacLean, G. L. (1967). Transport of water by adult sandgrouse to their young. *Condor*, **69,** 323
189. Smyth, M. and Bartholomew, G. A. (1966). Effects of water deprivation and sodium chloride on the blood and urine of the mourning dove. *Auk*, **83,** 597
190. Schmidt-Nielsen, B. and Schmidt-Nielsen, K. (1950). Do kangaroo rats thrive when drinking sea water? *Amer. J. Physiol.*, **160,** 291
191. Shkolnik, A. (1971). Diurnal activity in a small desert rodent. *Int. J. Biometer.*, **15,** 115
192. Horowitz, M. and Borut, A. (1970). Effect of acute dehydration on body fluid compartments in three rodent species, *Rattus norvegicus, Acomys cahirinus* and *Meriones crassus*. *Comp. Biochem. Physiol.*, **35,** 283
193. Hainsworth, F. R., Stricker, E. M. and Epstein, A. N. (1968). Water metabolism of rats in the heat: dehydration and drinking. *Amer. J. Physiol.*, **214,** 983
194. Borut, A., Horowitz, M. and Castel, M. (1972). Blood volume regulation in the spiny mouse: capillary permeability changes due to dehydration. *Symp. Zool. Soc. London*, **31,** 175
195. McNabb, A. F. M. (1969). A comparative study of water balance in three species of quail. *Comp. Biochem. Physiol.*, **28,** 1059
196. Poulson, T. L. (1965). Countercurrent multipliers in avian kidneys. *Science*, **148,** 389
197. Adolph, E. F. (1943). Do rats thrive when drinking sea water? *Amer. J. Physiol.*, **140,** 25
198. Bentley, P. J. (1955). Some aspects of the water metabolism of an Australian marsupial, *Setonyx brachyurus.*, *J. Physiol.* **127,** 1
199. Haines, H. (1964). Salt tolerance and water requirements in the salt water harvest mouse. *Physiol. Zool.*, **37,** 266
200. Richmond, C. R., Langham, W. H. and Trujillo, T. T. (1962). Comparative metabolism of tritiated water by mammals. *J. Cell. Comp. Physiol,*, **59,** 45
201. Macfarlane, W. V., Howard, B., Haines, H., Kennedy, P. S. and Sharpe, C. M. (1971). Hierarchy of water and energy turnover of desert mammals. *Nature (London)*, **234,** 483
202. Minnich, J. E. and Shoemaker, V. H. (1970). Diet behavior and water turnover in the desert iguana, *Dipsosaurus dorsalis. Amer. Midland Naturalist*, **84,** 496
203. Ohmart, R. D., Chapman, T. E. and Mcfarland, L. Z. (1970). Water turnover in roadrunners under different environmental conditions. *Auk*, **87,** 787
204. Edney, E. B. (1968). Transition from water to land in isopod crustaceans. *Amer. Zoologist*, **8,** 309
205. Macfarlane, W. V., Howard, B., Maloiy, G. M. O. and Hopcraft, D. (1972). Tritiated water in field studies of ruminant metabolism in Africa. *Proc. Symp. on the Use of Isotopes in Studies on the Physiology of Domestic Animals with Special Reference to Hot Climates*, (Athens: Int. At. Energy Agency)
206. Kamal, T. H., Shehata, O. and Elbana, J. M. (1972). Effect of heat and water restriction on body fluid compartments of farm animals. Tracer Bioclimatology Unit, Atomic Energy Establishment, Cairo, A.R.E.

207. Diamond, J. M. and Bossert, W. H. (1967). Standing gradient osmotic flow. A mechanism for coupling of water and solute transport in epithelia. *J. Gen. Physiol.*, **50,** 2061

208. Murrish, D. E. and Schmidt-Nielsen, K. (1970). Water transport in the cloaca of lizards: Active or passive? *Science*, **170,** 324

209. Lasiewski, R. C., Weathers, W. W. and Bernstein, M. H. (1967). Physiological responses of the giant hummingbird, *Patagona gigas*. *Comp. Biochem. Physiol.*, **23,** 797

210. Macfarlane, W. V. (1968). Comparative functions of ruminants in hot environments. *Adaptation of Domestic Animals*, 264–276 (E. S. E. Hafez, editor) (Philadelphia: Lea and Febiger)

211. Bartholomew, G. A., Hudson, J. W. and Howell, T. R. (1962). Body temperature, oxygen consumption, evaporative water loss, and heart rate in the Poor-Will. *Condor*, **64,** 117

212. Kinnear, J. A., Purohit, K. G. and Main, A. R. (1968). The ability of the tammar wallaby (*Macropus eugenii*, Marsupialia) to drink sea water. *Comp. Biochem. Physiol.*, **25,** 761

213. Kennedy, P. M. and Macfarlane, W. V. (1971). Oxygen consumption and water turnover of the fat tailed marsupials *Dasycercus cristicauda* and *Sminthopsis crassicaudata*. *Comp. Biochem. Physiol.*, **40A,** 723

214. Cloudstey-Thompson, J. L. (1970). Terrestrial invertebrates: *Comparative Physiology of Thermoregulation*, Vol. 1, 15–77 (G. C. Whittow, editor) (New York and London: Academic Press)

7
Thermoregulatory Behaviour

M. CABANAC
Université Claude Bernard, U.E.R. Médicale Lyon-Sud-Ouest

7.1 TEMPERATURE REGULATION

Living beings need a certain temperature to develop. In the animal kingdom, isothermic species have become more and more numerous in the course of evolution, and at the same time these species have become more and more complex. Mammals and birds differ from the lower animal classes in that their internal heat production is greater, and they are insulated by fur or feathers. They are called homeotherms[1], while the other classes are called temperature conformers[1]. In homeotherms, the control of the 'milieu interieur' is so perfect that an even temperature is maintained practically constant; therefore internal temperature can be said to be regulated. Physiologists agree on the name Temperature Regulation[1] for the function which keeps constant the body core temperature. Temperature regulation improves the freedom of organisms since it frees them from environmental constraints, but at the same time it renders them more fragile and dependent on their internal state. For example, plants can withstand changes in their temperature over the order of 50 °C, the range for temperature conformers is of the order of 30 °C, while in homeotherms a deviation of 5 °C from their normal temperature is a great challenge and can cause death.

7.1.1 Thermal balance

The processes involved in achieving the goal of constant body temperature obey the laws of thermodynamics. Specifically, the body heat budget is described by the following fundamental equation:

$$M \pm K \pm C \pm R - E \pm S = 0$$

where M=metabolic heat, K=conductive heat transfer, C=convective heat transfer, R=radiative heat transfer, E=evaporative heat loss and S=heat stored. When the value of this equation is zero, body temperature does not change. How is this sum kept equal to zero and thus temperature maintained constant? According to the environment or to circumstances, the living organism will be able to control one or the other of the parameters of the above equation in order to equilibrate the others. If he must work and thus

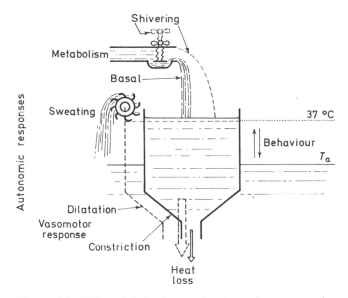

Figure 7.1 Roles of behaviour and autonomic responses in temperature regulation, shown with an analogue model of thermal balance in man. In this model, water is the analogue to heat, and water levels the analogue to temperatures. The tank, the analogue to the body, contains heat at 37 °C temperature. It is immersed in an infinite reservoir at variable ambient temperature (T_a). The organism exchanges heat with the environment by way of conduction, convection, radiation and evaporation; it also receives heat from its own metabolism. The figure represents the most frequent case where $T_a < 37$ °C, where the net result of heat exchange is a heat loss. At times T_a may be higher than 37 °C, and then the net result is a heat gain. The organism can regulate its temperature by (a) using autonomic reactions, which modify heat loss and heat production, and (b) by means of behaviour, which selected a new T_a.

increase his inner heat production, he will in the same time manage to increase his heat loss. If he is placed in a cold environment, he will limit his heat loss and increase his heat production. In both circumstances, his inner temperature will remain constant. To achieve this goal, the organism can use defence reactions: peripheral vasomotor responses, which primarily modify R and S, but also K and C, in the above equation; shivering, which may increase M; sweating and panting, which may increase E.

To summarise, the organism may be compared to an open container filled with water and dipped in water (Figure 7.1). In this model, volume is analogous to heat and temperature analogous to water level. In order to keep its level constant (constant temperature), the container can vary water intake (shivering, heat production), the diameter of the outlet (vasomotor response) and its own volume (vasomotor response), and can extract water actively with a pump (evaporative heat loss). The efficiency of these defence reactions is great in the short term: for example, a nude man can withstand without harm, environments up to 90 and 100 °C or down to −20 °C for up to 30 min at a time. On these occasions, his evaporative water loss may be as high as 1 l for $\frac{1}{2}$ h, and his resting metabolism may be multiplied by six or even ten[2]. These responses, called autonomic defence reactions are triggered and controlled by the nervous system, which disposes of information coming from temperature detectors. Specific brain centres integrate this information and process appropriate orders which are sent to the effectors. The result is a constant internal temperature.

7.1.2 Behaviour

With this model, it is immediately evident that the most efficient way to keep a steady level in the container is to move the relative positions of the container and the outside level. This is analogous to moving the body from a given thermal environment to another more favourable. This is what animals do by means of their behaviour. By their behaviour, they can modify the rate and direction of heat flowing between themselves and the environment. Do they use this opportunity during their life in natural environments or in laboratory experiments?

7.2 THERMAL BEHAVIOUR

Temperature-oriented behaviour exists in all animal species as soon as locomotion is possible. This type of behaviour covers the range of expressions from the simplest to the most sophisticated.

7.2.1 Posture

Changes in posture influence the ratio area/volume, and thus influence the heat flow between the organism and the environment. Certain positions improve heat loss, heat gain, or heat conservation. Among insects, such behaviour has been described in Orthoptera for heat gain as well as heat avoidance[3], and in Lepidoptera, which orient their wings with regard to the direction of the sun[4]. Such modified positions have also been described in amphibians[5], reptiles[6-8], seals and walruses[9,10], camels[11], and the albatross[12]. These species have been observed in conditions of heat stress or cold stress. According to their needs, they raise their bodies, extend their limbs, and position themselves perpendicular to the sun, or they crouch, retract their limbs, and face the sun. Identical behaviour can easily be observed in cattle and other domestic animals. This very simple vehaviour gives the organism some degree of control over heat flow, since it modifies the total surface exposed to the environment. For example, the surface area of a dog varies by a factor of 3, depending on whether it is seen from the back or from the side. In the same way the area of a human silhouette will be multiplied by a factor 3 or 1/3 according on whether the person assumes a crouching or expanded body position. This factor allows the organism to vary greatly the amount of heat it derives from solar irradiation, which has been evaluated at about 1039 W m^{-2} at noon time in Southern Arizona during summer[13]. On a lightly clothed manikin in human shape, it was estimated at 95 W m^{-2} in less severe conditions[14].

7.2.2 Avoidance of adverse environment and the search for favourable environment

As soon as animals can move, they respond to the ambient temperature by displacement. This is a very common observation in domestic animals, which seek sun to bask or move to rest in the shade. This simple behaviour has been described in a multitude of wild species, and it is impossible to report all of them since such examples have probably been studied in every class of animal. The list will be limited here to a few examples. Insects[15], crustacea[16], urodeles[17], frogs[5] and toads[18,19] bask in the sun, seek shade, and bury themselves to obtain heat, to avoid heat, or to avoid frost. Reptiles—turtles[20], lizards and snakes[6,21-24], also alternate shade and sun, and eventually bury themselves in the sand. The efficiency of this behaviour depends on the available environment. This environmental choice of behaviour is also seen in homeothermic species; for example, Arizona hares rest in shade and radiate their heat to the clear sky, which is radiatively no higher than 2 °C at the hottest part of the day[13]. A comparable behaviour is seen in semi-aquatic species. Theoretically, for equivalent temperature differences between body and environment, water is 25 times more efficient than air in removing heat from the body in the absence of convection. Actually, in nude man, the heat transfer coefficient is only four times greater in water than in air[25], but this is still a considerable difference. Indeed, many species use a water bath as a heat sink and alternate between air and water environments. Several examples will be found among the temperature conformers referred to above. The Walrus[9] and hippopotamus[26] are good examples of users of this behaviour, but eventually the rat will also use it if the opportunity is offered[27], and domestic animals often display it. Another form of this behaviour is huddling. Camels have been observed to gather and so avoid hot environmental radiations[11], but usually individuals are spread out in hot and warm environments, and gather only in cold environments. This is a common behaviour existing in many groups and it has been well described in bats[28]. This behaviour exists at high efficiency at birth in rats: 20-days-old rats at 21 °C ambient temperature can reduce by 32% their heat production just by huddling[29]. Avoidance of unfavourable environments and search for favourable environments have been studied experimentally in thermal gradients. In such a gradient, a free moving animal will, after an initial exploratory period, stabilise in its preferred thermal environment or thermopreferendum[30]. Quantitative results have been obtained on many species by this method. The unicellular organism, *Paramecium aurelia*[31], insects, Hymenoptera[32], Orthoptera[33], Coleoptera and Lepidoptera[34], arachnides[35] and among the vertebrates, fishes[36,37,38–41], amphibians[17,40,42], reptiles[43–47], mammals, pigs[48], rats[49], mice and wild mice[50], dogs[51,52], have all displayed thermal preferences in experimentally produced temperature gradients or in derivatives of this device, such as the double or triple shuttle box. This kind of experimental method has the advantage of being very close to a natural environment, and the field studies quoted above demonstrate that it is a fundamental response. While these types of behaviour are certainly very efficient in dealing with the animal's thermal problems, they have the disadvantage that all the animal's activity is devoted to improve its thermal environment. They are therefore competitive with other forms of behaviour. Their existence at a given time means that temperature is at that time the most important motivation for the subject.

7.2.3   Food and water intake

Food intake increases in all homeothermic species during long-term exposure to a cold environment (see Chapter 2). Conversely, an increase in ambient temperature usually reduces food intake. The amount eaten is proportional to the degree of cold[53]. This observation has led to the thermal theory of food intake[54]. In the same way, water intake increases when a subject is placed in a warm or hot environment[55]. These behavioural responses to ambient temperature are logical from an energy balance viewpoint. In a cold environment, the subject produces more heat; in a warm environment he loses more water to eliminate excess heat, and behaves so as to cover his energy and water balance. When a 10 kg animal chooses to behave so as to ingest food, its body temperature can theoretically be raised 1 °C by ingestion and metabolism of 2 g carbohydrates, a most readily available food. It will be able to lower by the same amount its body temperature by ingestion and evaporation of 14 g water. In a thermal sense the efficiency of eating and drinking is therefore great, if time is given for these autonomic reactions to occur. In the short term however, prior to the occurrence of their metabolism or evaporation the efficiency is lower. For example if all specific heats were equal to one, to raise its temperature by 1 °C the animal should ingest a mass of food or water equal to 1/10th its body weight if these substances are 10 °C higher than its own temperature. Even on the cold side, where the difference between food temperature and body temperature may be greater (up to 40 °C), a drop of 1 °C body temperature in a 10 kg animal requires ingestion of a mass of at least 250 g. The efficiency is improved if the animal can ingest ice as penguins do when overheated[56]. The thermal origin of water intake has been recently questioned and attributed to dehydration[57,58], but short exposures to hot environments caused increased water intake before any dehydration occurred[59,60]; therefore increased temperature may trigger water intake directly. Although the signals responsible for thermal behaviour are also capable of triggering food and water intake, and although this behaviour may improve the subject's thermal condition and energy balance, the thermal result appears as a delayed or minor effect. Therefore, although food and water intake play a role in energy balance, they should not, strictly speaking, be considered as a thermoregulatory behaviour, unless ingestion of cold or hot food leads to an immediate change in heat storage, as is the case with ice or cold water ingestion in great amounts. Temperature may be a signal for food intake, although there are exceptions in some animals[61], but this is a behaviour which serves not temperature balance but rather energy balance.

7.2.4 Specific natural behaviour

As described above, most species will, when necessary, try behaviourally to improve heat loss, heat gain or heat conservation by seeking appropriate environments and postures. Some species in addition show specific types of behaviour made possible by anatomical or ecological peculiarities, or made necessary by specific deficits. For example, penguins will ingest ice as reported above, and beavers show a propensity to immerse their big tail in water during heat waves[62]. Convective heat loss is increased by waving flippers in seals[63], ears in elephants, palmed feet in sea birds[12], and wings in ostriches[64]. Moreover, ostriches erect their feathers in order to shade their skin. A costly behaviour exists in some species incapable of autonomic evaporative heat loss; they spread saliva on their fur and skin, thus compensating behaviourally for their inability to use an autonomic defence against heat. This behaviour also exists in marsupials[65,66], although they also have autonomic heat loss responses as well, i.e. panting. This expensive behaviour is apparently the only way to fight hyperthermia in the rat[67], since experimental suppression of saliva secretion is followed by hyperthermia in rats placed in a warm environment[68]. A comparable behaviour exists in storks, which defaecate liquid excrements on their highly vascularised feet, and thus improve evaporative heat loss when ambient temperature increases[69]. Nocturnal life is probably a behavioural adaptation to desert environment mostly to avoid the diurnal heat stress. While it may appear that seasonal bird migrations are also an example of thermal behaviour, it is more probable that migrations are determined by food availability rather than directly by ambient temperature[70].

This is not a systematic review of specific behaviour, but gives an idea of the multiplicity of the possible solutions found by various species to the same problem.

7.2.5 Microenvironments

Animals are capable of controlling their environment by building nests or burrowing. By their behaviour, social insects render possible a quasi constancy of the colony's temperature. The constant nest temperature observed in termites, bees, wasps . . . is not a passive phenomenon. When ambient temperature drops, the heat production of the hive is increased due to individual activity[71-73]. At the same time, individual bees ventilate the hive to increase the supply of oxygen[73]. The heat production and the temperature of the wasps' nest are related to the size of the sugar stores contained within[74]. In warm environments, the behavioural ventilation is also increased to allow evaporation within the nest[75]; eventually bees[71], and wasps[74] will carry water from outside and place it on the combs to allow it to evaporate in the nest. Aside from social insects microclimate building is predominantly an activity of vertebrates. This includes fabrication and use of clothes and houses, and heating and cooling of the immediate microclimate. These activities have reached a very high level of technology and allow man and commensal species to live in a permanently favourable environment, even when outside conditions are extremely aggressive as found in polar, deep sea or lunar environments[76-80]. However, long before this technological stage had been reached, humans had been very efficient at building microclimates. The clothing of Lapps create for them a subtropical microclimate[81]. The same observation is true for bed temperature[82]. The use of camp fires supplies enough heat to keep people in heat balance at resting basal metabolism during nights with ambient temperature close to 0 °C[83].

Some animal species also display such behaviour. Excavating dens and building nests, besides allowing the animal to hide and escape from predators, certainly have thermal consequences as well. The temperature of the female rat's nest remains controlled between 14 and 18.5 °C. If ambient temperature increases, the mother moves the nest to colder environments. If ambient temperature decreases, she increases its insulation[84]. Humming-birds move and orient their nest, and the result is a constant nest temperature[85]. Comparable behaviour exists in other birds[86].

The result of these activities is therefore control over the immediate environment or microenvironment of the subject. There is practically no limit to the efficiency of these forms of behaviour, and they have the merit of giving the individual the freedom to perform other activities.

7.2.6 Operant response

For experimental purposes, devices have been built which allow the animal or subject under examination to obtain heat or cold, usually by pushing a lever. Each lever press provides a burst of cool air or a few seconds of radiant heat. In other cases, the bar press will remove for a few seconds an imposed

Table 7.1

Fish, *Carassius auratus*	— Rozin and Mayer 1961 (89)
Lizards, *Dipsausaurus dorsalis*	— Kemp 1969 (90)
Klauberina riversiana	— Regal 1971 (91)
Dove, *Streptojelia risoria*	— Budgell 1971 (241)
Mouse, *Mus musculus*	— Revusky 1966 (92)
	Baldwin 1968 (93)
	Baldwin and Ingram 1968 (94)

Table 7.1 (*continued*)

Rat, *Rattus norvegicus*	— Weiss 1957 (88)
	Weiss and Laties 1960 (95)
	Weiss and Laties 1961 (96)
	Laties and Weiss 1959 (97)
	Laties and Weiss 1960 (98)
	Yeh and Weiss 1963 (99)
	Carlton and Marks 1958 (100)
	Hamilton 1959 (87)
	Hamilton 1963 (101)
	Hamilton and Sheriff 1959 (102)
	Panuska and Popovic 1963 (103)
	Satinoff 1964 (104)
	Satinoff and Rutstein 1970 (105)
	Satinoff and Shan 1971 (106)
	Jakubczak 1966 (107)
	Carlisle 1966 (108)
	Carlisle 1966 (109)
	Carlisle 1968 (110)
	Carlisle 1968 (111)
	Carlisle 1969 (112)
	Carlisle 1969 (113)
	Carlisle 1970 (114)
	Rudiger and Seyer 1968 (115)
	Epstein and Milestone 1968 (116)
	Leeming and Crowder 1968 (117)
	Lipton 1968 (118)
	Lipton 1969 (119)
	Lipton 1971 (120)
	Lipton and Marotto 1969 (121)
	Lipton, Avery and Marotto 1970 (122)
	Corbit 1969 (123)
	Corbit 1970 (124)
	Corbit 1972 (125)
	Beckman and Carlisle 1969 (126)
	Beckman 1970 (127)
	Blass 1969 (128)
	Blass 1971 (129)
	Murgatroyd and Hardy 1970 (130)
	Wakeman, Donovick and Burright 1970 (131)
Pig, *Sus sus domesticus*	— Baldwin and Ingram 1968 (94)
	Baldwin and Ingram 1967 (132)
	Baldwin and Ingram 1967 (133)
	Baldwin and Ingram 1968 (134)
Dog, *Canis familiaris*	— Robinson and Hammel 1967 (135)
	Cabanac, Duclaux and Gillet 1970 (136)
	Duclaux and Cabanac 1971 (137)
Cat, *Felix domesticus*	— Weiss, Laties and Weiss 1967 (138)
Monkeys, *Papio papio*	— Pister, Jobin and Gale 1967 (139)
	Gale, Mathews and Young 1970 (140)
Saimiris sciureus	— Adair, Casby and Stolwijk 1970 (141)
	Adair 1971 (142)
	Adair and Stitt 1971 (143)
	Stitt, Adair, Nadel and Stolwijk 1971 (144)
Man,	— Cabanac, Cunningham and Stolwijk 1971 (145)
	Cabanac, Massonnet and Belaiche 1972 (146)
	Olesen and Fanger 1971 (147)
	Olesen, Bassing, J. J. and Fanger, P. O. 1972 (148)

infrared thermal stress. This method has the great experimental advantage that one can measure the number of bar presses, or better the time spent on the lever[87], and therefore obtain a quantitative behavioural response from the animal or subject. Animals will learn to make appropriate responses in these various kinds of apparatus. After the initial experiment by Weiss (1957)[88] on rats, this method has been widely used, mostly on rats but also on other species (see Table 7.1), to study thermoregulatory motivation. It must be remembered in considering experiments using this method, that bar pressing in itself, or suppression of bar pressing can be a non-specific response resulting from general excitation or apraxia. An experimental result should be considered to be specific only when the symmetrical response is also obtained (e.g. increased bar pressing for heat *and* decreased bar pressing for cold), when the response is a quantitative function of the environmental temperature, or when the effect is dose dependent. In using these techniques one must also take care to select the appropriate intensity of the rewarding stimulus. While the thermal efficiency of operant behaviour may be made as great as one desires, the probability that an animal will respond for a thermal stimulus falls off at very low and very high intensities. The optimum stimulus intensity must be located by trial and error. When these considerations are kept in mind, operant behaviour can be a very precise tool for the experimental analysis of thermal motivation.

The list of thermal behaviour outlined above does not pretend to be complete. Its purpose is to show that animals have evolved and/or can learn different ways of controlling heat flow between themselves and the environment. All the types of behaviour listed above tend, as stated in the Introduction, to modify the immediate environment of the subject and its heat exchange with the environment. The result is a net economisation of autonomic reactions. Food and water intake, on the other hand, do not immediately modify the microclimate, and thus are not thermoregulatory behaviours as has been discussed above. All the other forms of behaviour listed have effects in a very short period of time. They appear according to environmental, ethological or physiological constraints as various solutions to the same problem of thermal economy; therefore the differences among them will not, in the sequel, be stressed any more. In view of these similarities, the laws which describe thermally motivated behaviour can be largely elucidated by studying quantitatively anyone of the many examples of this behaviour.

7.3 QUANTITATIVE ASPECTS OF THERMAL BEHAVIOUR

As described above, thermal behaviour manifest itself in a number of ways. Experimental study of some specific types of thermal behaviour, using operant techniques has revealed that responses to thermal stresses are precisely related to thermal needs.

7.3.1 Variable environments

When animals are placed in a climatic chamber equipped with an operant system which they can use to obtain a change in the environment, their response depends on the ambient temperature. The warming response becomes more and more intense with decreasing ambient temperature. This was measured in rats[108,109,129,130], mice[93], pigs[132], dogs[136], cats[138]. Conversely, the cooling response increases with increasing ambient temperature in rats[116,124,129,130] and dogs[136]. In both circumstances, it is striking to observe that the behavioural response is practically proportional to ambient temperature. Since the heat exchange between the subject and its environment is directly proportional to the difference between the subject and his environmental temperature (this is not quite true since the rate of heat exchange is not strictly proportional to ambient temperature but on first approximation we may accept it), this result demonstrates a very tight quantitative adaptation of behaviour to the thermal stress and suggests also an adaptation to the thermal need.

7.3.2   Variable rewarding stimuli

An identical conclusion can be drawn from consideration of the results of experiments where the magnitude of the reward is varied. In cold environments, rats[95,101,111,113,114,122,124], mice[93] and pigs[134] increased their behavioural demand for heat when the magnitude of the reward, or its duration, decreased. The amount of heat demanded in a cold environment in a unit period of time can be computed, and shows a tendency to remain constant, provided the stimulus is not too weak, for a given environment[93]. However, the relationship between response and reward intensity or duration is not always linear. As a matter of fact, there seem to exist two factors preventing the animal from giving a response strictly proportional to environmental temperature. When the stimulus obtained by bar pressing is feeble, the animals seem to shun it as if it were worthless[114]. When the stimulus is intense, the magnitude of the response is limited by the existence of pain thresholds when the skin reaches 15 °C or 45 °C. The existence of these limiting factors for high and low stimulus intensities might explain why the response is not always a linear function of stimulus intensity throughout a broad range of stimulus conditions.

7.3.3   Variable subjects

From the observation of a rather precise adaptation of the behavioural heat intake or heat loss to the animals' need, it might be expected that one will also observe a modification of behaviour whenever the subject's ability to deal with thermal loads is modified. For example, it has been known for a long time that the rabbit's food intake is increased by fur clipping[53]. In the same way, clipping the rats' fur increased the rate of bar pressing for heat in cold environments[110,117]. Three special circumstances where heat producing and/or heat conserving autonomic mechanisms are known, or are suspected, to be modified, will be briefly reviewed here: these are cold 'acclimation'[1], changes in activity of the thyroid gland, and changes in the amount of energy available in the diet. Pathology and pharmacology will be studied in a following section.

7.3.3.1   Cold acclimation

Prolonged exposure to cold, either in a laboratory environment or in field experiments, results in an improvement of the efficiency of the heat conservation mechanisms. The rate of heat transfer from the subject to its environment is lowered by increased peripheral vasoconstriction and thickening of the fur. At the same time, its heat production increases either as a result of more powerful shivering or of the development of non-shivering thermogenesis, which is indicated by an increased basal metabolic rate[149] (see Chapter 2). Experimental measurement of operant behaviour gave conflicting results with regard to the effects of acclimation on thermally motivated behaviour. Rats[100], mice, and pigs[94], housed at low ambient temperatures, required more infrared heating rewards than their non-acclimated controls when exposed to a cool environment. This result is the opposite of what would be expected if acclimation results in an improvement of heat producing and heat conserving mechanisms. However, the opposite result has been obtained in rats[98], and in hairless mice[92]. The cold acclimated rats started using a lever delivering infrared heat later than did their controls, and asked for less heat once responding had begun. The hairless mice, during successive exposures to cold, asked for fewer and fewer rewards. The observation of thermal comfort in human subjects leads to comparable results. Human subjects in a sub-antarctic environment wore less and less clothing as the winter progressed[150]. Populations of people living chronically in a cold climate, who were therefore presumably cold acclimated, slept better than non-acclimated controls[151]. Finally, people of the meat-packing industry, working in a cold environment, preferred a slightly lower ambient temperature than did control subjects[147]. These results are in agreement with the hypothesis of an improvement in autonomic reactions leading to increased heat production and/or decreased heat loss in acclimated animals and men. As a result, there is a smaller need for heat in a cold environment, a decrease in heating behaviour, and a shift of comfortable temperature towards cooler values with the evolution of cold acclimation.

It is perhaps possible to interpret the contradictory behaviour displayed by mice and pigs by either absent or insufficient cold acclimation in these animals. The different results might alternatively be attributed to the use of different experimental procedures. For example, if animals are transferred from a cold acclimation room to a less-cold experimental chamber, they will retain for some time a heat debt in this new environment. Since pigs have a large mass, this heat debt might be large enough to mask the effects of acclimation on behaviour, especially if acclimation improves peripheral vasoconstriction which increases the heat debt. Such masking would not occur under conditions in which animals are housed and tested at the same ambient temperature.

7.3.3.2   Thyroid gland activity

The activity of the thyroid gland has effects on heat production. At thermal neutrality, an hyperactive thyroid gland will induce an increased rate of basal metabolism by as much as 100%. Conversely, a deficit in the gland secretion will result in a decreased basal metabolic rate by as much as 40%. Does this modified heat production influence thermal behaviour? Ablation of the thyroid gland in rats led to a decrease in basal heat production. These rats, when permitted access to a lever delivering infrared radiation, behave so as to obtain more heat than controls. Treatment of their metabolic deficit by chronic restitution of thyroid hormone, decreased this behaviour[97]. Reciprocally, administration of excess doses of thyroid hormone in dogs approximately doubled their basal metabolic rate. During the same period, their behavioural demand for heat in cold and cool environments was reduced, and the complementary demand for cold in warm and hot environments was increased[136].

These complementary observations show a close correlation between thyroid state and behaviour. Hypothyroidism leads to increased heat demand and hyperthyroidism to increased cold demand. In itself, thermal balance explains the well known chronic feeling of cold displayed by myxoedematous patients, as well as the thermophobia displayed by hyperthyroid patients. Therefore, there is no need to hypothesise a direct action of thyroid hormones on the nervous system and the patient's psychology to account for these symptoms.

7.3.3.3 Energy content of the diet

If the energy content of the diet is not sufficient, or if the diet lacks a nutrient essential to maintain the body weight, the animals increase their behavioural heat demand as if they compensated for this energy deficit by taking energy in another form[87,88,94,99,124]. In these experiments, the increased behavioural response is usually contemporaneous with a fall in rectal temperature due to the nutritional deficiency.

A symmetrical result was obtained after food intake, although the effect is quantitatively small. After a meal, there was a slight decrease of preferred ambient temperature in human subjects; unfortunately, this decrease did not reach the level of statistical significance[152]. Significant effects have been obtained in rats which bar pressed for less infrared radiation after a meal than after a fasted control period[102,124]. An increase in energy intake and increased specific dynamic action, were followed by an increased heat avoidance response[119] or by decreased bar pressing for heat[101]. Therefore human subjects and rats adapt their thermal behaviour to their decreased caloric need.

7.3.3.4 Miscellaneous (see also pathology section)

During muscular work a great amount of heat is produced within the body. Behavioural responses are used to help eliminate this heat, as has been shown by the measurement of thermal preference in man[145]. Extirpation of salivary glands in rats prevents these animals from using their physiological evaporative heat-loss response. This ablation is followed by a compensatory increase in bar pressing behaviour for heat avoidance[121].

All the examples reviewed in this section show a precise quantitative adjustment of behaviour to the subject's thermal needs. Behaviour resulting in heat gain appears each time heat loss is increased or heat production is decreased. Conversely, although there are fewer examples in the literature, behavioural heat loss occurs in circumstances where the subject gains an excess of heat from the environment or from his own metabolic activity. The result of such behaviour will be an improvement of the subject's thermal balance and a better defence of the constancy of his internal temperature. The question immediately arises: how is the control of this behaviour so well adapted to temperature regulation? The central nervous system responsible for the behaviour will need information on the subject's thermal needs. Since the subject's mass does not change, measurement of his temperature alone is sufficient to provide this information. The following sections will consider the sources of information about temperature which are available to the organism and will discuss the processing of this information by the central nervous system.

7.4 TEMPERATURE DETECTORS

In the course of evolution, animals have developed specialised organs or nervous regions which are more sensitive to temperature than average tissues. Nerve fibres leave these areas and carry messages toward the central nervous system. The term temperature *detector* rather than *receptor* has been proposed[153], as long as histologically specific organs have not been described at the endings of the neurones displaying this high sensitivity to temperature. Many examples of temperature detectors have been described in insects or other arthropods. Temperature detectors are usually located on the antennae[154,155], permitting detection of air temperature, and on the legs[32,156], permitting detection of ground temperature. Since the mass of these animals is small, it is likely that they only need to know environmental temperature, and not inner temperature as well, in order to select a favourable environment. Higher forms of life are more complex. These forms have multiple temperature detectors informing the central nervous system about body temperature as well as environmental temperature. These detectors have been studied by physiologists from two view points;

(a) that of electrical activity (by recording extracellular action potentials), and

(b) that of their capacity, when stimulated, to elicit autonomic reactions favourable to the organism's heat balance.

In addition, psychophysicists have described the relationship between skin temperature and thermal sensation. In the following, only the role of these detectors in the control of behaviour and not of autonomic responses, will be reviewed. According to the classical division of the body into two compartments, core and envelope, temperature detectors will be reviewed separately.

7.4.1 Peripheral detectors

The existence of skin temperature detectors is revealed by thermal sensation in everyday life. Thermal sensation is directly dependent upon skin temperature. Thermal stimulation of the skin gives rise to a dimension of conscious experience described by the words cold, cool, tepid, warm and hot. Temperature detectors send messages and give rise to sensations, but the histological structure of the receptor and the biophysical principle of translating temperature into nervous messages are still unknown.

7.4.1.1 Psychophysics

Skin thermal sensitivity is limited to very small punctuate areas[157]. These spots are sensitive to local temperature and to minute changes of their temperature[158–160]. The intensity of temperature sensation depends upon the number of thermal spots stimulated, i.e. depends upon the size of the surface stimulated[161–163], so that the larger the surface, the greater the sensation for a given stimulus. Within the limits of pain, 15 °C and 45 °C[164], the magnitude of thermal sensation is related to stimulus magnitude by a power law[165]. The thermal sensation resulting from application of a stimulus has an initial time-dependent component related to the speed of temperature change, and then a later steady component related to the stimulus temperature[166]. Thus, the initial value of temperature sensation will fall off to an asymptotic value, or adapt, if the stimulus and also the surface area stimulated remain constant[167]. Most psychophysical studies are conducted on human subjects, but the use of operant techniques allows one to obtain comparative responses in animals; this method shows that the skins of cat and man have similar threshold temperature sensitivities[168].

7.4.1.2 Electrophysiology (see Hensel, 1970[169] and Iggo, 1970[170])

Recording extracellular action potentials of sensory nerve fibres shows that some fibres respond to thermal stimulation of the skin[171]. The response consists of a complex change in the frequency of the action potentials seen after application of the stimulus. The frequency is a function of the adapting stimulus temperature, and also of the speed of change of the stimulus temperature[172]. The response to a changing temperature shows two populations of neurones. Some neurones increase their firing rate when stimulus temperature drops, and decrease it when stimulus temperature rises; they are described as cold units. The response of the other fibres is the mirror image; these units increase their firing rate for a rise and decrease it for a drop in temperature. The dynamic change may be an increase in frequency by 200-fold over the response to the adapting temperature. A plot of steady-state frequency against temperature gives a bell-shaped curve for an individual neurone. The peak of the bell curve for cold units occurs at about 26 °C and corresponds to a frequency less than 20 action potentials per second. The peak of the bell curve for warm units occurs at about 45 °C with a maximum frequency less than 50 action potentials per second. While temperature is primarily coded in terms of frequency it may also be coded by the pattern or grouping of action potentials over time[173].

Cold and warm fibres are myelinated or non-myelinated. Cold and warm firbes respond to stimuli limited to minute surfaces comparable to the minute cold and warm spots of human skin, but there is no proof that sensation is carried by these fibres. Indeed, the pattern of firing of the two groups of fibres does not coincide with the results of psychophysics. Although thermal potentials after skin stimulation have been traced up to the thalamus and cortex[174,175], and although these messages display the same temporal and dynamic characteristics as warm and cold fibres, it is still unproven whether sensation is mediated via these fibres. Theoretically, there is no need for a duality of specialised cold and warm sensors especially since there seems to exist a coding of information by means of the grouping of action potentials. The best evidence for such a role of cold and warm fibres is that the behaviour and electrophysiological responses to thermal stimulation of the cat's upper lip have an almost identical pattern[176].

7.4.1.3 Peripheral temperature and control of thermal behaviour

The fact that skin gives a sensation related to its temperature does not necessarily imply that cutaneous signals govern behaviour. What is the experimental evidence for the role of peripheral temperature detectors in controlling behaviour? Animal studies show that rats will bar press for heat in the cold and thus keep constant their mean sub-cutaneous temperature[96]. In a hot environment rats used operant behaviour to escape excessive heat, and their skin temperature beneath the infrared lamp remained consant[122]. Involvement of skin detectors was also shown by bar pressing behaviour for heat by rats placed in a cold environment: while skin temperature decreased, internal temperature remained nearly constant[110]. In the lizard *Tiliqua scincoides*, the peripheral acting signal is rather the temperature gradient across cutaneous tissue and temporal variations of this gradient[177]. In man, thermal sensation, besides having a discriminative component studied by psychophysicists, possesses an affective component reported in terms of pleasure and displeasure. This is another dimension of sensation, and in itself this dimension represent a motivation for behaviour. A skin temperature of 33 °C is usually considered as the neutral point[178]. Any displacement from this temperature leads to displeasure, and any change toward this temperature leads to pleasure[179,180] in men at rest and placed in thermal equilibrium in a neutral temperature. Operant responses by a human subject confirm the previous results based on comfort ratings. When this subject had the ability to adjust his ambient temperature, the final result of this behaviour was a steady mean skin temperature between 33 and 34 °C[148].

Peripheral temperature detectors certainly play an important role in behaviour, but this does not exclude the possibility that other detectors influence behaviour. Thermal behaviour relies also on temperature detectors placed deep inside the body core.

7.4.2 Internal detectors

The existence of internal thermal detectors is not as immediately evident as is the existence of skin detectors. Their existence has been postulated from the study of autonomic thermoregulatory responses, and then revealed experimentally[181,182]. They are theoretically necessary to permit precise control of internal temperature, i.e. temperature regulation. If the existence of internal sensitivity is a theoretical necessity from the viewpoint of temperature regulation, it is not so from the view point of behaviour. Since skin thermal stimulation gives a conscious sensation, apparently there is no need for a message coming from the thermal core. This point will be discussed later. Internal temperature has been shown to be capable of governing thermally adaptive behaviour in the absence of a peripheral signal of the same nature. During internal hypothermia, lizards[45], rats[103], dogs[51] and men[184,214], sought warmer environments while their skin was kept warm. During internal hyperthermia, dogs[51] and men[183,184] sought cooler environments in the absence of a warm skin signal. It is worth remembering that the internal temperature reflects the thermal balance of the whole organism. The above experiments did not give information on the site of the thermal detectors within the thermal core. Several internal thermal inputs have been discovered. The influence of head temperature can be deduced from the fact that there is a better correlation of behaviour with head temperature than with other internal temperatures in a lizard[22] or from early experiments where there was restlessness or narcosis during cooling or heating the carotid blood[185]. The main signal probably comes from the hypothalamus, but other thermal detectors have also been described in the core, and they will be reviewed here from the viewpoint of thermal behaviour.

7.4.2.1 The hypothalamus

The existence of both warm and cold sensitivities capable of triggering autonomic thermal reactions in the absence of skin inputs of the same nature (cold or warm) is shown by experiments which employ local thermal stimulation of the brain. After some controversy about internal cold sensitivity, its existence is no longer doubted (see reviews by Bligh, 1966[186] and Hammel, 1968[187]). The area most sensitive to local temperature stimuli seems to be the preoptic area and, more generally, the anterior hypothalamus. Recordings of extracellular unit activity have shown the existence of units responding to the local intracranial temperature[188]. Some increase their firing rate when local temperature increases (warm units) and others increase their firing rate when local temperature drops (cold units). The response is only static and never time-dependent, i.e. the neurones respond to the temperature but not to the speed of a temperature change. There is no direct evidence that these neurones are temperature *sensors* or play a role in temperature regulation. The same gap between electrophysiological observation and function exists here as with peripheral detectors (see reviews on these neurones by Hammel, 1965[189]; Hardy, 1969[190]; Hellon, 1970[191]; Eisenman, 1972[192]).

Postural adaptive reactions have been observed serendipidously when warming[193] or cooling[194] the hypothalamus. But it is only when the existence and role of hypothalamic thermal sensitivity had firmly been established that its possible role as a source of information in thermal operant behaviour was demonstrated[104]. Rats having access to a lever controlling short bursts of radiant heat increased their bar pressing rate when their hypothalami were cooled. This fundamental experiment has been confirmed in several classes of animals: fishes[39,195], reptiles[45,46], and in the following mammals, rat[124,130], pig[133], dog[135] and monkey[139-141].

Hypothalamic warm sensitivity has never been questioned as the main origin of autonomic thermoregulatory reactions. Experimental evidence confirms that it also has an influence on behaviour as well. Fishes[195,39], reptiles[45,46], and the following mammals: oppossums[196], rats[108,130,124], pigs[133], and monkeys[140,141], worked one way or another to decrease their ambient temperature when their hypothalami were heated. In all these experiments, there was observed a hypothalamic sensitivity to actual temperature only, and not to the rate of change of hypothalamic temperature. This is quite logical from a finalistic viewpoint, since internal temperature changes are slow and the time derivative of temperature is negligible. The hypothalamic temperature sensitivity had the same order of magnitude when measured by behavioural or autonomic responses. In rats the magnitude of the behavioural response was proportional to the magnitude of the hypothalamic stimulus:

$$R = a \ (T_{hy} - T_{set})^{124,130,141}$$

where R is the behavioural response, T_{hy} hypothalamic temperature, and T_{set} the hypothetical set point temperature.

As already mentioned, warming the hypothalami in penguins led them to ingest ice and as a result their cloacal temperature dropped[56]. Apart from these examples, there is a controversy about the effect of hypothalamic thermal stimulation on food and water intake. Classically in goats, heating the hypothalamus increases water intake and decreases food intake. Conversely, cooling the hypothalamus decreases water intake and increases food intake[197]. There have been opposite results with rats: heating the hypothalamus was accompanied by increased food intake whereas cooling the hypothalamus caused decreased food intake[198,199].

7.4.2.2 Extrahypothalamic detectors

Although the hypothalamus is considered to be the main source of thermal inputs in the control of autonomic reactions, other internal influences on autonomic reactions have also been described. Is behaviour also influenced by these detectors? If the hypothalamus is cooled for 2 h the behavioural response returns to near control level[141]. This result indicates that signals from extrahypothalamic thermosensitive structures can effectively override the hypothalamic signal. Midbrain temperature displacements did not have any effect on behaviour in squirrel monkeys[143], although midbrain cooling may be followed by shivering in anaesthetised rabbits. Conversely, thermal stimulation of the rat's medulla was followed by a corrective behaviour: heating up to 40–43 °C was followed by heat avoidance and cooling down to 28–30 °C increased heat demand[120]. This medullary stimulus was capable of multiplying the control response by a factor of approximately 2. The same kind of stimulation has not been shown to be very efficient in arousing autonomic responses. The autonomic effects of medullary thermal stimulation were limited to vasomotor changes; however, the lack of other autonomic responses may be due to the use of anaesthesia in these rather early experiments.

The spinal cord has repeatedly shown a thermal sensitivity capable, in anaesthetised as well as unanaesthetised animals, of arousing a very complete pattern of autonomic responses including panting, shivering, piloerection, cutaneous vasomotor changes and changes in vascular distribution and vegetative ganglia tonus (see reviews by Thauer, 1970[200] and Klussman and Pierau, 1972[201]). Information on the influence of spinal cord temperature sensitivity on behaviour is limited to unpublished observations. Dogs chronically implanted with spinal thermodes decreased their heat seeking behaviour in warm as well as cold environments when their spinal cords were heated. They behaved as if a spinal signal was simply added during the stimulation to the other signals controlling the bar press behaviour. The response to spinal cord heating was not time dependent. Cooling the spinal cord did not modify the behaviour although the cold stimulus did induce shivering[202]. Opposite results were obtained on the pig. Warming the spinal cord had practically no behavioural effect; on the other hand, cooling the spinal cord was followed by a corrective behavioural response and furthermore this response was highly time-dependent. The most obvious response of these pigs to the cold stimulus was a change in posture followed by increased bar pressing for heat[203]. Finally, frogs placed in a thermal gradient left their 25 °C thermopreferendum to swim toward cooler waters when their spinal cord was locally heated. The temperature of the new thermopreferendum was inversely proportional to the amount of heat produced in the spinal canal by the electric heater[204].

Observation of autonomic responses after warm stimulation in the abdominal cavity has led to the conclusion that there exists in this area thermal detectors at least capable of arousing heat defence mechanisms in sheep[205,206]. General abdominal thermal stimulation produced corrective behaviour in dogs[51,52], and in frogs[40], but this kind of stimulus, although abdominal in origin, could have influenced other internal detectors not specifically located in the viscera. For this reason, the use of a rectal probe limiting the stimulus to the viscera was a better approach[142]. The results permit the conclusion that there exists a signal of abdominal origin which influences behaviour. The signal had the same behavioural effects as other internal signals, i.e. cooling triggers a heating behaviour and warming a cooling behaviour, but its influence was only 1/3rd the influence of a hypothalamic stimulus.

In sum, a multiplicity of thermal detectors influence behaviour, and although some differences exist here and there between the capacity for a given detector to arouse both autonomic and behavioural reactions, in viewing the evidence as a whole, it is tempting to think that autonomic and behavioural reactions have common sources of information, and that no detector has only behavioural or only autonomic influences.

7.5 INTEGRATION OF THE INFORMATION

In the previous sections it has been seen that homeothermic organisms use This behaviour is quantitatively adapted to the thermal needs of the organsm. their behavioural patterns in order to correct or prevent thermal aggressions. To reach this goal, the organism receives information about his environment from his peripheral detectors and about his *milieu interieur* from his internal detectors. All the known temperature detectors are capable of triggering or influencing thermal behaviour one way or another. Is it possible to know how this information is used by the central nervous system and combined to produce the behavioural response? This is a very difficult question to answer due to the multiplicity of the inputs and outputs, and the complexity of specifying, measuring and controlling them. For example the information from the skin has at least three relevant dimensions: surface, time and temperature. There are two possible experimental ways to measure the output: by observing the behaviour in animals or humans, and by obtaining subjective ratings in humans. Regarding the inputs, the general experimental method consists in holding constant the thermal state of the animal or human subject and displacing only one variable, here a detector's temperature, over the whole range of possible values. Then another variable is selected for study until all the possible combinations are explored.

At present very little is known about interaction of thermal stimuli in the control of thermal behaviour. In the first place not many studies have systematically explored several inputs at once and measured the behavioural response. Furthermore, the proximal stimulus is in many cases not known, therefore disallowing precise experimentation. Finally, it is sometimes difficult to compare results that have been obtained in different experiments, since the observed behavioural responses and the species are different, and often the results do not superimpose. General trends, though, can be recognised.

7.5.1 Skin and hypothalamus

As already mentioned the behavioural response for environmental temperature changes is proportional to hypothalamic temperature[124,130,141]. When the skin temperature is modified and the hypothalamic temperature clamped, the behavioural response is affected by this input as well. Skin and hypothalamic temperatures have influences of the same magnitude and sign, e.g. increasing either one or the other will increase the behavioural warm defence response.

The way these inputs combine is not certain, however. There may be a simple addition of signals in which the response is the sum of the two independent responses determined by the temperatures of the skin and of the hypothalamus individually[125,141]. Or the combination may be multiplicative rather than additive; this possibility is characterised by an absence of any response when one signal is zero, for example in a neutral environment when the skin is neither warm nor cold[130,133]. From these experiments it is also possible to deduce the relative influence of hypothalamic and peripheral signals on thermal behaviour. In the rat there is some evidence that skin temperature is weighed over hypothalamic temperature by a ratio of 3:1[125]. In the squirrel monkey, skin temperature is also favoured over hypothalamic temperature by a ratio of 1.5:1[144].

7.5.2 Skin and spinal cord

In dogs, the behavioural response for environmental heating and cooling was modified by spinal heating as if a new input was added at all environmental temperatures, and presumably for a range of skin temperatures[202].

In frogs placed in an aquatic temperature gradient, spinal heating was followed by a new behavioural choice of environmental water. The choice of water temperature was the behavioural response and this behaviour in turn produced a new skin signal[204]. An inverse relationship was found between skin temperature and the amount of heat produced near the spinal cord. This result has the same significance as the above: skin and spinal cord temperatures have the same sign for the nervous system, and both signals are added.

7.5.3 Skin and core

In several studies the temperature of the internal compartment was considered to be uniform, which is a good approximation to natural conditions. It was this simplified variable which was combined with skin temperature changes. In lizards, the behavioural choice between two environments depended on both the internal temperature and the temperature gradient between the core and surface. As the skin was warmed, cooler internal temperatures were tolerated; the reverse was true in cold environments[46,47]. In man, preferred hand temperature was affected both by the average skin temperature and by the internal temperature. Mean skin and internal temperatures had the same influence on preferred temperature, with internal temperature predominating over skin temperature by a factor of at least 4. This information seemed to combine according to a multiplicative model[146].

7.5.4 Hypothalamus and viscera

Comparison of the relative effectiveness of these two temperatures in the behavioural choice for ambient temperature in monkeys showed a preponderance of hypothalamic over visceral. Hypothalamic displacements were three times more efficient than rectal displacements. The combination of these two inputs seems to be multiplicative, since the influence of rectal temperature shifts was a change in the gain of the combined T_s, T_{hy} thermostat[142].

7.5.5 Internal set temperature

Internal temperature is quite constant during usual life circumstances. This temperature is so constant that it may be regarded as regulated. Classically, this control was considered to rely on an internal set point[207], which implies that there exists an analogous temperature reference in the central nervous system. Recently, another model was proposed where the control could be accomplished by multiple negative feed-back loops[208]. The controlled temperature level, whether it is achieved by a dynamic equilibrium or a regulation, can be shifted in fever from 37 °C in the human species toward higher values. Fever is defined as control of internal body temperature at a value greater by two standard deviations than the mean specific temperature in resting conditions[1]. In man, the lower value for fever is about 37.5 rectal, although 38 °C is a surer sign of fever. What happens to behaviour during fever?

When dogs were given the behavioural ability to bar press in order to correct a large range of ambient temperatures, their response was proportional to ambient temperature, as reported above. Their behaviour was minimum for an ambient temperature about 30 °C. When rendered feverish by administration of a pyrogenic substance, their demand for heat was increased and their demand for cold decreased at all ambient temperatures. The minimum behaviour now occurred at a much higher ambient temperature, about 40 °C, showing an increase in the value of thermal neutrality by about 10 °C[136]. This result shows that core temperature was controlled at a higher level, and demonstrates that behaviour was at the service of the regulated set temperature. Comparable results have been obtained in feverish cats placed in cold environments[138], and in baboons[140]. Men displayed a preference for higher hand temperatures when feverish than when non-feverish, all other things being equal. Pleasure given by thermal sensations was therefore directly dependent on the level of regulation of the inner temperature. Thus pleasure is a motivation for behaviour adapted to defence of the set temperature[209]. This point will be discussed later.

7.5.6 Conclusions

There exist multiple temperature detectors near the surface of the body, or placed deep within the body. All the identified detectors capable of triggering behaviour had influences of the same sign, and their individual influences are additive. The results reported above give some information on the way the total thermal inputs combine. So far, the models produced fail to integrate all the information available to the central nervous system. This is not only because not all the inputs have been considered, but also because the actual inputs are undoubtedly more complex than the physical variables recorded to date. For example, skin temperature is taken as a single variable, although rare are the cases where the total surface of the skin is at the same temperature. The practice of weighting inputs according to the area of the surface where temperature is measured depends for its validity on the unproven assumption that thermal detectors have the same density on the skin surface. The phasic aspect of the response is most often ignored, so that the actual signal is only approximated. As long as these approximations are obligatory, one does not lose much precision in lumping all the internal detectors into one. The models built on these approximations have already shown a certain amount of predictive value. At present there seems to be a great analogy between the two systems responsible for autonomic and behavioural responses, with respect to their inputs, integration rules, and the notion of controlled temperature. From the still limited evidence available, they may be considered to be identical.

Little is known about the organisation of the nervous network responsible for temperature regulation, but there does exist already some evidence for a distinction between behavioural and autonomic brain 'centres'.

7.6 CENTRES

Temperature regulation is not possible after a brain transection lower than the hypothalamus[210], and obviously behaviour will not appear in an 'unconscious' animal. It is possible, however, to place in the anterior part of the lower brain stem limited lesions which do not affect behaviour but do impair temperature regulation. Although the deficit observed after a lesion is difficult to localise in the chain between stimulus and response, these results deserve attention, even if they do not lead to a general theory of thermoregulatory 'centres', precisely because they show that the system is not as simple as might be thought. A good example of puzzling results is seen in rats with combined hypothalamic lesions and decortication. In the same animal a hypothalamic lesion is produced on one side and spreading depression on the other side of the brain; these rats display opposite responses according to the behavioural opportunity offered to them. If they are placed in a thermal gradient, thermoregulatory behaviour is suppressed[49], while with a bar pressing response this behaviour is increased[115].

After the discovery of temperature sensitivity in the hypothalamus, most of the lesions experimentally produced were localised in this area. Unfortunately the results are not coherent. Almost all the experiments reported below have been carried out on rats. This is a special animal, since its main defence against heat is behavioural.

7.6.1 Anterior hypothalamic lesions

In dogs, anterior hypothalamic lesions left animals with an intact perception of skin temperature, but with a deficit in sensitivity to internal temperature. These animals were able to defend themselves against hypothermia by shivering only in a cold environment[211]. Similarly in rats, these lesions usually led to a loss of the ability to keep a constant internal temperature in a mild cold environment[105], in severe cold stress[112], or in warm stress[118,68]. This impairment of temperature regulation was accompanied by a compensatory behaviour, i.e. the behaviour was increased compared to the control level. For example, compared to controls, lesioned rats in a cold environment sought more heat[112,105,131 (septal lesions)], and in a warm environment, avoided heat more often[118]. These results seem very simple and they are logical from a teleological point of view. In this situation, rats have a deficit in their autonomic thermoregulatory responses and compensate for this deficit by relying more on behaviour. This result does not agree with the notion that the neural structures responsible for all aspects of temperature regulation—behavioural and autonomic responses—are restricted to the hypothalamus. Suppression of the autonomic response by hypothalamic lesions fits with the accepted scheme, but the persistence of an adaptive behavioural response implies that

   (a) there are thermoregulatory 'centres' situated outside the lesion, presumably caudaly to it,

   (b) behavioural responses can use internal inputs from elsewhere than the anterior hypothalamus to ensure homeothermy,

(c) the nervous networks responsible for autonomic and behavioural reactions can be separated.

Other experimental data different from the above results, are simpler to interpret. Removal of the whole rostral brain was followed by an increased rectal temperature in warm and cold environmental temperatures, and by increased bar pressing for heat, decreased saliva spreading, and bar pressing for cool showers at all environmental temperatures[129]. The logical interpretation of this thorough experiment is that temperature regulation *per se* is not impaired by such lesions. The complete rostral lesion appears to elevate the level of the set temperature, and behaviour simply defends this new level. The parallel observation that rats with anterior hypothalamic lesions became hyperthermic and lost their thermoregulatory behaviour in a warm environment[68] is consistent with the above interpretation.

7.6.2 Lateral hypothalamic lesions

Damage to the lateral hypothalamus led to conflicting results. In a warm environment, the rat's main response is salivary secretion and spreading of saliva on its fur. Lateral hypothalamic lesions were followed in one study by a suppression of the saliva secretion, but the grooming behaviour, i.e. the behavioural response itself, was left intact[212]. In another study, the grooming behaviour and voluntary bath immersion were suppressed or considerably reduced, resulting in a lower tolerance to heat stress[68]. In a cold environment another situation was found: cold avoidance was suppressed[49], and nest building and bar pressing for heat decreased at least temporarily[106], while rectal temperature was maintained at normal. These results seem to show that lateral hypothalamic lesions and anterior hypothalamic lesions have opposite effects. The former suppress motivation for behaviour leaving autonomic reactions unaffected, while the effects of the latter are just the reverse. However, these results were not entirely clear cut and perhaps need further confirmation.

7.7 MOTIVATION AND COMFORT

The correlation between thermoregulatory behaviour and the motivation for this behaviour is good if the subject has no other priorities. While it is unlikely that behaviour occurs without motivation, motivation can occur in the absence of behaviour; this divorce of behaviour from motivation may happen even in well planned experiments. Such dissociation between motivation and its behavioural expression has been emphasised with other types of behaviour, such as food intake[213]. It is therefore of interest to explore motivation as such. It is difficult to speak of the mental state or of the perception of an animal, particularly when the animal is low on the phylogenetic scale. But man can communicate and thus, by using human subjects, the experimenter can explore this new field. In the above sections, it has been assumed that thermoregulatory behaviour is motivated by what man describes as thermal comfort or discomfort. In the present section this motivation will be studied, not in terms of behaviour, but in terms of subjective reports. It is assumed that the effective part of conscious perception of thermal states is the motivation for thermoregulatory behaviour.

7.7.1 Role of internal temperature

The strong influence of internal temperature on the perception of thermal comfort is shown by responses and ratings given by subjects immersed in a water bath. In a well-stirred bath skin temperature is clamped. If comfort changes in such a bath, the origin of the change cannot be attributed to signals from the skin. In a bath, thermal discomfort appeared to depend on internal temperature. Subjects felt uncomfortably warm when hyperthermic[183,184], and uncomfortably cold when hypothermic[184]. In an air environment, where mean skin temperature cannot be clamped but can still be monitored, this temperature 'was not a dependable criterion of thermal comfort'[78,214,215]. These observations are strictly parallel with the observations in animals that thermoregulatory behaviour depends on internal temperature. But it is possible to go further in the analysis of the conscious phenomenon. Internal temperature may have its influence in a variety of ways:

(a) the direct perception of internal temperature is a possibility, i.e. there may be a sensation initiated in the hypothalamus or in other internal detectors;

(b) thermoregulatory reactions, such as sweating and shivering, are perceived by consciousness and are elicited by internal temperature displacements, and this perception may be the origin of thermal discomfort;

(c) alliesthesia.

7.7.2 Alliesthesia

One of the primary components of thermal comfort is the pleasure aroused by a peripheral stimulus; this in turn depends on internal temperature. To a hypothermic subject, a cool 20 °C stimulus will feel unpleasant, but to a hyperthermic subject the same stimulus will feel very pleasant. Therefore the pleasure or displeasure given by the stimulus will depend on the subject's internal state. This phenomenon is called alliesthesia[1]. The internal signal responsible which gives rise to an alliesthesic change is the difference between the set temperature (or level of regulation) and the actual internal temperature[209].

7.7.2.1 Quantification of alliesthesic changes

The most-preferred skin temperature selected by human subjects was a function of their internal temperature and of their mean skin temperature[146]. For each given mean skin temperature, the preferred hand temperature was inversely proportional to internal temperature. Mean skin temperature did not modify this proportional relationship but simply changed the gain of the system. A warm hand temperature was chosen by hypothermic subjects, and a cold hand temperature by hyperthermic subjects. Thus, those skin stimuli which are pleasurable will have the effect of correcting internal temperature in proportion to the magnitude of its deviation from the set point.

7.7.2.2 *Spatial summation*

Although alliesthesic changes in themselves seem capable of motivating adapted thermoregulatory behaviour, there is only indirect evidence for their participation in the global perception of thermal comfort. It is probable that thermal comfort is made up of a sum of elementary effects identical to hand alliesthesia described above. As a matter of fact, when one looks only at the discriminative part of sensation, warm sensation shows spatial summation[162]. It is reasonable to suppose that alliesthesia affects this global peripheral sensory input. If this is true, thermal comfort is the sum of all peripheral sensations, plus an affective factor determined by internal temperature. This way of looking at comfort is tempting, since, for example, comfort persists when only one side of the body is cooled and the other side warmed[216,218], or when the body receives asymmetric thermal radiations producing up to a 10 or 13 °C difference between front and back temperatures[217].

7.7.3 Thermoregulatory autonomic responses

Any displacement of internal temperature in man is followed by the corrective autonomic reactions of shivering or sweating. The onset of sweating is contemporaneous with the onset of discomfort[219,220]. Interruption of shivering is contemporaneous with an improvement in comfort[221]. The question arises whether these reactions, which are conscious but not voluntary, are at the origin of the perception of thermal discomfort. As a matter of fact, in some languages, to shiver is to feel cold, and to sweat is to feel warm.

However, there is so far no experimental evidence on the degree of participation of autonomic reactions in thermal discomfort. It may be noted in this context that temperature conformers have no autonomic defence, but still display a behaviour very well adapted to their temperature regulation. Conversely, shivering elicited by cooling the spinal cord is not accompanied by a thermoregulatory operant behaviour. From these dissociations between autonomic and behavioural responses, it may be suspected that autonomic reactions are not the major component of thermal discomfort.

7.7.4 Perception of hypothalamic temperature

There is a possibility that internal temperature is perceived consciously as a sensation. Since manipulations of internal temperature have many effects which can be perceived consciously, it is difficult to confirm or to rule out this possibility. Although the only way to solve this problem would be to thermally stimulate the hypothalamus in man, preferably on the experimenter himself, animal experimentation has yielded valuable information on this question. Corbit[123] has given rats the opportunity to thermally stimulate their own brain. When heat stressed, these animals cool their hypothalami by pressing a lever. The rate of bar pressing for brain cooling is quite similar to the rate measured when rats bar press to cool their skin by the same amount, and the same model describes both types of behaviour. Nevertheless, this experiment does not answer the question of whether hypothalamic temperature is directly perceived, since there is a possibility that this intracranial self-stimulation is perceived via alliesthesic changes of peripheral sensations, or via autonomic reactions. But in a second experiment[125], the rats had the choice between two possible types of behaviour, pulling a chain to cool their skin or pressing a bar to cool their hypothalamus. To an increase in hypothalamic temperature alone, they responded by pressing the lever. To an increase in ambient temperature alone, they responded by pulling the chain. To increases in both hypothalamic and ambient temperature, they responded with both types of behaviour. This result does not say whether there is an hypothalamic 'sensation', but it shows that signals coming from the skin or from the hypothalamus produce different conscious states, since the rats were able to discriminate between them and to make appropriate responses. It is quite remarkable that these successful experiments consisted in self-cooling of the brain; in the opposite situation, rats[222] or pigs[133] given the opportunity to *warm* their brain did not use the operant behaviour to do so.

7.7.5 Conclusion

Thermal comfort is the absence of unpleasant feeling regarding temperature. Affective perception of thermal stimuli exists already at birth and in premature infants[223,224]; it is therefore certainly innate and not acquired. Thermal comfort and its opposite, discomfort, rely heavily upon internal temperature sensitivity. If this is true, how is it that mean skin temperature is kept so constant by behavioural means in man and rat and has been considered as the basis for comfort? The answer is probably that, for a given thermal environment and a subject at rest, constant skin temperature is the result of a thermal equilibrium. Skin is not only a source of information, but also an interface between environment and thermal core. As a matter of fact, when men switched from rest to activity, comfort was maintained by a lowering of mean skin temperature by more than 2 °C[148], or the lowering of a limited skin area (the hand) by more than 20 °C[145]. It is highly likely that comfort in man reflects not only the hypothalamic temperature but rather all detected temperatures, and thus indirectly reflects the general heat balance. It is possible that internal temperature is perceived as such, but in natural conditions alliesthesia applied to peripheral sensation alone seems sufficient to account for thermal comfort. Finally, it is possible that autonomic reactions play a role in the perception of discomfort. A model proposed by Hardy (1970)[225] includes all these inputs.

7.8 PATHOLOGY AND PHARMACOLOGY

The following section will describe thermoregulatory behaviour and the experience of thermal comfort in various circumstances.

7.8.1 Forced vasodilation

An increased heat loss due to an exaggerated peripheral vasodilation is usually correlated with a feeling of cold and search for heat. Such a situation was observed in men[226,227], in dogs[51] and in the baboon[139], after treatment with Tolazoline, a strong peripheral vasodilator. A comparable situation exists in patients suffering from erythrodermia[228], and, to a lesser extent, in normal subjects with a chronic vasodilation[229]. In all these situations, skin temperature was raised by the acute or chronic vasodilation, but the subjects or animals compensated the resulting forced heat-loss with their behaviour. All these results emphasise the primary role of internal temperature detectors in controlling thermoregulatory behaviour and comfort since the result of behaviour was to defend internal temperature while aggravating skin temperature.

7.8.2 Ethyl alcohol

In a cold environment, the main result of ethyl alcohol intake was a loss or decrease in cold discomfort and a facilitation of sleep[230,231]. At the same time, the intoxication was deleterious to the subjects' thermal balance since rectal temperature tended to drop compared to that of the control subjects.

7.8.3 Catecholamines

In rats, intrahypothalamic acetylcholine was followed by a dose-dependent decrease of warming behaviour and a drop in hypothalamic temperature[126]. Conversely, intrahypothalamic noradrenaline in rats was followed by increased bar pressing for heat and elevated hypothalamic temperature[127]. Whenever an internal temperature shift followed intracisternal noradrenaline in dogs, the operant behaviour for heat or for cold always facilitated the internal shift[137]. Therefore, after catecholamine administration, the behaviour was adapted to the new temperature level (see Chapter 2).

7.8.4 Hypnosis

In a cold environment, hypnosis was correlated with decreased shivering, a drop in rectal temperature, and an improvement of thermal comfort[232]. A comparable situation was observed in subjects who submitted to simulated warm stimulation; they presented a localised vasodilation in the pseudo-stimulated skin and reported a warm sensation[233].

7.8.5 Indifference to pain

Two patients suffering from indifference to pain showed no alliesthesia toward thermal sensation. In fact, these patients were completely ignorant of thermal comfort or discomfort[234]. Shivering and sweating were not affected in these subjects. Thus autonomic responses were not sufficient to create thermal discomfort. Regarding temperature regulation, this syndrome suppresses completely the motivation for behaviour, but leaves intact autonomic reactions.

7.9 CONCLUSIONS

Behaviour appears as an extremely efficient way to gain or lose heat, and must be viewed as a physiological means of achieving the goal of temperature regulation. It is the only possible response in temperature conformers who must depend solely on behaviour to thermoregulate. For example lizards by their behaviour achieve an optimal body temperature which oscillates between a voluntary hypothermia at night[44] and the highest body temperature compatible with health[235]. In species where the newborn are dependent, such as in human species, temperature regulation is also accomplished by behaviour, but the negative feed-back loop is longer than in the adult since it is the parent's behaviour which is regulatory. In species where the newborn is independent, the behaviour is as well adapted to temperature regulation as in the adult. The only difference may be that preferred ambient temperature is higher during the first days of life[48,236].

A closer examination of the above results emphasises the duality of thermal information, internal core and periphery. Which of them is the most important? The smaller variations in internal temperature and its constancy as compared to the wide range of peripheral variations, confirms the privileged position of internal temperature in man. It is possible, in the light of this review, that this is not so with other species, and that the relative influence of peripheral and internal sensitivities could be a function of the mass of the subject. In man and other big species, the main factor would be internal; in small species such as the rat, the main factor would be superficial sensitivity. In smaller species, such as arthropods, it is sufficient that the organism have a peripheral sensitivity in order to permit thermotropism toward a favourable ambient temperature, since the mass is small and equilibration time is also small. In the *milieu interieur*, there is no doubt that the hypothalamus is the keystone of the system. Within the hypothalamus, the functional organisation is still unclear.

Unlike other functions, where behaviour is the only way to satisfy the physiological goal (e.g. food intake), temperature regulation is accomplished by two means: behavioural and autonomic. In the intact animal, behaviour obeys the same laws which describe autonomic regulatory responses. How does the homeothermic organism choose between one or the other of these possibilities? The various circumstances reviewed above do not allow a firm conclusion, but it is remarkable that any time a given response is imposed— forced vasodilation in the dog or desalivation in the rat—the homeotherm reacts with the response available—increased behaviour in the first case, increased autonomic response in the second. Therefore, in critical situations, behavioural or autonomic responses seem completely interchangeable. Thus, they are complementary rather than competitive. It is more difficult to sort out the extent to which behavioural and autonomic responses are used in daily life. Observation of human life does show a progressive decrease of autonomic reactions with the evolution of technology. Man finds and uses more and more sophisticated thermoregulatory behaviour, which is non-competitive with other behaviour. However, in animals the use of behaviour to reach a thermoregulatory goal may compete with other behaviour aiming at other physiological or non-physiological goals.

Thus, observations under natural or near-natural conditions are necessary complements of laboratory work[237]. These observations permit the exploration of several forms of behaviour at the same time. For example, piglets 'will tolerate a certain amount of thermal discomfort before modifying their specific behaviour pattern, especially when the discomfort is endured for the sake of obtaining food'[238]. The presence of a dark shelter modified the thermoregulatory behaviour of a lizard; with such a shelter the animal eventually went into a state of cold lethargy[47]. A hot environment reduced hypothalamic electrical self-stimulation in rats, while a cold environment increased this behaviour[239]. In turn, the onset of self-stimulation was contemporaneous with an increased body temperature[240]. These examples illustrate that during its life, the living organism chooses among various needs the one it will satisfy at each instant. The resulting observable behaviour is the outcome of many conflicting motivations. It is the beauty of living beings that they are able to integrate simultaneously all this information and decide at a given instant the best possible behaviour.

Acknowledgement

The author is deeply indebted to Dr. E. F. Rabe for critically reading the manuscript and for the long hours he spent improving the English version.

References

1. Bligh, J. and Johnson, K. G. (1972). Glossary on thermal physiology and temperature regulation. *Internat. Union Physiol. Sci.* (IUPS) (In press)
2. Chatonnet, J. and Minaire, Y. (1966). Comparison of energy expenditure during exercise and cold exposure in the dog. *Fed. Proc.*, **25**, 1348
3. Fraenkel, G. (1929). Untersuchungen über Lebensgewohnheiten, Sinnesphysiologie und Sozialpsychologie der wandernden Larven der afrikanischen. Wanderheuschrecke *Schistocerca gregaria F. Biol. Zentralblatt.*, **49**, 657
4. Clench, H. K. (1966). Behavioral thermoregulation in butterflies. *Ecology*, **47**, 1021
5. Brattstrom, B. H. (1963). A preliminary review of the thermal requirements of amphibians. *Ecology*, **44**, 238
6. Saint-Girons, H. and Saint-Girons, M. C. (1956). Cycle d'activité et thermorégulation chez les reptiles (lézards et serpents). *Vie et milieu*, **7**, 133
7. Bartholomew, G. A. (1966). A field study of temperature relations in the Galapagos marine iguana. *Copeia*, **2**, 241
8. De Witt, C. B. (1971). Postural mechanisms in the behavioral thermoregulation of a desert lizard, *Dipsausaurus dorsalis*. *J. Physiol.* (*Paris*), **63**, 242
9. Fay, F. H. and Ray, C. (1968). Influence of climate on the distribution of Walruses, *Odobenus rosmarus L.* I evidence for thermoregulatory behavior. *Zoologica*, **53**, 1
10. Ray, C. and Smith, M. S. R. (1968). Thermoregulation of the pup and adult Weddell Seal, *Leptomychotes wedelli* (*Lesson*), in antarctica. *Zoologica*, **53**, 33

11. Pilters-Gauthier, H. (1961). Observations sur l'écologie du dromadaire dans le sahara nord occidental. *Mammalia*, **25**, 195
12. Bartholomew, G. A. (1964). The roles of physiology and behaviour in the maintenance of homeostasis in the desert environment. *Soc. Exp. Biol.* (*Cambridge Univ. Press*), **18**, 7
13. Schmidt-Nielsen, K., Dawson, T. J., Hammel, H. T., Hinds, D. and Jackson, D. C. (1965). The Jack Rabbit—a study in its desert survival. *Hvalraadets Skrift*, **48**, 125
14. Breckenridge, J. R. and Goldman, R. F. (1971). Solar heat load in man, *J. Appl. Physiol.*, **31**, 659
15. Heath, J. E., Hanegan, J. L., Wilkin, P. J. and Heath, M. S. (1971). Thermoregulation by heat production and behavior in insects. *J. Physiol.* (*Paris*), **63**, 267
16. Miller, D. C. and Verberg, F. J. (1968). Some thermal requirements of Fiddler Crabs of temperate and tropical zones and their influence on geographic distribution. *Amer. Zoologist*, **8**, 459
17. Licht, P. and Brown, A. G. (1967). Behavioral thermoregulation and its role in the ecology of the red-bellied newt, *Taricha rivularis. Ecology*, **48**, 598
18. Cunningham, J. D. (1963). Additional observations on the ecology of the Yosemite Toad, *Bufo canorus. Herpetologica*, **19**, 56
19. Tester, J. R. and Breckenridge, W. J. (1964). Winter behaviour patterns of the Manitoba toad *Bufo hemiophrys*, in northwestern Minnesota. *Ann. Acad. Sci. Fennicae*, **71**, 423
20. Boyer, D. R. (1965). Ecology of the basking habit in turtles. *Ecology*, **46**, 99
21. Mayew, W. W. (1963). Temperature preferences of *Sceloporus orcutti. Herpetologica*, **18**, 217
22. Heath, J. E. (1964). Head body temperature differences in horned lizards. *Physiol. Zool.*, **37**, 273
23. Stewart, G. R. (1964). Thermal ecology of the garter snakes *Thamnophis sirtalis concinnus* (Hallowell) and *Thamnophis ordinoîdes* (Baird and Girard). *Dissert. Abstr.*, **25**, 2116
24. McGinnis, S. M. and Dickson, L. L. (1967). Thermoregulation in the desert iguana *Dipsausaurus dorsalis. Science*, **156**, 1757
25. Colin, J. M., Timbal, J., Guieu, J. D., Boutelier, Ch. and Houdas, Y. (1970). Combined effect of radiation and convection. *Physiological and behavioral temperature regulation*, 81 (J. D. Hardy, A. P. Gagge and J. A. J. Stolwijk, editors) (Springfield: Charles C. Thomas Publishers)
26. Cena, K. (1964). Thermoregulation in the hippopotamus. *Internat. J. Biometeorol.*, **8**, 57
27. Stricker, E. M., Everett, J. C. and Porter, R. E. A. (1968). The regulation of body temperature by rats and mice in the heat: Effects of desalivation and the presence of a water bath. *Communic. Behavioral Biology*, **2**, 113
28. Licht, P. and Leitner, P. (1967). Behavioral responses to high temperatures in three species of california bats. *J. Mammology*, **48**, 52
29. Cosnier, J., Duveau, A. and Chanel, J. (1965). Consommation d'oxygène et Grégarisme chez le rat nouveau-né. *C. R. Soc. Biol.*, **159**, 1579
30. Viaud, G. (1955). Le thermopréférendum et les thermotropismes. *Le comportement des homéothermes vis à vis du stimulus froid*, C35 (Paris, C.N.R.S., editor)
31. Mendelssohn, M. (1895). Ueber den Thermotropismus einzelliger Organismen *Arch. Ges. Physiol.*, **60**, 1
32. Herter, K. (1923). Untersuchungen über den Temperatursinn der Hausgrille (*Acheta domestica L*) und der roten Waldameise (*Formica rufa L*) *Biol. Zentbl.*, **43**, 282
33. Chauvin, R. (1948). Sur le preferendum thermique des insectes. *Physiologica Comparata et Oecologica*, **1**, 76
34. Amos, T. G., Waterhouse, F. L. and Chetham, N. A. (1968). Temporal distribution of *Tribolium castaneum* (Herbst) and *Cadra cautella* (Walker) on temperature gradients. *Experientia*, **24**, 86
35. Kraft, B. (1967). Thermopreferendum de l'araignée sociale, *Agelena consociata Denis. Insectes sociaux.*, **14**, 161.
36. Shelford, V. E. and Powers, E. B. (1915). An experimental study of the movements of herring and other marine fishes. *Biol. Bull.*, **28**, 315

37. Fry, F. E. J. (1964). Animals in aquatic environments: fishes. *Handbook of Physiology*, Sect. IV, 715 (Washington: *American Physiological Society*)
38. Hammel, H. T., Strømme, S. B. and Myhre, K. (1969). Forebrain temperature activates behavioral thermoregulatory response in arctic Sculpins. *Science*, **165**, 83
39. Crawshaw, L. I. and Hammel, H. T. (1971). Behavioral thermoregulation in two species of antarctic fish. *Life Science*, **10**, 1009
40. Cabanac, M. and Jeddi, E. (1971). Thermopréférendum et thermorégulation comportementale chez trois poïkilothermes. *Physiol. Behav.*, **7**, 375
41. Neill, W. H., Magnuson, J. J. and Chipman, G. G. (1972). Behavioral thermo-regulation by fishes: a new experimental approach. *Science*, **176**, 1443
42. Lillywhite, M. B. (1971). Temperature selection by the bullfrog *Rana catesbeiana*. *Comp. Biochem. Physiol.*, **40**, 213
43. De Witt, C. B. (1967). Precision of thermoregulation and its relation to environ-mental factors in the desert iguana *Dipsausaurus dorsalis*. *Physiol. Zool.*, **40**, 49
44. Regal, P. J. (1967). Voluntary hypothermia in reptiles. *Science*, **155**, 1551
45. Hammel, H. T., Caldwell, F. T. and Abrams, R. M. (1967). Regulation of body temperature in the blue tongued lizard. *Science*, **156**, 1260
46. Myhre, K. and Hammel, H. T. (1969). Behavioral regulation of internal tempera-ture in the lizard *Tiliqua scincoides*. *Amer. J. Physiol.*, **217**, 1490
47. Cabanac, H. P. and Hammel, H. T. (1971). Comportement thermorégulateur du lézard *Tiliqua scincoides*: réponses au froid. *J. Physiol. (Paris)*, **63**, 222
48. Mount, L. E. (1963). Environmental temperature preferred by the young pig. *Nature (London)*, **199**, 1212
49. Rudiger, W. and Seyer, G. (1965). Lateralisation of cortico-hypothalamic relations as revealed by thermosensitive behaviour in the rat. *Physiol. Bohem.*, **14**, 515
50. Ogilvie, D. M. and Stinson, R. H. (1966). Temperature selection in *Peromyscus* and laboratory mice *Mus musculus*. *J. Mammal.*, **47**, 655
51. Cabanac, M., Chatonnet, J. and Duclaux, R. (1965). Influence de la température centrale sur le choix de l'ambiance thermique chez le chien. *J. Physiol. (Paris)*, **57**, 574
52. Cabanac, M., Duclaux, R. and Chatonnet, J. (1966). Influence d'une élévation passive de la température interne sur le comportement thermorégulateur du chien. *J. Physiol. (Paris)*, **58**, 214
53. Gasnier, A. and Mayer, A. R. (1939). Recherches sur la régulation de la nutrition. III mécanismes régulateurs de la nutrition et intensité du métabolisme. *Ann. Physiol.*, **15**, 186
54. Brobeck, J. R. (1948). Food intake as a mechanism of temperature regulation. *Yale J. Biol. Med.*, **20**, 545
55. Adolph, E. F. (1947). *Physiology of man in the desert*. 357 (New York: Interscience ed.)
56. Hammel, H. T. (1971). Regulation of temperature in ectoterms by behavioral responses. *International Congress of the International Union of Physiological Sciences*. (1971: München). Invited lecture
57. Hainsworth, F. R., Stricker, E. M. and Epstein, A. N. (1968). Water metabolism of rats in the heat: dehydration and drinking. *Amer. J. Physiol.*, **214**, 983
58. Carlisle, H. T. (1971). Fixed ratio polydipsia: thermal effects of drinking pausing and responding. *J. Comp. Physiol. Psychol.*, **75**, 10
59. Grace, J. E. and Stevenson, J. A. F. (1971). Thermogenic drinking in the rat. *Amer. J. Physiol.*, **220**, 1009
60. McFarland, D. J. and Budgell, P. W. (1970). Determination of a behavioural transfer function by frequency analysis. *Nature (London)*, **226**, 966
61. Hamilton, C. L. (1971). Food intake and temperature stress in the monkey. *Proc. Soc. Exp. Biol. Med.*, **136**, 207
62. Steen, I. and Steen, J. B. (1965). Thermoregulatory importance of the beaver's tail. *Comp. Biochem. Physiol.*, **15**, 267
63. Bartholomew, G. A. and Wilke, F. (1956). Body temperature of the northern fur seal. *J. Mammal.*, **37**, 327
64. Helmendach, R. H., Dent, H. D. and Brown, E. P. (1965). Observations concerning temperature regulatory mechanisms in the ostrich *Struthio camelus The Physio-logist*, **8**, 190

65. Martin, C. J. (1903). Thermal adjustment and respiratory exchange in monotremes and marsupials. A study in the development of homeothermism. *Phil. Trans. Roy. Soc.*, **195**, 1
66. Bartholomew, G. A. (1956). Temperature regulation in the macropod marsupial. *Setonix brachyrus. Physiol. Zool.*, **29**, 26
67. Hainsworth, F. R. (1967). Saliva spreading, activity and body temperature regulation in the rat. *Amer. J. Physiol.*, **212**, 1288
68. Stricker, E. M. and Hainsworth, F. R. (1970). Evaporative cooling in the rat: effects of hypothalamic lesions and chorda tympani damage. *Can. J. Physiol. Pharmacol.*, **48**, 11
69. Kahl, M. P. (1963). Thermoregulation in the wood stork with special reference to the role of the legs. *Physiol. Zool.*, **36**, 141
70. Blondel, J. and Frochot, B. (1972). Pourquoi les oiseaux migrent. *La Recherche*, **3**, 621
71. Lindauer, M. (1951). Die Temperaturregulierung der Bienen bei Stocküberhitzung. *Naturwissenschaften*, **38**, 308
72. Lindauer, M. (1954). Temperaturregulierung und Wasserhaushalt im Bienenstaat. *Z. Vergleish. Physiol.*, **36**, 391
73. Stussi, T. (1967). Thermogenèse de l'abeille et ses rapports avec le niveau thermique de la ruche. *Thèse Doctorat Etat. Sci.*, Univ. Lyon.
74. Roland, C. (1969). Rôle de l'involucre et du nourrissement au sucre dans la régulation thermique à l'intérieur d'un nid de Vespides. *C.R. Acad. Sc.*, **269**, 914
75. Hazelhoff, E. H. (1954). Ventilation in a bee hive during summer. *Physiol. Comp. Oecol.*, **3**, 343
76. Stolwijk, J. A. J. (1970). Thermal loads in lunar ambulation. *Aerospace Medicine*, **41**, 1266
77. Fanger, P. O. (1970). Thermal comfort, analysis and applications in environmental engineering. *Danish Technical press*. 244 (København)
78. Gagge, A. P., Stolwijk, J. A. J. and Hardy, J. D. (1967). Comfort and thermal sensations and associated physiological responses at various ambient temperatures. *J. Environmental Res.*, **1**, 1
79. Gagge, A. P., Stolwijk, J. A. J. and Nishi, Y. (1971). An effective temperature scale based on a simple model of human physiological regulatory response. *Ashrae Transactions*, **77**, 247
80. Hardy, J. D. (1971). Thermal comfort and health. *Ashrae Journal*, February, 43
81. Scholander, P. F., Andersen, K. L., Krog, J., Lorentzen, F. V. and Steen, J. (1957). Critical temperature in Lapps. *J. Appl. Physiol.*, **10**, 231
82. Goldsmith, R. and Hampton, I. F. G. (1968). Nocturnal microclimate of man. *J. Physiol. (London)*, **194**, 32
83. Scholander, P. F., Hammel, H. T., Hart, J. S., Le Mesurier, D. H. and Steen, J. (1958). Cold adaptation in Australian Aborigines. *J. Appl. Physiol.*, **13**, 211
84. Gelineo, S. and Gelineo, A. (1952). La température du nid du rat et sa signification biologique. *Bull. Acad. Serbe. Sci.*, **2**, 197
85. Horvath, O. (1964). Seasonal differences in rufous hummingbird nest height and their relation to nest climate. *Ecology*, **45**, 235
86. Howell, T. R. and Bartholomew, G. A. (1962). Temperature regulation in the sooty tern, *Sterna fuscata. Ibis. G.B.*, **104**, 98
87. Hamilton, C. L. (1959). Effect of food deprivation on thermal behaviour of the rat. *Proc. Soc. Biol. Med.*, **100**, 354
88. Weiss, B. (1957). Thermal behaviour of the subnourished and pantothenic-acid-deprived rat. *J. Comp. Physiol. Psychol.*, **50**, 481
89. Rozin, P. N. and Mayer, J. (1961). Thermal reinforcement and thermoregulatory behavior in the Gold fish, *Carassius auratus. Science*, **134**, 942
90. Kemp, F. D. (1969). Thermal reinforcement and thermoregulatory behavior in the lizard *Dipsausaurus dorsalis. Anim. Behav.*, **17**, 446
91. Regal, P. J. (1971). Long term studies with operant conditioning techniques of temperature regulation patterns in reptiles. *J. Physiol. (Paris)*, **63**, 403
92. Revusky, S. H. (1966). Cold acclimatization in hairless mice measured by behavioural thermoregulation. *Psychonom. Sci.*, **6**, 209

93. Baldwin, B. A. (1968). Behavioural thermoregulation in mice. *Physiol. Behav.*, **3**, 401

94. Baldwin, B. A. and Ingram, D. L. (1968). The effects of food intake and acclimatization to temperature on behavioural thermoregulation in pigs and mice. *Physiol. Behav.*, **3**, 395

95. Weiss, E. and Laties, V. G. (1960). Magnitude of reinforcement as a variable in thermoregulatory behavior. *J. Comp. Physiol. Psychol.*, **53**, 603

96. Weiss, B. and Laties, V. G. (1961). Behavioral thermoregulation. *Science*, **133**, 1338

97. Laties, V. G. and Weiss, B. (1959). Thyroïd state and working for heat in the cold. *Amer. J. Physiol.*, **197**, 1028

98. Laties, V. G. and Weiss, B. (1960). Behavior in the cold after acclimatization. *Science*, **131**, 1891

99. Yeh, S. D. J. and Weiss, B. (1963). Behavioral thermoregulation during vitamin B_6 deficiency. *Amer. J. Physiol.*, **205**, 857

100. Carlton, P. L. and Marks, R. A. (1958). Cold exposure and heat reinforced operant behavior. *Science*, **128**, 1344

101. Hamilton, C. L. (1963). Interaction of food intake and temperature regulation in the rat. *J. Comp. Physiol. Psychol.*, **56**, 476

102. Hamilton, C. L. and Sheriff, J. R. (1959). Thermal behavior of the rat before and after feeding. *Proc. Soc. Exp. Biol. Med.*, **102**, 746

103. Panuska, J. A. and Popovic, V. (1963). Learning in hypothermic rats. *J. Appl. Physiol.*, **18**, 1016

104. Satinoff, E. (1964). Behavioral thermoregulation in response to local cooling of the rat brain. *Amer. J. Physiol.*, **206**, 1389

105. Satinoff, E. and Rutstein, J. (1970). Behavioral thermoregulation in rats with anterior hypothalamic lesions. *J. Comp. Physiol. Psychol.*, **71**, 77

106. Satinoff, E. and Shan, S. S. Y. (1971). Loss of behavioral thermoregulation after lateral hypothalamic lesions in rats. *J. Comp. Physiol. Psychol.*, **77**, 302

107. Jakubczak, L. F. (1966). Behavioral thermoregulation in young and old rats. *J. Appl. Physiol.*, **21**, 19

108. Carlisle, H. J. (1966). Behavioural significance of hypothalamic temperature sensitive cells. *Nature (London)*, **209**, 1324

109. Carlisle, H. J. (1966). Heat intake and hypothalamic temperature during behavioral temperature regulation. *J. Comp. Physiol. Psychol.*, **61**, 388

110. Carlisle, H. J. (1968). Initiation of behavioral responding for heat in cold environment. *Physiol. Behav.*, **3**, 827

111. Carlisle, H. J. (1968). Peripheral thermal stimulation and thermoregulatory behavior. *J. Comp. Physiol. Psychol.*, **66**, 507

112. Carlisle, H. J. (1969). Effect of preoptic and anterior hypothalamic lesions on behavioral thermoregulation in the cold. *J. Comp. Physiol. Psychol.*, **69**, 391

113. Carlisle, H. J. (1969). Effect of fixed ratio thermal reinforcement on thermoregulatory behavior. *Physiol. Behav.*, **4**, 23

114. Carlisle, H. J. (1970). Intermittent heat as a reinforcer for rats in the cold. *Physiol. Behav.*, **5**, 861

115. Rudiger, W. and Seyer, G. (1968). Thermosensitive bar pressing behavior of the rat with unilateral lesion in the hypothalamus and during cortical spreading depression. *Acta Biol. Exp.*, **28**, 375

116. Epstein, A. N. and Milestone, R. (1968). Showering as a coolant for rats exposed to heat. *Science*, **160**, 895

117. Leemming, F. C. and Crowder, W. F. (1968). Response rate as a function of magnitude and schedule of heat reinforcement. *J. Exp. Psychol.*, **76**, 74

118. Lipton, J. M. (1968). Effect of preoptic lesions on heat escape responding and colonic temperature in the rat. *Physiol. Behav.*, **3**, 165

119. Lipton, J. M. (1969). Effects of high fat diets on caloric intake, body weight, and heat escape responses in normal and hyperphagic rats. *J. Comp. Physiol. Psychol.*, **68**, 507

120. Lipton, J. M. (1971). Behavioral temperature regulation in the rat: effect of thermal stimulation of the medulla. *J. Physiol. (Paris)*, **63**, 325

121. Lipton, J. M. and Marotto, D. R. (1969). Effects of desalivation on behavioral thermoregulation against heat. *Physiol. Behav.*, **4**, 723

122. Lipton, J. M., Avery, D. D. and Marotto, D. R. (1970). Determinants of behavioral thermoregulation against heat: thermal intensity and skin temperature levels. *Physiol. Behav.*, **5,** 1083

123. Corbit, J. D. (1969). Behavioral regulation of hypothalamic temperature. *Science*, **166,** 256

124. Corbit, J. D. (1970). Behavioral regulation of body temperature. *Physiological and Behavioral Temperature Regulation*, chap. 53, 777 (J. D. Hardy, A. P. Gagge and J. A. J. Stolwijk, editors) (Springfield: Charles C. Thomas)

125. Corbit, J. D. Control of thermoregulatory behavior. *Control of Metabolism* (J. D. Sink, editor) (New York: Academic Press). In press

126. Beckman, A. L. and Carlisle, H. J. (1969). Intrahypothalamic infusion of acetylcholine in the rat. *Nature (London)*, **221,** 561

127. Beckman, A. L. (1970). Effect of intrahypothalamic norepinephrine on thermoregulatory responses in the rat. *Amer. J. Physiol.*, **218,** 1596

128. Blass, E. M. (1969). Thermoregulatory adjustments in rats after remove of the frontal poles of the brain. *J. Comp. Physiol. Psychol.*, **69,** 83

129. Blass, E. M. (1971). Effects of frontal pole area ablation on temperature regulation in the rat. *J. Comp. Physiol. Psychol.*, **74,** 233

130. Murgatroyd, D. and Hardy, J. D. (1970). Central and peripheral temperatures in behavioral thermoregulation of the rat. *Physiological and behavioral temperature regulation*, Chap. 58, 874 (J. D. Hardy, A. P. Gagge, J. A. J. Stolwijk, editors) (Springfield: Charles C. Thomas)

131. Wakeman, K. A., Donovick, P. J. and Burright, R. G. (1970). Septal lesions increase bar pressing for heat in animals maintained in the cold. *Physiol. Behav.*, **5,** 1193

132. Baldwin, B. A. and Ingram, D. L. (1967). Behavioural thermoregulation in pigs. *Physiol. Behav.*, **2,** 15

133. Baldwin, B. A. and Ingram, D. L. (1967). The effect of heating and cooling the hypothalamus on behavioural thermoregulation in the pig. *J. Physiol. (London)*, **191,** 375

134. Baldwin, B. A. and Ingram, D. L. (1968). Factors influencing behavioural thermoregulation in the pig. *Physiol. Behav.*, **3,** 409

135. Robinson, J. J. and Hammel, H. T. (1967). Behavioral thermoregulation in response to heating and cooling of the hypothalamic preoptic area of the dog. *Report AMRL-TR-67-144-*, Wright Patterson AFB-Ohio

136. Cabanac, M., Duclaux, R. and Gillet, A. (1970). Thermoregulation comportementale chez le chien. Effet de la fièvre et de la thyroxine. *Physiol. Behav.*, **5,** 697

137. Duclaux, R. and Cabanac, M. (1971). Effets de la noradrénaline intracérébrale sur le comportement thermorégulateur chez le chien. *J. Physiol. (Paris)*, **63,** 246

138. Weiss, B., Laties, V. G. and Weiss, A. B. (1967). Behavioral thermoregulation by cats with pyrogen-induced fever. *Arch. Int. Pharmacodyn.*, **165,** 467

139. Pister, J. D., Jobin, M. and Gale, C. C. (1967). Behavioral responses to anterior hypothalamic cooling in unanesthetized baboon. *Physiologist*, **10,** 279

140. Gale, C. C., Mathews, M. and Young, J. (1970). Behavioral thermoregulatory responses to hypothalamic cooling and warming in baboons. *Physiol. Behav.*, **5,** 1

141. Adair, E. R., Casby, J. U. and Stolwijk, J. A. J. (1970). Behavioral temperature regulation in the squirrel monkey: changes induced by shifts in hypothalamic temperature. *J. Comp. Physiol. Psychol.*, **72,** 17

142. Adair, E. R. (1971). Displacements of rectal temperature modify behavioral thermoregulation. *Physiol. Behav.*, **7,** 21

143. Adair, E. R. and Stitt, J. T. (1971). Behavioral temperature regulation in the squirrel monkey: effects of midbrain temperature displacements. *J. Physiol. (Paris)*, **63,** 191

144. Stitt, J. T., Adair, E. R., Nadel, E. R. and Stolwijk, J. A. J. (1971). The relation between behavior and physiology in the thermoregulatory response of the squirrel monkey. *J. Physiol. (Paris).*, **63,** 424

145. Cabanac, M., Cunningham, D. J. and Stolwijk, J. A. J. (1971). Thermoregulatory set point during exercise: a behavioral approach. *J. Comp. Physiol. Psychol.*, **76,** 94

146. Cabanac, M., Massonnet, B. and Belaiche, R. (1972). Preferred skin temperature as a function of internal and mean skin temperature. *J. Appl. Physiol.* (In press)
147. Olesen, S. and Fanger, P. O. (1971). Can man be adapted to prefer a lower ambient temperature? *Proc. 5th Internat. Congress for Heating, Ventilating & Air Condition.*, **1**, 27 (1971: København)
148. Olesen, S., Bassing, J. J. and Fanger, P. O. (1972). Physiological comfort conditions at sixteen combinations of activity, clothing, air velocity and ambient temperature. *Ashrae Trans.* (In press)
149. Bargeton, D. (1955). L'adaptation au froid: réactions à long terme de la thermo-régulation. *Le confort des homéothermes vis à vis du stimulus froid.* C_{47} (Paris, C.N.R.S. ed)
150. Palmai, G. (1962). Thermal comfort and acclimatization to cold in a sub-antarctic environment. *Med. J. Aust.*, **1**, 9
151. Andersen, K. L. (1963). Comparison of scandinavian Lapps, Arctic fishermen and Canadian Arctic Indians. *Fed. Proc.*, **22**, 834
152. Fanger, P. O. (1972). Conditions for thermal comfort. Opening review paper. *Proc. Sympos. on thermal comfort and moderate heat stress* (CIB Commission W45 London)
153. Ström, G. (1960). Central nervous regulation of body temperature. *Handbook of Physiology*, Section II, 1173
154. Gebbhardt, H. (1951). Lokalisatorischer Nachweis von Thermoreceptoren bei *Dorcus parallelepipedus L.* und *Pyrrhocoris apterus L. Experientia*, **7**, 302
155. Loftus, R. (1966). Cold receptor on the antenna of *Periplaneta americana. Z. vergl. Physiol.*, **52**, 380
156. Alexander, A. J. and Ewer, D. W. (1958). Temperature adaptative behaviour in the Scorpion *Opisthophthalmus latimanus Koch. J. Exp. Biol.*, **35**, 349
157. Blix, M. (1882–1883). Experimentela bidrag till lösning of frägan om hudnervernas specifika energi. *Upsala Läkaref. Förh.*, **18**, 87 and 427
158. Bazett, H. C., McGlone, B. and Brocklehurst, R. J. (1930). The temperatures in tissues which acompany temperature sensations. *J. Physiol. (London)*, **69**, 88
159. Oppel, T. W. and Hardy, J. D. (1937). Studies in temperature sensation. II. The temperature change responsible for the stimulation of the heat end organs. *J. Clin. Invest.*, **16**, 525
160. Ebaugh, F. G. and Thauer, R. (1950). Influence of various environmental tempera-tures on cold and warmth thresholds. *J. Appl. Physiol.*, **3**, 173
161. Hardy, J. D. and Oppel, T. W. (1937). Studies in temperature sensation. III. The sensitivity of the body to heat and spatial summation of the end organ responses. *J. Clin. Invest.*, **16**, 533
162. Stevens, J. C. and Marks, L. E. (1971). Spatial summation and the dynamics of warmth sensation. *Perception Psychophysics*, **9**, 391
163. Stevens, J. C. and Banks, W. P. (1971). Spatial summation in relation to speed of reaction to radiant stimulation. *Abstracts. Internat. Symposium on Environ-mental Physiology* (1971: Dublin)
164. Hardy, J. D. (1953). Thresholds of pain and reflex contraction as related to noxious stimulation. *J. Appl. Physiol.*, **5**, 725
165. Stevens, J. C. and Stevens, S. S. (1960). Warmth and cold: dynamics of sensory intensity. *J. Exper. Psychol.*, **60**, 183
166. Kenshalo, D. R. (1969). Psychophysical studies of temperature sensitivity. *Contributions to Sensory Physiology*, **4** (W. D. Neff, editor) (New York: Academic Press)
167. Vendrik, J. H. (1970). Psychophysics of the thermal sensory system and statistical detection theory. *Physiological and Behavioral Temperature Regulation.* Chap 55, 819 (J. D. Hardy, A. P. Gagge, J. A. J. Stolwijk, editors) (Springfield: Charles C. Thomas)
168. Brearley, E. A. and Kenshalo, D. R. (1970). Behavioral measurements of the sensitivity of cat's upper lip to warm and cool stimuli. *J. Comp. Physiol. Psychol.*, **70**, 1
169. Hensel, H. (1970). Temperature receptors in the skin. *Physiological and behavioral temperature regulation*, Chap. 30, 442 (J. D. Hardy, A. P. Gagge, J. A. J. Stolwijk, editors) (Springfield: Charles C. Thomas)

170. Iggo, A. (1970). The mechanisms of biological temperature regulation. *Physiological and behavioral temperature regulation*, Chap. 28, 391 (J. D. Hardy, A. P. Gagge, J. A. J. Stolwijk, editors) (Springfield: Charles C. Thomas)

171. Zotterman, Y. (1936). Specific action potentials in the lingual nerve of the cat. *Scand. Arch. Physiol.*, **75**, 105

172. Hensel, H. and Zotterman, Y. (1951). Quantitative Beziehungen zwischen der Entladung einzelner Kältefasern und der Temperatur. *Acta Physiol. Scand.*, **23**, 291

173. Iggo, A. and Iggo, B. J. (1971). Impulse coding in primate cutaneous thermoreceptors in dynamic thermal conditions. *J. Physiol. (Paris)*, **63**, 287

174. Landgren, S. (1970). Projections from thermoreceptors into the somatosensory system of the cat's brain. *Physiological and Behavioral Temperature Regulation*. Chap. 31, 454 (J. D. Hardy, A. P. Gagge, J. A. J. Stolwijk, editors) (Springfield: Charles C. Thomas)

175. Poulos, D. A. (1971). Central processing of peripheral temperature information. *Proc. Internat. Union Physiol. Sci.*, **8**, 86

176. Kenshalo, D. R. and Brearley, E. A. (1970). Electrophysiological measurements of the sensitivity of cat's upper lip to warm and cool stimuli. *J. Comp. Physiol. Psychol.*, **70**, 5

177. Cabanac, H. P. and Hammel, H. T. unpublished. Personal communication.

178. Hardy, J. D. (1953–54). Control of heat loss and heat production in physiologic temperature regulation. *Harvey Lectures*, **49**, 242

179. Winslow, C. E. A., Herrington, L. P. and Gagge, A. P. (1937). Relation between atmospheric condition, physiological reactions and sensations of pleasantness. *Amer. J. Hyg.*, **26**, 103

180. Winslow, C. E. A. and Herrington, L. P. (1949). Temperature and human life. *Princeton University Press* (Princeton)

181. Fredericq, L. (1882). Sur la régulation de la température chez les animaux à sang chaud. *Arch. Biol.*, **3**, 687

182. Richet, Ch. (1884). De l'influence de la chaleur sur la respiration et de la dyspnée thermique. *C.R. Acad. Sci.*, **XCIX**, 279

183. Benzinger, T. H. (1963). Peripheral cold and central warm reception, main origins of human discomfort. *Proc. Nat. Acad. Sci.*, **49**, 832

184. Chatonnet, J. and Cabanac, M. (1965). The perception of thermal comfort. *Internat. J. Biometeorol.*, **9**, 183

185. Kahn, R. (1904). Uber die Erwärmung des Carotidenblutes. *Arch. f. Physiol. Suppl.* 81

186. Bligh, J. (1966). The thermosensitivity of the hypothalamus and thermoregulation in mammals. *Biol. Rev.*, **41**, 317

187. Hammel, H. T. (1968). Regulation of internal body temperature. *Ann. Rev. Physiol.*, **30**, 641

188. Nakayama, T., Eisenman, J. S. and Hardy, J. D. (1961). Single unit activity of anterior hypothalamus during local heating. *Science*, **134**, 560

189. Hammel, H. T. (1965). Neurones and temperature regulation. *Physiological Regulation and Control*, **5**, 71 (W. S. Yamamoto, J. R. Brobeck, editors) (Philadelphia: Saunders)

190. Hardy, J. D. (1969). Brain sensors of temperature. *Brody Memorial Lecture VIII*. 28 (Univ. of Missouri Publ.)

191. Hellon, R. F. (1970). Hypothalamic neutons responding to changes in hypothalamic and ambient temperatures. *Physiological and Behavioral Temperature Regulation*, Chap. 32, 463 (J. D. Hardy, A. P. Gagge, J. A. J. Stolwijk, editors) (Springfield: Charles C. Thomas)

192. Eisenman, J. S. (1972). Unit activity studies of thermoresponsive neurons. *Essays on Temperature Regulation*, Chap. 6, 55 (J. Bligh, R. Moore, editors) (Amsterdam: North Holland Publ.)

193. Hardy, J. D., Fusco, M. and Hammel, H. T. (1958). Responses of conscious dog to local heating of anterior hypothalamus (film). *Physiologist*, **6**, 34

194. Freeman, W. J. and Davis, D. D. (1959). Effects on cat of conductive hypothalamic cooling. *Amer. J. Physiol.*, **197**, 145

195. Strømme, S. B., Myhre, K. and Hammel, H. T. (1971). Forebrain temperature activates behavioral thermoregulatory response in arctic sculpins. *J. Physiol. (Paris)*, **63**, 433

196. Roberts, W. W., Berquist, E. H. and Robinson, T. C. L. (1969). Thermoregulatory grooming and sleep like relaxation induced by local warming of preoptic area and anterior hypothalamus in Opossum. *J. Comp. Physiol. Psychol.*, **67**, 182

197. Andersson, B., Gale, C. C. and Sundsten, J. W. (1963). The relationship between body temperature and food and water intake. *Olfaction and Taste*, 361 (Y. Zotterman, editor) (Oxford: Pergamon Press)

198. Spector, N. H., Brobeck, J. R. and Hamilton, C. L. (1968). Feeding and core temperature in albino rats: changes induced by preoptic heating and cooling. *Science*, **161**, 286

199. Hamilton, C. L. and Ciaccia, P. J. (1971). Hypothalamus, temperature regulation and feeding in the rat. *Amer. J. Physiol.*, **221**, 800

200. Thauer, R. (1970). Thermosensitivity of the spinal chord. *Physiological and Behavioral Temperature Regulation*, Chap. 33, 472 (J. D. Hardy, A. P. Gagge, J. A. J. Stolwijk, editors) (Springfield: Charles C. Thomas)

201. Klussman, F. W. and Pierau, F. K. (1972). Extrahypothalamic deep body thermosensitivity. *Essays on Temperature Regulation*. Chap. 8, 87 (J. Bligh, R. Moore, editors) (Amsterdam: North Holland Publ.)

202. Cormareche, M. and Cabanac, M. Influence de stimulation thermiques dela moelle epiniere sur le comportement thermoregulateur du chien. *Pflügers Arch*. In press

203. Carlisle, H. J. and Ingram, D. L. unpublished

204. Duclaux, R., Fantino, M. and Cabanac, M. (1972). Comportement thermorégulateur de la grenouille, influence de stimulations thermiques spinales. *Pflügers Arch*. In press

205. Bligh, J. (1961). Possible temperature sensitive elements in or near the vena cava of sheep. *J. Physiol. (London)*, **159**, 85

206. Rawson, R. O., Quick, K. P. and Coughlin, R. F. (1969). Thermoregulatory responses to intra abdominal heating of sheep. *Science*, **165**, 919

207. Hardy, J. D. (1965). The "set point" concept in physiological temperature regulation. *Physiological Controls and Regulations*, Chap. 6, 98 (Yamamoto, W. S. and J. R. Brobeck, editors) (Philadelphia: Saunders)

208. Mitchel, D., Atkins, A. R. and Wyndham, C. H. (1972). Mathematical and physical models of thermoregulation. *Essays on Temperature Regulation*. Chap. 5, 37 (J. Bligh and R. Moore, editors) (Amsterdam: North Holland)

209. Cabanac, M. (1969). Plaisir ou déplaisir de la sensation thermique et homéothermie. *Physiol. Behav.*, **4**, 359

210. Bard, P., Woods, J. W. and Bleier, R. (1970). The effects of cooling heating and pyrogens on chronically decerebrate cats. *Physiological and Behavioral Temperature Regulation*. Chap. 36, 519 (J. D. Hardy, A. P. Gagge and J. A. J. Stolwijk, editors) (Springfield: Charles C. Thomas)

211. Murgatroyd, D., Keller, A. D. and Hardy, J. D. (1958). Warmth discrimination in the dog after a hypothalamic ablation. *Amer. J. Physiol.*, **195**, 276

212. Hainsworth, F. R. and Epstein, A. N. (1966). Severe impairment of heat-induced saliva spreading in rats recovered from lateral hypothalamic lesions. *Science*, **153**, 1255

213. Miller, N. E., Bailey, C. J. and Stevenson, J. A. F. (1950). Decreased "hunger" but increased food intake resulting from hypothalamic lesions. *Science*, **112**, 256

214. Pirlet, K. (1962). Die Verstellung des Kerntemperatur Sollwertes bei Kältebelastung. *Pflügers Archiv.*, **275**, 71

215. Topliff, E. D. L. and Livingstone, S. D. (1970). Thermal comfort in relation to mean skin temperature. *Canadian J. Physiol. Pharmacol.*, **48**, 98

216. Bøje, O., Nielsen, M. and Olesen, J. (1948). Undersøgelser over betydningen af ensidig straalingsafkøling. *Boligopvarmningsudvalgets Med. No 9*

217. Olesen, S., Fanger, P. O., Jensen, P. B. and Nielsen, O. J. (1972). Comfort limits for man exposed to aysmmetric thermal radiation. *Proceed. Sympos. on Thermal Comfort and Moderate Heat Stress*. London. CIB Commission W45

218. Hall, J. F. and Klemm, F. K. (1969). Thermal comfort in disparate thermal environments. *J. Appl. Physiol.*, **27**, 601

219. Hindmarsh, M. E. and Macpherson, R. K. (1962). Thermal comfort in Australia. *Aust. J. Sci.*, **24**, 335

220. Winslow, C. E. A., Herrington, L. P. and Gagge, A. P. (1937). Physiological reactions of the human body to various atmospheric humidities. *Amer. J. Physiol.*, **120**, 288
221. Fay, T. and Smith, G. W. (1941). Observations on reflex responses during prolonged periods of human refrigeration. *Arch. Neurol. Psychiat.*, **45**, 215
222. Carlisle, H. J. unpublished. Personal communication
223. Brück, K., Parmelee, A. H. and Brück, M. (1962). Neutral temperature range and range of thermal comfort in premature infants. *Biol. Neonat.*, **4**, 32
224. Brück, K. (1968). Which environmental temperature does the premature infant prefer? *Pediatrics*, **41**, 27
225. Hardy, J. D. (1970). Thermal comfort: skin temperature and physiological thermoregulation. *Physiological and Behavioral Temperature Regulation*, 856 (J. D. Hardy, A. P. Gagge and J. A. J. Stolwijk, editors) (Springfield: Charles C. Thomas)
226. Brack, W. (1941). Aus der Praxis für die Praxis ueber die Behandlung von Kalteschäden mit Priscol. *Schweiz Med. Wschr.*, **71**, 1559
227. Roch-Besser, B. (1950). La Benzy-imidazoline (Priscol), étude pharmacodynamique et applications cliniques. *Helvetica Med. Acta Suppl.* **27**, 158
228. Thiers, H., Chatonnet, J., Cabanac, M. and Michel, P. (1966). Le frisson et l'incomfort thermique des erythrodermies. Leur valeur seméiologique. Leur interprétation physiopathologique. *Lyon Medical*, **50**, 1395
229. Driver, A. F. M. (1964). Sensitivity to heat and cold of summer and winter preferrers. *Ergonomics*, **7**, 475
230. Keatinge, W. R. and Evans, M. (1960). Effect of food, alcohol and hyoscine on body temperature and reflex responses of men immersed in cold water. *Lancet*, **2**, 176
231. Andersen, K. L., Hellstrøm, B. and Lorentzen, F. V. (1963). Combined effect of cold and alcohol on heat balance in man. *J. Appl. Physiol.*, **18**, 975
232. Kissen, A. T., Reifler, C. B. and Thaler, V. H. (1964). Modification of thermoregulatory responses to cold by hypnosis. *J. Appl. Physiol.*, **19**, 1043
233. Haslam, D. (1963). Changes in skin temperature during the heat illusion test. *Nature (London)*, **198**, 219
234. Cabanac, M., Ramel, P., Duclaux, R. and Joli, M. (1969). Indifférence à la douleur et confort thermique. Etude expérimentale de deux cas. *Presse Médicale*, **77**, 2053
235. Licht, P. (1965). The relation between preferred body temperatures and testicular heat sensitivity in lizards. *Copeia*, **4**, 428
236. Bashcnina, N. V. and Borovskaja, E. M. (1963). The peculiarity of development of heat regulation in vole during the first month after birth. *Bjull. Moskov. Obshch. Ipyatel Prirody Otd. Biol.*, **68**, 34
237. Bligh, J. and Harthoorn, A. M. (1965). Continuous radiotelemetric records of the deep body temperature of some unrestrained African mammals under near natural conditions. *J. Physiol. (London)*, **176**, 145
238. Ingram, D. L. and Legge, K. F. (1970). The thermoregulatory behavior of young pigs in a natural environment. *Physiol. Behav.*, **5**, 981
239. Briese, E., Echevarria, Y. and De Quijada, M. G. (1966). Ambient temperature and self stimulation. *Acta Physiol. Lat. Amer.*, **16**, 209
240. Briese, E. (1965). Hyperthermia in self stimulating rats. *Acta Physiol. Lat. Amer.*, **15**, 357
241. Budgell, P. (1971). Behavioural thermoregulation in the barbary dove *Streptopelia risoria*. *Anim. Behav.*, **19**, 524

8
Physiological Responses and Adaptations to High Altitude

S. LAHIRI
University of Pennsylvania

List of abbreviations

ADP	Adenosine diphosphate
ATP	Adenosine triphosphate
DPNH	Reduced diphosphopyridine nucleotide
FVC	Forced vital capacity
K_m	Substrate concentration or pressure at half maximum rate
P_{ACO_2}	Partial pressure of CO_2 in alveolar air
P_{AO_2}	Partial pressure of O_2 in alveolar air
P_{aCO_2}	Partial pressure of CO_2 in arterial blood
P_{aO_2}	Partial pressure of O_2 in arterial blood
P_{ICO_2}	Partial pressure of CO_2 in inspired air saturated at body temperature
P_{IO_2}	Partial pressure of O_2 in inspired air saturated at body temperature
P_{vCO_2}	Partial pressure of CO_2 in venous blood
P_{vO_2}	Partial pressure of O_2 in venous blood
P_B	Barometric pressure
$P_{50\,7\,4}$	P_{O_2} (mmHg) at 50 per cent saturation with O_2 at pH 7.4 at a specified temperature
$\dot{Q}$	Blood flow (cardiac output) in $1 \ \mathrm{min}^{-1}$
RQ	Respiratory quotient $(\dot{V}_{CO_2})/(\dot{V}_{CO_2})$
$S_{aO_2}\%$	Per cent saturation of arterial blood with O_2
$\dot{V}_E$	Expiratory air flow (ventilation) in $1 \ \mathrm{min}^{-1}$
$\dot{V}_A$	Alveolar air flow (ventilation) in $1 \ \mathrm{min}^{-1}$ at body temperature, pressure, saturated
$\dot{V}_A/\dot{Q}$	Alveolar ventilation perfusion ratio
$\dot{V}_{CO_2}$	CO_2 output in $1 \ \mathrm{min}^{-1}$ at standard temperature, pressure, dry
$\dot{V}_{O_2}$	O_2 uptake in $1 \ \mathrm{min}^{-1}$ at standard temperature, pressure, dry

8.1 INTRODUCTION

At sea level the O_2 stores of the human body can support life for only 5 min at the resting metabolic rate[1] when the O_2 supply is terminated. At high altitude, where P_{IO_2} is lower, the O_2 stores are also decreased. Since resting metabolic rate does not decrease at altitude, the O_2 stores will last even less time than at sea level. This continuing threat of oxygen shortage is further compounded by the narrow pressure difference for O_2 between the air source and the sink in the mitochondrial material of the cells where it is consumed. The body responds to this threat by making short-term and long-term adjustments, not only to ensure an adequate supply of O_2 to the tissues but also to use O_2 at a normal rate. The purpose of this chapter is to present our current understanding of the adaptive mechanisms.

In recent years, three key observations have stimulated a great deal of research work: (1) the realisation that the control of ventilation in natives of high altitude is modified in the sense that their hypoxic response is blunted[2-4]; (2) in the field of O_2 transport, the observation that deoxygenation of haemoglobin in red blood cells increases 2,3-diphosphoglycerate concentration which in turn decreases affinity of haemoglobin for oxygen[5,6] and (3) the possibility that lung growth may be stimulated by chronic hypoxia[7].

Although much of the following discussion pertains to human adaptation to the hypoxia of high altitude, results on other species have been incorporated in so far as they enhanced understanding of the human phenomena or help to derive a general biological principle.

Although this chapter concerns hypoxia of high altitude, it is worth noting that environmental conditions other than inspired oxygen tension (P_{IO_2}) change as one moves from sea level to high altitude. Of these, a decrease in ambient temperature and humidity may assume great physiological significance, particularly in influencing physical performance. It is important to remember that subjects adapted to hypoxia of high altitude are also adapted to these other environmental conditions. The problem of hypoxia will be considered from the point of view of successive oxygen tensions in the transport system between atmospheric air and the mitochondrial system: ambient air→lungs→arterial blood→capillary blood→cells→mitochondria, and the control of reaction of oxygen at the sites in mitochondria.

8.2 REGULATION OF PULMONARY VENTILATION

8.2.1 Initiation of chemoreflexes

The ventilatory effect of acute hypoxia is mediated through the peripheral chemoreceptors within the carotid and aortic bodies in mammals. Complete denervation of all these structures abolishes the prompt ventilatory response to acute hypoxia in man and animal. Both whole nerve and single fibre preparations of the carotid sinus nerve of the cat have shown that chemoreceptor activity increases progressively as P_{aO_2} is decreased from a very high to a low value[8,9]; no threshold value was found. There is no evidence to date that the peripheral chemoreceptor discharge for a given decrease in P_{aO_2} is diminished by chronic hypoxia. Åstrand[10] was the first to demonstrate that the carotid chemoreceptor afferent activity of the cat was normal after several days of chronic hypoxia at 4000 m, and Hornbein and Severinghaus[11] reported that the hypoxic response of the carotid chemoreceptor afferent of cats born and raised at 4000 m was not less than that of sea level cats.

8.2.2 Ventilatory response

The ventilatory response to hypoxia, on the other hand, seems to show a threshold value. In acute hypoxia, the ventilatory response using steady state methods is barely measurable at a P_{aO_2} above 60 mmHg[12] yet a few days of chronic hypoxia of the same degree increases ventilation considerably. The question of what initiates this change during chronic hypoxia has not been answered satisfactorily. That mild hypoxia ($P_{aO_2} \sim 60$ mmHg) is a ventilatory drive can be shown by various techniques, e.g. by the transient 'O_2 test'[13], by a combination of muscular exercise and hypoxia[14] and by hypoxia on a background of hypercapnia[15]; these conclusions concerning ventilation also correspond to the continuous relation between chemo-receptor activity and P_{aO_2}. Consequently, the observed ventilatory threshold for hypoxia does not correspond to the continuing increase of chemoreceptor activity as P_{aO_2} decreases below the sea level value. The question then remains: what prevents the continuing increase in ventilation during acute hypoxia? Further consideration of acclimatisation (changing response to a continued stimulus after the initial response) to P_{aO_2} above 60 mmHg will be resumed after documenting the clearer picture at P_{aO_2} below 60 mmHg.

8.2.2.1 *Peripheral v. central drive*

The concomitant respiratory alkalosis during acute hypoxia limits the stimu-latory effect of hypoxia on ventilation. Before the discovery of medullary chemosensitivity to CO_2-H^+ it was generally believed that arterial blood pH returned towards normal after an initial rise through renal compensation, and this restored blood [H^+] stimulated ventilation until the full effect of hypoxia was reached. As the phenomenon of medullary chemosensitivity was unravelled, Kellogg[16] pointed out convincingly that ventilatory acclima-tisation preceded the return of arterial blood pH to normal and Severinghaus *et al.*[17] subsequently showed that cerebrospinal fluid (CSF) pH returns to normal ahead of arterial blood pH during high altitude acclimatisation to 3880 m. They argued that since the medullary chemosensitive area is readily influenced by the CSF pH the ventilation increase in the second phase was related to this prompt restoration of CSF pH, thereby substantiating Kellogg's original hypothesis. Thus, we may tentatively conclude at this stage that ventilatory acclimatisation to chronic hypoxia is a central rather than a peripheral chemoreflex phenomenon.

8.2.2.2 Cerebral acidosis

Under conditions of severe hypoxia, cerebral acidosis may occur because of an augmented anaerobic metabolism. This acidosis component has been demonstrated by exposing animals to hypoxia in which the arterial chemo-receptors have been surgically denervated[18]. However, if this cerebral acidosis is gradually compensated in this preparation by an increase of medullary [HCO_3^-], then ventilatory drive (and consequently ventilation) may be expected to decrease with time unlike the normal process of ventilatory response to chronic hypoxia. This time course of the long-term effect of hypoxia on CSF acid-base and ventilation in the completely chemoreceptor-denervated animal is not available. However, our unpublished observations on the time course in the bilaterally carotid chemoreceptor-denervated goats exposed to 5000 m for several weeks showed that both arterial blood and CSF acidity were no greater than at sea level despite a small decrease of [HCO_3^-]. Consistent with the observed hyperventilation in the animals, these data suggested that some respiratory drive other than cerebral acidosis is involved.

8.2.2.3 Central sensitisation

There is a third possible mechanism for acclimatisation to chronic hypoxia which may be described as 'central sensitisation'[15]. According to this idea central arousal develops slowly during chronic hypoxia and also disappears slowly during de-acclimatisation. This idea gained further support recently because of the uncertainty of the explanation for the following observations: (1) mild *acute* hypoxia of P_{aO_2} 60 mmHg in man increased ventilation[12] and increased arterial blood and CSF/pH only slightly (Dempsey, personal communication) but in the chronic states a distinct increase in ventilation occurred while the pH of arterial blood and CSF continued to increase, (2) the data of Severinghaus *et al.*[17] and Pauli *et al.*[19] show that although CSF pH turned alkaline following initial hypoxic hyperventilation during altitude (3200–3800 m) acclimatisation, further change in ventilation was not associated with any consistent change of CSF pH in all the subjects, (3) CSF pH does not seem to be regulated similarly in sojourners and natives at high altitude[36, 37]. Thus, the theory that reversal of CSF pH from alkaline to normal value accounts for the increase in ventilation during chronic hypoxia[17] needs re-examination.

It is relevant to bring up at this point that animals and man after denervation of either carotid or both aortic and carotid bodies at sea level gradually increase their arterial P_{CO_2} and [HCO_3^-] in blood[20, 21], presumably because of loss of ventilatory drive from the chemoreceptors. Our own unpublished data on goats and sheep showed gradual increases in P_{CO_2} and [HCO_3^-] in arterial blood and CSF at sea level after bilateral carotid sinus nerve section; there was also a corresponding decrease in P_{aO_2}. This mild hypoxia, in the absence of carotid bodies, did not induce increases in ventilation as seen in normal animals exposed to an equivalent altitude, and is *not* consistent with

the suggestion that ventilatory acclimatisation may not involve the participation of arterial chemoreceptors[18].

8.2.3 Role of carbon dioxide

The fact that alveolar or arterial P_{CO_2} is low in the altitude acclimatised
sojourners and residents has been well documented since Fitzgerald[22], and
it has repeatedly been found that CO_2 threshold for ventilatory stimulation
is decreased[23] correspondingly. It is generally found that ventilatory sensitivity
to CO_2 (slope of the $\dot{V}_E$-P_{aCO_2} response curve) is increased in man acclimatised to high altitude[24], although the reason for this is not clear. A decrease
in CSF and blood [HCO_3^-] as it occurs in acclimatised subjects would increase
[H^+] at a given P_{CO_2} and therefore stimulate ventilation but a change in
P_{CO_2} is unlikely to have caused any greater increase in [H^+] than at sea level.
This reasoning is substantiated by the observation that $\dot{V}_E$-P_{aCO_2} slope is
not changed by metabolic acidosis in man where [HCO_3^-] is decreased to a
similar degree[25]. It seems that the increase in CO_2 sensitivity in acclimatised
man is associated with hypoxia for some unknown reason. Such notion is
also supported by the observation[26] that 8 h of chronic hypoxia in man
produced an extra ventilatory drive not accounted for by hypocapnia and
the consequent acid-base adjustment which is known to follow hypoxic
hyperventilation.

On the other hand, altitude polycythemia increases the buffering power
of blood and may, therefore, decrease respiratory sensitivity to CO_2. However, the observations are neither consistent[3, 4, 27] nor convincing.

8.2.4 Acid-base homeostasis

8.2.4.1 Role of renal function

It has repeatedly been found in man that arterial blood is alkaline not only
during acute hypoxia but it remains relatively alkaline (pH > 7.4) for a long
time in acclimatised sojourners[15, 28]. However, the native residents of high
altitude have an arterial pH comparable to the normal value at sea level[29, 36].

It is generally agreed that renal blood flow is reduced in high altitude
natives[30]. The renal plasma flow is decreased in proportion to the increase in
haematocrit, but the filtration fraction and clearance are increased so that
the kidney function is maintained within the normal limits. Despite this, the
compensatory adjustment to hypoxic respiratory alkalosis seems slow. A
comparative study of the effect of hypocapnia with and without hypoxia on
arterial acid-base balance is worthy of experimental investigation.

8.2.4.2 Role of cerebral blood flow and metabolism

Acute hypoxia increases cerebral blood flow but the concomitant respiratory
alkalosis makes this increase self-limiting because acute hypocapnic alkalosis
decreases the flow. Thus, normocapnic acute hypoxia increases the flow

further[31]. Fencl et al.[32] investigated ventilation and cerebral blood flow (indirectly by arteriovenous O_2 and CO_2 differences) during acute arterial acid-base changes, and concluded that both are a unique function of CSF pH. But the similarity of responses between ventilation and cerebral blood flow ends there. During acclimatisation to hypoxia in man cerebral blood flow diminishes[33] whereas ventilation continues to increase. This decrease in cerebral blood flow in spite of a less alkaline CSF and blood pH is inconsistent with the notion of synergistic control of cerebral blood flow and ventilation. The initial transient increase in cardiac output during acclimatisation may contribute to the initial increase in cerebral blood flow but it is not supposed to do so in the face of autoregulation[34]. It is also unlikely that a small increase in P_{aO_2} through hyperventilation should have caused this gradual but profound change in cerebral blood flow.

It is not known for certain how cerebral blood flow reacts to prolonged or lifelong hypoxia. The study of Milledge and Sørensen[35] on cerebral arterio-venous O_2 difference implied that it is low in high altitude natives (4300 m) and is reduced further when they breathe 100% O_2. Roy, however (S. B. Roy, personal communication), found a relative increase in cerebral blood flow in high-altitude natives. Lahiri and Milledge[36] reported that the CSF pH in native residents of the Himalayas was closer to that of the lowlanders at sea level than to lowlanders acclimatised at high altitude. Sørensen and Milledge[37] reported even more acid CSF pH in the Andean high-altitude natives. It is not certain at this moment why CSF is more acid in these highlanders but this acidity in blood and CSF would constitute a greater component of their ventilatory drive if their respiratory sensitivity to CO_2-H^+ were the same as in the sea level natives. A knowledge of cerebral blood flow and metabolism is necessary to understand this phenomenon. The importance of this CO_2-H^+ stimulus will be discussed further in connection with the hypoxic drive in a later section.

8.2.5 Increased hypoxic sensitivity

There is not conclusive evidence at this date to prove that ventilatory sensitivity to hypoxia is increased at any stage of altitude acclimatisation. One group of investigators[38] claimed that hypoxic sensitivity in recent sojourners at 3100 m increased and remained elevated for more than 45 days even after return to sea level during rest and exercise. Michel and Milledge[24] measured hypoxic sensitivity of human subjects at intervals over several months at 5880 m but did not observe any pronounced or systematic change. Lahiri[39] followed indices for hypoxic sensitivity in three subjects before and after ascent to 4540 m for 11 days and also found no measurable change in hypoxic sensitivity, although CO_2 sensitivity increased. Hypoxic ventilation increased as acclimatisation progressed but so did ventilation during acute normoxia. Inspection of other published data[40, 41] also suggests that there is no change. Thus, the phenomenon of hypersensitisation has not been seen by all investigators who looked for it. Indeed, the balance of evidence suggests that no important increase in hypoxic sensitivity occurs during chronic hypoxia.

8.2.6 Blunted respiratory sensitivity in high-altitude natives

Although it was usually thought that maximum ventilatory response for a given degree of hypoxia is achieved by complete acclimatisation to high altitude, the natives of high altitude have been found to show relative hypoventilation[42, 43]. Chiodi[42] concluded that the peripheral chemoreceptor activity might be decreased after prolonged acclimatisation to hypoxia. He found higher P_{aCO_2} and lower ventilatory response to pure O_2 breathing among natives or long-term residents at various high altitudes than in short-term residents. He also performed 'CO$_2$ sensitivity' tests on these subjects, but the inspired-gas mixtures in this experiment consisted of CO_2 in air at various altitudes, and therefore, also presented an increased hypoxic stimulus as altitude increased. Thus, his results relate to a combination of hypoxic and hypercapnic effects rather than to the effect of hypercapnia alone. Nevertheless, hyposensitivity to hypoxia in the native residents can be detected in these results.

Hurtado[43], on the other hand, compared native residents of Morococha (4540 m) and Lima (sea level). He emphasised the similarities between the two groups of permanent residents in terms of homeostasis, such as pH of arterial blood; he also pointed out the differences such as levels of ventilation, P_{aCO_2} and haemoglobin concentration which helped to reduce the P_{O_2} gradient from inspired air to the tissues. In testing respiratory sensitivity to CO_2, Hurtado[43] followed the time course of changes in ventilation and P_{ACO_2} for 6 min after the change of inspired gas mixture which consisted of $P_{ICO_2} = 37.4$ mmHg at both elevations but $P_{IO_2} = 83.5$ mmHg at 4540 m (therefore hypoxic) and 150 mmHg at sea level. The author ascribed the ventilatory response to 'CO$_2$ sensitivity' and found it to be greater in the Morococha residents, but apparently did not take the differences in P_{AO_2} between the two groups into account. Of particular importance was his observation that ventilatory response did not decrease when P_{IO_2} was raised in the Morococha experiments because it indicated that ventilation of high-altitude natives did not show a normal sensitivity to a change of P_{AO_2}. Yet in explaining higher normal resting P_{ACO_2} in the high altitude natives compared with acclimatised lowlanders, Hurtado attributed the difference to lower CO_2 sensitivity in their control of ventilation.

Inspection of early observations made on various expeditions[22, 44, 45, 46] shows that the native high-altitude residents have higher levels of P_{ACO_2} and lower levels of P_{AO_2} or $S_{aO_2}\%$ than the sojourners[54]. It has been pointed out that a part of this higher P_{ACO_2} is due to a higher RQ in high-altitude natives. Through the same mechanism of RQ they also raise their P_{AO_2} for a given P_{IO_2}. All these observations on the natives of the Andes indicated that there was an important difference in the hypoxic drive of ventilation between acclimatised lowlanders and highlanders.

Meanwhile during the Himalayan Scientific and Mountaineering Expedition, 1960–61, ventilatory measurements on a Sherpa subject at 5800 m showed that he ventilated less than did the acclimatised lowlanders at rest and during exercise[47]. Thus, it was apparent that natives of high altitude, irrespective of their geographic location ventilate less than the sojourners in spite of prolonged chronic hypoxia. This observation set the stage for a future expedition in the Himalayas to study Sherpa physiology[48]. The need for further studies of the control of ventilation in high altitude natives was also echoed by Dejours at the Interlaken Symposium in 1962. Such studies were

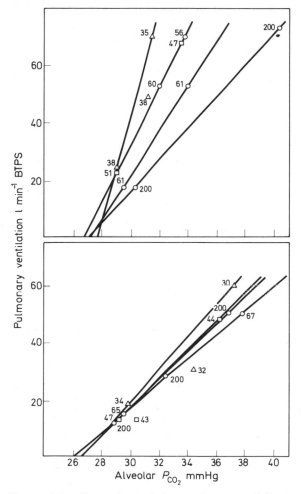

Figure 8.1. Comparison of the steady state ventilatory responses to acute changes of P_{AO_2} and P_{ACO_2} in sojourner (upper panel) and Sherpa high-altitude native (lower panel) at 4880 m. $\dot{V}_E$ is plotted against P_{ACO_2} at various levels of P_{AO_2} (shown by numbers on the lines). Hypercapnia stimulated $\dot{V}_E$ in both subjects but the lack of hypoxic effect in Sherpa subject is striking. (From Milledge and Lahiri[3], by courtesy of the Editor, *Respiration Physiology* and the authors.)

first done apparently independently by three groups of investigators, two in the Andes[2,4] and the other[3] in the Himalayas. These studies used standard tests previously developed[13,15,49,50] and the results showed that the hypoxic ventilatory drive in the altitude natives was blunted[2,3,4].

Milledge and Lahiri[3] reported for the first time that this blunted response in a Sherpa subject was not reversed by 6 weeks of residence at sea level. Figure 8.1 compares a typical ventilatory response to hypercapnia and hypoxia of a Sherpa high-altitude native with that of a sojourner at 4880 m. The ventilatory effect of an acute reduction of P_{AO_2} was small in the Sherpa compared to the response in the sojourner. This hypoxic insensitivity persisted at sea level. Lahiri et al.[51] re-examined the question of irreversibility and showed that 10–12 months of deacclimatisation afforded no increase in sensitivity. Similar findings were obtained by Sørensen and Severinghaus[52] in nine high-altitude natives who had moved to sea level at ages from 2 and 27 y and had lived there for 2–16 y. On the average, their hypoxic response was about one-fifth of the sea level natives. There was, thus, no evidence that this characteristic is changed in the natives of high altitude, either in adults or in children who migrated to sea level and were normoxic.

The obvious question whether this characteristic is genetic or developed during lifelong hypoxaemia has been raised, but has not been solved satisfactorily. The most direct evidence would be obtained from the sensitivity to hypoxia of the offspring of high-altitude natives born at sea level but that has not been obtained. However, work has developed into two other rewarding lines.

8.2.6.1 Effect of lifelong hypoxia

Husson and Otis[53] previously compared the effect of right to left shunt hypoxia and altitude hypoxia in lowlanders, and provided evidence that lifelong hypoxia caused an increased arterial P_{CO_2}. Inspection of these and other data on cyanotic subjects at sea level and comparison with those of high-altitude natives have suggested that adult cyanotic subjects do hypoventilate for a comparable degree of hypoxaemia as do the high altitude natives[54]. Sørensen and Severinghaus[55] tested hypoxic sensitivity in patients with tetralogy of Fallot after surgical correction and found that normal sensitivity was not recovered even after 1–7 years of normoxia. These results were in line with the idea of irreversibly blunted hypoxic response in high altitude natives. Edelman et al.[56] studied subjects with cyanotic congenital heart disease (10–37 years old) using transient N_2 tests and found that they were similar to high-altitude natives. But, several months after surgical correction their hypoxic sensitivity had returned to that of the normal sea level natives. These observations show that while lifelong hypoxia causes blunting of respiratory response to hypoxia it need not be irreversible as in high-altitude natives.

8.2.6.2 Prolonged hypoxia: childhood v. adulthood

Another line of work consists of studying sea level natives who have been exposed to hypoxia for various durations at various ages. Compiling and analysing the blood gas and alveolar gas data of adult human subjects Lahiri[54] found that P_{AO_2} and P_{ACO_2} were similar in short-term and long-term residents at high altitudes whereas P_{AO_2} was lower and P_{ACO_2} higher in high altitude natives. Only Chiodi's[42] data appeared to suggest that this hypoventilation might also have developed in the migrant long-term residents, but uncertainty as to the ancestry of the subjects makes it difficult to arrive at a definite conclusion. Furthermore, not only did the ventilatory response of Andean and Himalayan natives to hypoxia remain unchanged[3,51,52,57] at sea level but sea level natives also did not acquire a blunted hypoxic response[51,58] at altitude. Admittedly there were variations of response in sea level natives but it was not correlated with the duration of high-altitude exposure.

The results of similar studies on the natives of the Rockies (Leadville, 3100 m) appear to be different. Earlier studies on this population[59] showed that their ventilatory response to hypoxia during rest and exercise was not different from those of recent sojourners. Later studies[27,38,60] reported that the native residents of Leadville did show depressed sensitivity in 'isocapnic hypoxia' test compared to recent sojourners. In general, they also agreed that long-term residence of the sojourners reduced their hypoxic response. Weil et al.[27] suggested that this decrease in ventilatory sensitivity was a gradual process, and implied that it requires 12 years or more to acquire half-sensitivity. On the basis of this argument, Byrne-Quinn et al.[61] went on to show that the hypoxic sensitivity of children aged 9–10 years born in Leadville (3100 m) was similar to a control group living in Denver (1600 m). This report is in contrast with the following observation. One of the cyanotic subjects of Edelman et al.[56], who was only 10 years old, showed profound ventilatory hyposensitivity to hypoxia. Also, ventilatory studies on a 10-year-old Sherpa child at 3800 m showed little hypoxic response (Lahiri, unpublished).

However, the two sojourners in the study of Weil et al.[27] who had the longest hypoxic exposure and were most desensitised were also necessarily the oldest. The authors did not provide adequate control data to discount the age factor. In the study of Byrne-Quinn et al.[61] the children living at 3100 m had a P_{ACO_2} level 2–3 mmHg higher than those at 1600 m; in some the P_{ACO_2} was 35–38 mmHg which is in the range normally found at sea level. These data alone suggest that Leadville children hypoventilated in spite of hypoxia. However, the determination of hypoxic sensitivity by the method of 'isocapnic hypoxia' at a single P_{CO_2} — higher (mean, 34.3) for the Leadville group and lower (mean, 32.8) for the Denver group at Denver, made interpretation of their results susceptible to error.

Furthermore, working with the same groups of adult subjects at Leadville, Weil et al.[27] found no discernable difference in the ventilatory responses between native residents and recent newcomers during hypoxic exercise whereas Dempsey et al.[60] asserted that it is during hypoxic exercise that the differences became evident. Obviously, the entire picture of the problem investigated in the Leadville population has not emerged clearly.

In essence, the theory of acquired attenuation states that a prolonged hypoxic exposure of several years is required to develop blunted response independent of age and of history and ancestry of the subject. The single common factor which determines the sensitivity is the duration of exposure. Unfortunately, sufficient good data from a single group of investigators to support such a general conclusion is as yet unavailable. The data from different groups of investigators are difficult to compare because the sensitivity of hypoxia is not uniformly defined. However, we expressed the results obtained by each investigative group on the high altitude residents as a percentage of control, at sea level or at altitude. These derived values then allow comparison of all the results as a first approximation. An important difference was found between the results obtained in the Andean and Himalayan studies and those in the Leadville population and are shown separately in Figures 8.2 and 8.3. Figure 8.2 depicts sensitivity to hypoxia as a function

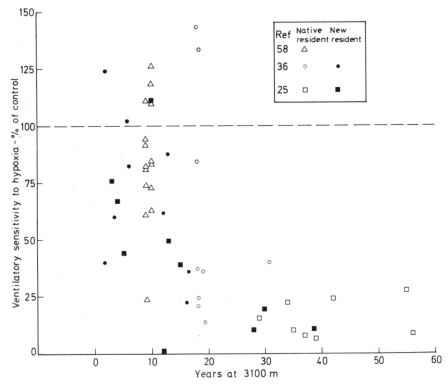

Figure 8.2. Effect of duration of hypoxia on ventilatory sensitivity in new (closed symbols) and native (open symbols) residents at Leadville (3100 m). Duration of chronic hypoxia of more than 10 years appears to decrease ventilatory sensitivity to hypoxic stimulus. The hypoxic sensitivity was computed from the following source references: 27, 38, 61.

of length of exposure to altitude in the Leadville studies[27, 38, 61]. The high-altitude natives at young age showed similar sensitivity as newcomers who have only comparable duration of exposure. Inspection shows that as time passes, hyposensitivity tends to develop, and a rapid change occurs between 10 and 20 years of exposure. Although there are paramount difficulties with each of these studies taken separately, as pointed out previously, the pooled data seem to reinforce the suggestion[27, 38] that prolonged residence at 3100 m does attenuate the sensitivity.

However, a similar picture is not apparent from the Andean and Himalayan studies[2, 3, 4, 24, 39, 42, 43, 47, 51, 54, 57, 58] as shown by the averaged data in Figure 8.3. In these locations it seems that the new and native residents of high altitude belong to two distinct populations independent of the duration of altitude exposure—the normal newcomers retained their sensitivity whereas the native residents consistently showed hyposensitivity. However, the data covering the

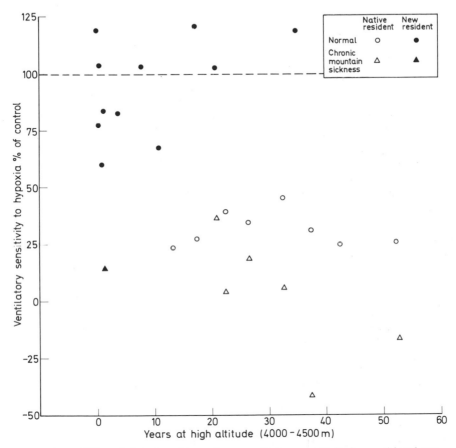

Figure 8.3. Effect of duration of hypoxia on ventilatory sensitivity in new (closed symbols) and native (open symbols) residents at high altitude (4000–4500 m) in the Andes and Himalayas. The hypoxic sensitivity was computed from the following source references: 2, 3, 4, 24, 39, 42, 43, 47, 51, 52, 54, 57 and 58. The values for the same duration of hypoxia were averaged to obtain the plot. The sensitivity appears to be independent of the duration of chronic hypoxia.

duration of exposure between 10 and 20 years, which is apparently crucial because the change in hypoxic sensitivity may occur during this crucial period, are few. Nonetheless, consideration of the data in detail indicate that there is no time-dependent relation.

One similarity between the two series of studies, however, is that there was no time dependence of the sensitivity in the normal subjects after 20 years of exposure. There is no apparent reason why it did not decrease further with time as found in the subjects with chronic mountain sickness (see later).

Thus it is reasonable to conclude tentatively that adult individuals with lifelong hypoxia do show blunted ventilatory response to hypoxia and that it develops during childhood. Evidence for the hypothesis that prolonged hypoxia in adult individuals leads to blunted response is inconclusive.

8.2.6.3 Chronic mountain sickness

The outstanding diagnostic features of patients who develop 'chronic mountain sickness' are profound arterial hypoxia, erythrocythemia and pulmonary arterial hypertension[62]; all examined so far have shown very little ventilatory response to hypoxia and consequently they also are CO_2 retainers. Not only the native altitude dwellers but also lowlanders[4] (we also came across two such lowlander patients at 4540 m in Peruvian Andes, 1966–67, during preliminary screening procedures) develop this disorder. If chronic mountain sickness is a consequence of loss of hypoxic ventilatory sensitivity it may be surmised that these lowlanders also decreased their sensitivity. However, it is possible that all these lowlanders and highlanders were potentially poor responders but did not show it under sea level normoxic condition. When patients with chronic mountain sickness are moved down to sea level, they gradually lose their pulmonary hypertension and erythrocythemia[63]. They presumably retain a blunted hypoxic ventilatory response but no data are available. There are instances at sea level that some lowlanders may develop a similar disease[64, 65] without any initial hypoxic exposure at all (idiopathic hypoventilator). If this disease is identical with chronic mountain sickness, the argument that the natives of high altitude develop relative insensitivity to hypoxia as a result of chronic exposure to hypoxia becomes untenable.

8.2.6.4 Lifelong hypoxia v. genetic effect

Because the sea level man shows a blunted hypoxic response as a result of lifelong or prolonged hypoxia does not necessarily mean that this phenomenon is the same as that found in the high-altitude natives. All evidence shows that it is a permanent feature of the high-altitude natives; there is, however, no general agreement as to whether the phenomenon is permanent in the sea level natives with lifelong hypoxia. There is no doubt that we will see more investigations of this problem.

With respect to the genetic aspect of hypoxic sensitivity, it is worth noting that most of the Peruvian sea level subjects are likely to have a mixed ancestry of Indian altitude dwellers and European or American immigrants. It is curious that hypoxic sensitivity of these subjects is systematically low compared to say normal European and American subjects on whom most data have been obtained. For example, two Peruvian sea level subjects of Lahiri et al.[39, 51] appeared to be half Indian, and they showed feeble hypoxic response. The Peruvian sea level subjects of Sørensen and Severinghaus[58] showed half of the response of the European and American immigrants[4], suggesting that part of this sensitivity may be race related.

8.2.6.5 Euoxic ventilatory drive in the high-altitude natives

Although little or no ventilatory response to hypoxia is found in the high altitude natives[3, 4, 58] during conventional steady-state testing, they do respond to the transient O_2 test[2, 66] during rest and exercise. In 'transient tests' alveolar P_{O_2} is momentarily changed by inhaling a breath or two of pure O_2, and the transient change in ventilation is recorded breath by breath. This prompt transient ventilatory response reflects activity of peripheral chemoreflex uncomplicated by secondary changes which follow in the course of time. They also lower ventilation as a result of O_2 inhalation during exercise[47, 57, 66-69]. Thus, the altitude natives do have a hypoxic drive, although apparently small.

Not only do high altitude natives have a greater hypoxic stimulus by virtue of their lower arterial P_{O_2} at a given high altitude, but also a greater central stimulus as a result of a more acid CSF pH than in lowlanders acclimatised to the same altitude[36, 37].

Sørensen and Milledge[37] proposed that the low CSF pH was sufficient to account for the ventilatory acclimatisation of the high-altitude natives in the absence of a functioning hypoxic drive from peripheral chemoreceptors. Sørensen[18] substantiated this contention by showing a similar decrease in CSF [HCO_3^-] in intact and bilaterally chemoreceptor-denervated rabbits after exposure to hypoxia ($P_B = 470$ mmHg) for 24 h and suggested that this cerebral acidosis which may not be compensated provides a persistent respiratory stimulus. This hypothesis contradicts the one put forward by Severinghaus et al.[17] proposing that it is the active regulation of CSF pH from alkaline to its normal acidity which promotes ventilatory acclimatisation to chronic hypoxia. The weakness of the hypothesis that intact peripheral chemoreceptors are not essential to the ventilatory acclimatisation to hypoxia is focused by the following argument. If a given ambient hypoxia causes the same ventilatory acclimatisation in normal and chemoreceptor-denervated animals it follows that they will have the same arterial P_{O_2} which is expected to cause the same cerebral acidosis. It is known, however, that central activity potentiates the peripheral chemoreflex effect of hypoxia on ventilation. Accordingly, intact animals will achieve a greater ventilation and consequently a greater arterial P_{O_2} in response to the same hypoxic environment. Thus, intact and peripheral chemoreceptor-denervated animals cannot achieve the same ventilatory acclimatisation at the same ambient hypoxia. It seems that Sørensen's interpretation of reduction of CSF [HCO_3^-] taken alone as a measure of cerebral acidosis and ventilatory acclimatisation in his two preparations may not be entirely valid. However, the important point is that highlanders do not respond in the same way as did Sørensen's denervated rabbits. These highlanders do hypoventilate relative to sojourners[3, 4, 42, 58] and do respond to transient O_2 test[2, 66]. My own assessment is that the raised acidity interacting with the small hypoxic drive provides the major stimulus to resting ventilation in high-altitude natives. In a review article on carotid body, Biscoe[83] discussed that an increase in activity in nerves efferent to peripheral chemoreceptors in chronic hypoxia would decrease hypoxic sensitivity. But then the crux of the problem is why carotid and aortic chemoreceptor efferent activity should be greater in high-altitude natives. No answer is immediately available.

Milledge and Sørensen[36] measured cerebral arterio-venous O_2 difference in the high-altitude natives in the Andes (4300 m) and from the large $(a-v)_{O_2}$ difference (7.89 vol.%) they concluded that the cerebral blood flow was low in their subjects. This conclusion was based on the assumption that the cerebral O_2 uptake was the same as in normal sea level subjects. These authors[37] confirming Lahiri and Milledge[36] also reported that high-altitude natives show greater cerebral anaerobic metabolism which caused greater CSF acidity. Thus the implication is that at high-altitude the natives have high total cerebral metabolic rate (aerobic plus anaerobic). It is not clear what enhanced anaerobic metabolism if cerebral O_2 uptake were normal. On the other hand, it is possible that cerebral O_2 uptake was actually low. The available data thus do not present a clear picture of cerebral metabolism and blood flow in natives to high altitude. This area of physiological function in chronic hypoxia needs comprehensive investigation, not only because of the importance in its own right, but also from the point of view of control of ventilation.

It is well documented[43, 66] that at high altitude, native subjects hyperventilate while breathing O_2 at sea level P_{IO_2} for several minutes. The mechanism of this phenomenon is unclear. However, Sørensen and Milledge[35] found that in high-altitude natives pure O_2 breathing increased $(a-v)_{O_2}$ difference suggesting a decrease in cerebral blood flow. The likely increase in P_{vCO_2} might have increased central P_{CO_2}-H^+ stimulus which in balance stimulated ventilation because the contribution of hypoxic drive was small to start with. An investigation in the medullary acid-base metabolism and blood flow during transition from hypoxia to hyperoxia would be of great interest. The hyperventilation on sea level P_{IO_2} does not persist because at sea level these subjects decrease ventilation and increase alveolar and arterial P_{CO_2}[51, 54] suggesting that important cerebral acid-base changes take place in response to O_2.

Of interest are the observations that P_{AO_2} at which ventilation is stimulated is lower in the highlanders than in the lowlanders[54, 57] and that the degree of hypoxic insensitivity is directly proportional to the level of chronic hypoxia[56].

8.2.6.6   Animal model

The need to investigate the blunting of the human ventilatory response to hypoxia in depth had led to a search for an animal model. High-altitude animals, llamas and yaks, studied at high altitude (3880–4300 m) showed normal hypoxic responses[70, 71]. So did the goats and sheep born at high altitude[71, 72, 73]. Lefrançois et al.[2] examined anaesthetised dogs at 4800 m and Hornbein and Sørensen[74] decerebrate cats at 4300 m and found normal responses comparable to sea level values. Tenney et al.[75], however, found that blunted response to acute hypoxia was developed in intact adult sea level cats when exposed to 6000 m for 5 days. Mid-collicular decerebration, however, practically returned the hypoxic response to normal. Incidentally Tenney's results suggest that even if the cats of Hornbein and Sørensen[74] were actually insensitive to the hypoxic stimulus decerebration abolished the blunting. This interpretation combined with the evidence of normal activity of the cut peripheral end of the carotid sinus nerve of high-altitude cats[11] suggest that the chemoreceptor drive *per se* is normal in the subjects with blunted ventilatory response. Consistent with this hypothesis is the postulate of Tenney *et al.*[75] that a suprapontine inhibition of hypoxic drive was induced by severe chronic hypoxia in cats. There were two other remarkable features of Tenney's cat preparation: (1) the attenuation was reversible at sea level just as it was acquired in a few days; (2) when the response was attenuated, the animals continued to hyperventilate, no matter what the P_{aO_2} was at sea level. These features are not quite the same as found in high-altitude natives.

Grover *et al.*[76] made the interesting observation that some cattle species, when moved to high altitude, decrease their P_{aCO_2} only transiently. The authors interpreted this reversal of P_{aCO_2} to normal sea level values as a loss of ventilatory response to chronic hypoxia. As pointed out by Lahiri *et al.*[71, 73] this type of P_{CO_2} change is peculiar to ruminants and its interpretation is complicated because of rumen acid-base transport (Lahiri, DeLaney and Fishman, unpublished). Rumen normally contains very high concentrations of CO_2 (25–65%) varying with the state of feeding and rumen metabolism. As seen in sheep a considerable amount of this CO_2 finds access to blood depending on the rumen epithelial blood flow. Under the right conditions CO_2 transfer from this source can increase CO_2 output ($\dot{V}_{CO_2}$) of the animal by more than 50% raising the respiratory quotient significantly. Increases in the concentrations of short-chain fatty acids (e.g. butyric acid) in the rumen also increases transport adding fixed acid to blood. The total transfer of CO_2 and short-chain fatty acids from rumen to blood is further facilitated by an increase in rumen blood flow caused, in turn, by CO_2 and fatty acids. Acute arterial hypoxia usually increases this blood flow. Although these observations do not demonstrate a direct influence of rumen on arterial blood gases and pH during chronic hypoxia, it could be visualised that during the first few hours of high-altitude acclimatisation an appropriate change in rumen metabolism and blood flow might occur causing metabolic acidosis. These two factors, hypoxia and acidosis, would increase ventilation promptly lowering P_{aCO_2} and arterial CO_2 content. Such changes would explain the unusually rapid fall in P_{aCO_2} observed in goats[73] and sheep (Lahiri, unpublished) without a corresponding rise in arterial pH unlike man during acclimatisation to high altitude. During the later part of chronic hypoxia, the metabolic acid component would presumably decrease, thereby withdrawing a part of the ventilatory stimulus. The resulting decrease in ventilation would increase P_{aCO_2} and arterial CO_2 content as seen in ruminants during acclimatisation to high altitude. It is expected that rumen CO_2 will have its own influence superimposed on these changes.

The species of cattle studied by Grover *et al.*[76] also developed relentless pulmonary hypertension at altitude. This study was extended by Bisgard et al.[77] who reported that ventilation of the calves at 4000 m responded normally to acute changes in P_{aO_2}. Furthermore, carotid chemodenervation in these species increased P_{aCO_2} remarkably, i.e. about 20 mmHg, suggesting a strong hypoxic drive to ventilation at 4000 m[78]. This presence of normal hypoxic ventilatory drive in the calves is in conformity with the observation of Lahiri[71] in 1–3 year old cows and yaks. Furthermore, inspection of the blood data of Hall et al.[79] suggests that all of their high-altitude animals except one hyperventilated normally as altitude increased. Thus there is no evidence that ventilatory response to hypoxia is attenuated in high-altitude animals.

8.2.6.7 Role of neonatal hypoxia

Lahiri and co-workers[80] approached the problem of attenuated ventilatory response to hypoxia from a developmental point of view. On the basis of the observation[81] that newborn (up to age 11 days) at sea level show a profound depression of ventilation within a minute after exposure to mild hypoxia ($P_{IO_2} = 100$ mmHg), they postulated that human infants born at high altitude presumably share this initial depression, and those who survive presumably maintain ventilation and hypoxic response at a low level. There is, as yet, no information about respiration in human infants at high altitude. It is well known that carotid arterial blood of human foetuses at sea level is in the range of 40 mmHg when maternal P_{aO_2} is around 100 mmHg. At a maternal P_{aO_2} of 50 mmHg at high altitude, foetal carotid arterial P_{O_2} is expected to be about 30–35 mmHg. In the normal newborn at sea level, P_{aO_2} increases to 60–70 mmHg immediately after birth and gradually increases to the order of 80–90 mmHg in about 2 weeks as the ductus arteriosus closes; at 4500 m P_{aO_2} would be expected to remain lower than 50 mmHg. This low P_{aO_2} in turn keeps pulmonary arterial pressure high and consequently the ductus remains open for a longer period. If the ventilatory response of high-altitude infants was conditioned by persistent hypoxia, their ventilation presumably would be less than that of the sea level infant which rapidly became normoxic after birth.

To test this hypothesis, we attempted to reproduce the human infant phenomenon in newborn animals. It was found that in the newborn lamb and kid, breathing a hypoxic gas mixture (P_{IO_2} down to 60 mmHg; P_{aO_2} of the order of 25 mmHg) produced a sustained hyperventilation for the duration of the experiment. However, at P_{aO_2} of 15–20 mmHg, ventilation continued at a lower level than during air breathing. In kittens this sustained depression of ventilation was obtained at a P_{IO_2} of about 70 mmHg. According to these results, cats born and raised at 5000–6000 m would be expected to show a blunted response to hypoxia. This prediction seems to be in conformity with the observation of Tenney et al.[75] who showed that exposure of adult cats to 380 mmHg (c. 6000 m) decreases ventilatory response to acute change of P_{IO_2}. Our results offered a tentative explanation why goats and sheep born and raised below 6000 m did not show blunted ventilatory response to hypoxia; because ambient hypoxia presumably did not cause any initial depression of ventilation in the neonatal stage.

Not clear is how the depressed ventilation in the newborn during hypoxia was sustained. Schwieler[82] observed an increase of carotid chemoreceptor activity due to hypoxia in anaesthetised kitten while ventilation decreased. We found an increase in arterial acidity in our unanaesthetised preparation under the hypoxic condition. Thus, it may be inferred that the ventilation decreased despite increases in chemoreceptor stimulation and activity suggesting that the inhibition was central.

8.2.6.8   Effect of erythrocythaemia

The contribution of erythrocythaemia to blunted ventilatory response as seen in the high-altitude natives is likely to be small because the subjects show the same blunted response at sea level and altitude independent of their red cell concentrations[3,52]. There is, however, intrinsic interest in this subject because the increased O_2 content of the blood during erythrocytosis would raise P_{vO_2} at a given P_{aO_2}, other conditions remaining constant (see section on O_2 transport). If the peripheral chemoreceptors are sensitive to such changes in P_{vO_2} as a result of erythrocythaemia, chemoreceptor and consequently ventilatory response to arterial hypoxia may decrease. The question remains to be solved[83].

8.2.6.9   Hypoxic chemoreflex v. central depression

Although the transient 'N_2/O_2 test'[2,66] and 'CO_2 tests'[84] did show decreased ventilatory responses in the high-altitude natives, the physiologic tests did not identify the receptor sites responsible for the blunted respiratory sensitivity. These tests do not distinguish between desensitisation at the peripheral receptor sites and inhibition (or block) in the reflex pathways central to the receptors. However, these tests do demonstrate that the blunted response involves reflex pathways and not excessive cerebral medullary depression as may happen during steady state hypoxia[51,85,86].

The size and histologic structure of the carotid chemoreceptor tissue in high-altitude sheep (Lahiri and Pietra, unpublished) and cats (Hornbein, personal communication) which have been found functionally normal appeared also essentially normal. Edwards et al.[87] reported a change in the proportion of dark and white Type I cells in high-altitude guinea-pigs but nothing is known as to the functional significance of such a change. There are reports available on the enlargement of carotid bodies in chronic cor pulmonale[88] and in inherited disease of chemoreceptor tissues but there are no functional studies available in such patients.

In summary, with respect to control of ventilation in rest, it can be stated that (1) at sea level, hypoxic ventilatory drive and response play a small part; CO_2-H^+ drive predominates; (2) during acute hypoxia, hypoxic drive and response predominate whereas CO_2 drive is negligible; (3) in the course of acclimatisation to hypoxia, CO_2 drive increases and the response eventually exceeds the sea level value while hypoxic response is maintained unchanged; the combination of the two stimuli producing a multiplicative effect; (4) in chronic exposure of sea level natives or man with lifelong hypoxia, hypoxic response is small whereas CO_2 response appears to be normal.

8.2.7 Hypoxic exercise

It is generally well known that exercise increases the stimulating effect of acute hypoxia on ventilation at sea level. Although the mechanism is not understood, the enhanced effect clearly involves the chemoreflex mechanism[14] because it disappears promptly with a breath of O_2. A similar conclusion was reached by Lahiri et al.[66, 67, 69] studying the effect of chronic hypoxia on the sojourners to high altitude. This enhancement of hypoxic effect on ventilation during exercise occurred in spite of alkalosis[66, 68] (Masson and Lahiri, unpublished). Altitude natives, however, ventilate relatively less than sojourners and maintain their arterial P_{CO_2} and pH during moderate exercise. It seems that hypoxic sensitivity determines the ventilatory augmentation during hypoxic exercise, and arterial pH follow this response without visibly influencing ventilation.

We have previously indicated that CSF is more acid in the high-altitude natives at high altitude[36, 37]. If increased CSF acidity were responsible for the augmented ventilation in hypoxic exercise there should have been a pronounced increase in ventilation in the high-altitude natives during exercise. The fact that this is not so suggests that factors other than a chemical agent may be involved.

8.2.8 Temperature regulation: interaction between hypoxia and cold

Acute exposure of a newborn infant to hypoxia at sea level promptly decreases his ventilation and lowers body temperature and O_2 uptake[81, 89] particularly if the ambient temperature is below 34–35 °C (neutral thermal environment). At high altitude, particularly in the Himalayas, the newborn is immediately exposed to a very low temperature because of the lack of adequate heating. This combination of cold temperature and hypoxia of high altitude presumably lowers body temperature of the newborn. This initial response of the newborn after birth to altitude environment may alter their temperature regulation in adult life, just as initial ventilatory response may lead to blunted hypoxic sensitivity as discussed previously. Little is known about developmental adaptation to environment.

8.3 O_2 AND CO_2 TRANSPORT BY LUNGS AND BLOOD

Most forms of life are dependent on molecular oxygen, much of which is contained in the atmospheric air. But life originated in water and the organism received O_2, in soluble form, which moved from the water surface into the depth primarily by convection. In stagnant waters the organisms moved to the surface in search of oxygen. As the ambient temperature increased, the amount of soluble oxygen decreased and purely aquatic life became unbearable. Thus, the organism began to acquire O_2 directly from the air which eventually led to the advent of air breathing and development of lungs—an example of fundamental adaptation to oxygen want. Parallel with this development were the changes in the transport of oxygen by the circulatory system on the one hand and by circulating fluid, i.e. blood, on the other. From this point of view, adaptation to altitude hypoxia is in continuity with the evolutionary process—oxygen-linked biological evolution.

This section deals with the structural and functional adaptation of these systems to hypoxia. In doing so I have used lessons from the field of comparative physiology.

8.3.1 Gas diffusion in the lung

It is expected that with the growth of the whole body from young to adult age its component parts, including the lungs, will also grow in approximate proportion[90]. It is also reasonable that large animals will generally have lungs with a large surface area so that a large amount of O_2 could diffuse through according to the demand of the metabolic rate. Tenney and Remmers[7] pointed out that while these general expectations hold good, small animals which have a greater specific O_2 consumption (O_2 uptake per unit mass) have disproportionately large lung volumes and surface area. As a corollary to the concept of optimal design for functional needs they also raised the question whether or not changes can be induced in the morphologic dimensions of lung by environmental stress, such as oxygen want.

This speculation seems to be substantiated by the observation in chronically hypoxic animals only if the lung volumes are expressed as a function of body weight[91,92] (Brody, personal communication). It seems that growth of the lungs was not retarded by chronic hypoxia whereas body growth was. Increased environmental P_{O_2} on the other hand retarded lung growth and decreased its gas-exchange surface area.

Hurtado[43] emphasised great thoracic development and large residual volume in high-altitude natives of the Peruvian Andes, and Baker[93] reported a slow post-natal growth in this population. Working on boys of 11–20 years of age in Peru, Frisancho[94] reported that chest circumference and forced vital capacity (FVC) are greater in the native subjects at 4300 m in spite of their smaller body stature. His data relating FVC to age or body stature show that the curve for highlanders paralleled that of lowlanders with higher FVC. The extrapolated intercept suggests that the difference may have occurred at birth; if not, hypoxia increased the rate of lung growth prior to age 11. At lower altitudes this difference in FVC is not obvious[4,96,98] (also our own unpublished observation on Sherpas). Diffusing capacities of the lungs for CO of the native residents of the Andes[95], Himalayas[47,96] and Rockies[97,98] have been found to be large compared to the sea level natives but Sherpa altitude natives are not particularly known for their large thoracic lung volumes. More recently Saldaña (M. Saldaña, personal communication) found that the alveoli of adult high-altitude natives (3840 m) are large in diameter (286 μm v. 264 μm) and greater in number (336×10^6 v. 283×10^6) than in sea level dwellers of the same size. This form of adaptation is unlike the adaptation in small animals which achieve greater surface area by internal partitioning[7] for a given lung volume.

Most investigators are inclined to believe that diffusing capacity in adult sojourners after several months of exposure to altitude does not increase[98,99]. However, if exposed during childhood, sojourners may achieve lung diffusing capacity similar to that in native residents of high altitude[97]. Post-natal increase in alveolar number (over tenfold) continues up to age 8–20 years and in diameter (1–2 times) for the next 10–15 years[100] in man. Hypoxia may have influenced both of these determinants of diffusing capacity in high-altitude natives and migrants during childhood. These changes, once achieved, are expected to be permanent. Accordingly, the diffusing capacity of the high altitude native was found to be high after several weeks of de-acclimatisation at sea level[96].

8.3.2 Oxygen transport by blood

The two basic respiratory properties which can modify oxygen transport are oxygen capacity and oxygen affinity.

8.3.2.1 *Erythrocytosis, O_2 capacity and content*

Stimulation of the erythropoietic system increases erythrocytosis within hours after hypoxic exposure in man[101]. In several weeks the expanded red-cell mass tends to achieve a steady level. In a serial study on the same individuals Pugh[102] found a prompt decrease in plasma volume in the early phase of acclimatisation which apparently persisted in the fully acclimatised sojourners and native residents. The mechanism for this plasma volume shrinkage is not known. Both acclimatised sojourners and high-altitude natives conform to this finding[103]. A similar situation is found in chronic hypoxia of cyanotic heart disease[104].

This red-cell response to chronic arterial hypoxia is linearly related to arterial O_2 saturation (S_{aO_2} %). The compiled results obtained in the Andes are shown in Figure 8.4. The lower the P_{aO_2} and S_{aO_2} % the greater is the O_2 capacity. The net result is a somewhat increased oxygen content in arterial blood in the healthy normal sojourners and native residents. Accordingly, the O_2 capacity increased by 0.38 vol. % and O_2 content by 0.12 vol. % for a decrease of 1% in S_{aO_2}.

By the standard of maternal arterial P_{O_2} all foetuses are hypoxic, and foetal blood O_2 capacity is greater than maternal blood. At high altitude both maternal and foetal O_2 capacities are apparently higher than at sea level[105]. However, for a given level of hypoxic stimulation (carotid P_{aO_2} approximates 22 and 19 mmHg at sea level and 4300 m respectively), foetal O_2 capacity is a great deal lower than in adults as shown in Figure 8.4. After birth, blood haemoglobin concentration presumably decreases further

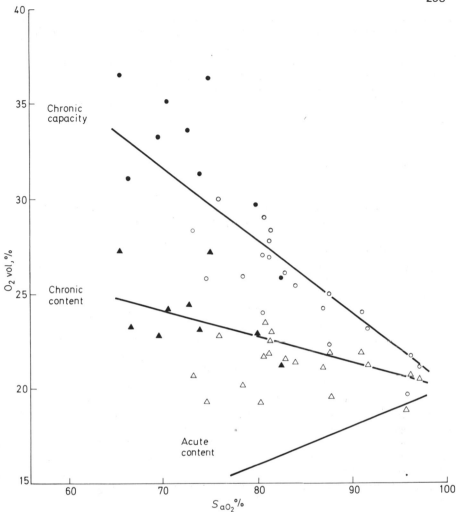

Figure 8.4. Effect of hypoxia on oxygen content (triangles) and capacity (circles) of human subjects. Open symbols are for normal healthy sojourners and native residents and closed symbols are for subjects with chronic mountain sickness. The line describing oxygen content during acute hypoxia is based on O_2 capacity of 20 ml/100 ml blood, and shows a linear decrease as S_{aO_2}% decreases. The data for chronic hypoxia are compiled from the following references: 4, 29, 42, 45, 57, 63 and 130. The O_2 capacity response to chronic hypoxia is such that O_2 content is somewhat greater than the sea level value at a given altitude.

before reaching adult values as seen at sea level[106] but the mechanism is un-solved.

8.3.2.2 Effect of haemoglobin concentration

The role of increased haemoglobin concentration in blood on O_2 transport can be visualised in terms of its effect on P_{vO_2}. This is depicted in Figure 8.5

relating P_{vO_2} to P_{aO_2} for an extraction of 10 vol. % O_2 from O_2 capacity of 14.3, 20.0 and 33.3 vol. %. This shows that starting with P_{aO_2} of 50 mmHg, for example, the values for P_{vO_2}s respectively are 12.6, 21.2 and 28.8 mmHg. That is, if blood can be circulated normally, higher haemoglobin concentration ensures adequate tissue P_{O_2} for normal aerobic metabolism assuming that P_{vO_2} usually reflects the balance between supply and use of oxygen. Thus, the erythropoietic response to hypoxia is evidently appropriate to minimise tissue hypoxia.

8.3.2.3 O_2 and haemoglobin affinity

The sigmoid shape of the oxygen equilibrium curve which is due to conformational changes in the molecule is of unique biological significance at sea level. At high altitude, however, the physiological use is limited to only a part of the curve, and the sigmoid shape loses some of its significance.

In recent years, because of the discovery that certain organic phosphates, notably 2,3-diphosphoglycerate (2,3 DPG), which are present in large concentrations in normal human red cells decrease oxygen affinity and that deoxygenated haemoglobin binds 2,3 DPG and increases concentration of 2,3 DPG by relieving product inhibition of 2,3 DPG mutase[5], the effect of acclimatisation to hypoxia on the O_2 equilibrium curve has been re-investigated. Lenfant et al.[107] and Mulhausen et al.[108] reported that within a few hours of human subjects' exposure to hypoxia, oxygen affinity of blood (indicated by P_{O_2} at 50% saturation with O_2 at 37°C and pH 7.4: $P_{50_{7.4}}$) decreased with a concomitant increase in 2,3 DPG concentration. Torrance et al.[109] also observed that $P_{50_{7.4}}$ as well as 2,3 DPG concentration of red cells of the native residents of high altitude were similarly high (about 30 mmHg at 4540 m). Similar changes were found in hypoxic patients with cyanotic heart disease[107] but not in prolonged carbon monoxide exposure[108]. Baumann et al.[110] also showed increases in 2,3 DPG and P_{50} in rats and guinea pigs during chronic hypoxia at 4000 m. Thus, the general finding is that acclimatisation to hypoxia in adult man and animals increased, rather than decreased $P_{50_{7.4}}$.

The finding of a shift of $P_{50_{7.4}}$ to a higher value led to the teleological explanation that it is an advantageous adaptive mechanism delivering O_2 to the tissues at higher P_{O_2}[36, 107]. More recently, Lenfant et al.[111] reconsidered their position. They also found that the subjects made acidotic prior to altitude ascent showed no increase in 2,3 DPG and no shift of $P_{50_{7.4}}$ but apparently unimpaired tolerance to hypoxia manifested by a sense of well being and ability to perform physical work well. Duhm and Gerlaich[112] reported that experimentally induced respiratory acidosis abolished the effect of hypoxia on the increases of 2,3 DPG concentration and $P_{50_{7.4}}$ in the rats. These data indicate that the 2,3 DPG depend on the increase in intraerythrocyte pH due to respiratory alkalosis and deoxygenation of haemoglobin A. Thus, the original reasoning that deoxyhaemoglobin increased 2,3 DPG concentration, and consequently decreased O_2 affinity, was not validated. This situation, however, raises the difficulty as to what keeps the 2,3 DPG concentration and $P_{50_{7.4}}$ high, since the respiratory alkalosis is largely compensated during acclimatisation, particularly in high-altitude natives who show a normal blood pH. The intra-erythrocyte increase of pH due to arterial deoxygenation (about 20%) at 4540 m seems to be too small to account for the reported increase in $P_{50_{7.4}}$. There may be yet other unidentified factor(s).

The mechanism of how 2,3 DPG changes O_2-Hb affinity has not been clearly worked out but kinetic studies showed that it increases O_2-Hb association at high P_{O_2} and increases dissociation at low P_{O_2}—an interaction which contributes to the sigmoid shape of the O_2-Hb equilibrium curve. In the complete absence of phosphates O_2-Hb (in solution) affinity increases enormously and the curve appears hyperbolic with $P_{50_{7.4}}$ less than 1 mmHg (Forster, personal communication).

An examination of the effect of change of $P_{50_{7.4}}$ on the relation between P_{AO_2} and P_{vO_2} for various levels of oxygen extraction is informative. An example is shown in Figure 8.5 for P_{50} values 26.6 to 30.6 mmHg for three blood samples with O_2 capacities of 14.3, 20.0 and 33.3 vol. %. For all these

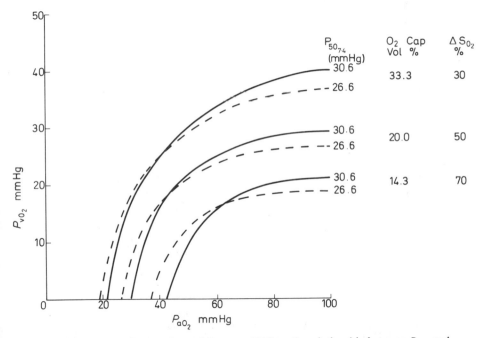

Figure 8.5 Effect of O_2 capacity and $P_{50_{7.4}}$ at 37°C on the relationship between P_{aO_2} and P_{vO_2} at three levels of O_2 extraction (ΔS_{O_2} % = 30, 50 and 70). The arterial pH is considered constant at 7.4 but the venous blood pH varies according to CO_2 output at RQ = 0.8 for a given ΔS_{O_2} %, taking the effect of *in vivo* CO_2 buffering and haemoglobin desaturation into account.

An increase of O_2 capacity raises P_{vO_2} at any P_{aO_2} at a constant P_{50} and ΔS_{O_2}%. For a greater ΔS_{O_2} %, P_{vO_2} is lower at a given P_{aO_2}.

An increase in $P_{50_{7.4}}$ from 26.6 to 30.6 mmHg, other conditions being equal, raises P_{vO_2} in the range of higher P_{aO_2} but makes it lower (note the cross-over points) in the hypoxic range. These cross-over points correspond to P_{aO_2} at which gain in unloading tension equals loss of O_2 loading due to an increase in P_{50}. An increase in O_2 capacity decreases this null-point P_{aO_2} and an increase in ΔS_{O_2} % increases it.

situations, 10 vol. % O_2 extraction is considered. Each of these samples shows clearly that down to a certain arterial P_{O_2}, depending on the O_2 capacities, the P_{vO_2} increases with the increase of $P_{50_{7.4}}$: However, at lower arterial P_{O_2}, P_{vO_2} is also lower when $P_{50_{7.4}}$ is higher. This arterial point roughly corresponds to P_{aO_2} at the altitude (4540 m) where this $P_{50_{7.4}}$ shift is found. This figure also shows that at higher O_2 extraction (ΔS_{O_2} %) the advantage of a greater $P_{50_{7.4}}$ is lost at even a higher P_{aO_2}. But an increase in O_2 capacity improves the condition greatly.

To conclude, it must, however, be pointed out that although $P_{50_{7.4}}$ may increase in sojourners, the *actual* P_{50} within the first few hours at high altitude is bound to decrease below the sea level value due to alkalosis. The actual P_{50} will depend on the balance of the effects of erythrocyte H^+ and 2,3 DPG concentrations which in turn are interdependent in a complex way. That the current theories of this cellular adaptation do not account for all the observations suggests that our knowledge in this regard is incomplete.

8.3.2.4 *High altitude animals*

This increase in P_{50}, however, is not found in animals native to high altitude[79, 113]. These animals (alpaca, guanaco, llama and vicuña) showed $P_{50_{7.4}} = 18$–21 mmHg which did not apparently change with the change of altitude, although their ventilation changed.

As for the adaptive value of high O_2 affinity, a teleologic view is that O_2 procurement from the atmosphere may be accomplished effectively. Without it no amount of adjustment would be of any value. Once this first step is accomplished the rest depends on the internal adjustment at the tissue level. A similar argument applies to foetal blood. The foetuses of the high altitude animals presumably have even lower values for $P_{50_{7.4}}$ which increases to their adult value after they are born.

The red cells of these animals native to high altitude have two other unusual features: they are packed with greater concentration of haemoglobin (40%) and are smaller in size (diameter = 6.5 μm)[79, 114]. Thus, blood in these animals can carry O_2 in a more concentrated form and have greater surface areas for gas exchange. They also do not show a significant polycythemic response, although the turn-over rate of erythrocytes is increased at high altitude[114]. There is, however, one exception to this rule: the yak, a traditionally high-altitude animal in the Himalays, shares none of these peculiarities. Rather it is very similar to sea level man[115].

Schmidt-Neilsen and Larimer[116] reported that small animals who have a greater specific $\dot{V}_{O_2}$ showed a higher P_{50}. They might have over-estimated $P_{50_{7.4}}$ since the authors equilibrated blood of all the animals with P_{CO_2} of 40 mmHg at 37 °C whereas some small animals have lower P_{aCO_2} than 40 mmHg. With the available corrected figures (Lahiri, unpublished) the importance of the relationship between specific $\dot{V}_{O_2}$ and $P_{50_{7.4}}$ is somewhat diminished. However, the relationship indicates another aspect of adaptation to oxygen demand.

It is conceivable that a larger Bohr effect would facilitate O_2 transport from lungs to tissues. Accordingly, Riggs[117] found that Bohr effect in haemoglobin solution positively correlated with the specific $\dot{V}_{O_2}$ in mammals. However, working with whole blood, Hilpert et al.[118] could not confirm this observation. No specific explanation is known for this discrepancy. Be that as it may, it appears that Bohr effect does not change with transition during neonatal adjustment[106] nor during adaptation to hypoxia[107].

The role of reticulocytes in O_2 transport relative to erythrocytes deserves mention because its concentration is increased during acclimatisation. Presumably these cells have high concentration of 2,3 DPG and a high $P_{50_{7.4}}$ but they also have a high O_2 uptake relative to the mature red cells. All these properties of reticulocytes may be more of a theoretical than practical interest but the fact that the mature mammalian red cells have low oxygen uptake is in itself an improved property as an oxygen carrier.

8.3.3 CO_2 transport

Transport of CO_2 at high altitude, unlike O_2, has not received much attention. However, it is worthy of mention that the total Haldane effect (defined for the present purpose as the difference in total CO_2 contents between fully oxygenated and deoxygenated blood at the normal arterial P_{CO_2}) assumes a proportionately larger value because of the increase in haemoglobin concentration of blood. This increase in the Haldane effect potentially widens arterio-venous (a-v) difference for CO_2 in blood for a given change in P_{CO_2} at a given RQ. Since it is the a-v difference rather than the absolute value of total CO_2 in blood that matters with respect to transport of CO_2 from tissues to lung the process of balanced elimination of CO_2 is likely to be facilitated at high altitude. Increased haemoglobin content also means that a greater proportion of combined CO_2 is carried as carbamino compounds. This reaction is direct and fast and does not directly involve a shift of ions across cell membranes. Moreover, a greater concentration of carbamate minimises pH change due to the oxygen linked Bohr effect[119]. Higher haemoglobin levels also increase the buffering power of blood. Thus, the high O_2 capacity which results from a hypoxic stimulus not only copes with the problems of adequate O_2 delivery to tissues but also 'spreads protective wings' over CO_2 transport to lung.

However, CO_2 transport could become limiting during strenuous muscular exercise at high altitude when S_{aO_2} % decreases: desaturated arterial blood will have less CO_2 carrying capacity for the same difference in (v-a) P_{CO_2} because of the Haldane effect; in transporting the excess CO_2 the venous P_{CO_2} would have to be raised, unduly increasing $[H^+]$ and presumably disturbing various CO_2-H^+ related physiological functions.

8.4 CARDIOVASCULAR ADAPTATION

8.4.1 Circulating arterial O_2

The increase in erythrocyte volume while increasing O_2 capacity also increases blood viscosity which may limit the blood flow. The advantage of increased

O_2 capacity follows the rule of diminishing returns at rest, and even more so during exercise. In the resting dogs the optimum O_2 delivery appears to be around the normal haematocrit (45–50 vol. %) with normal blood volume and viscosity. However, increased blood volume changes haematocrit optimum for blood flow to a higher value[120]. The increased blood volume and red cell mass at high altitude may thus counterbalance the effect of increased haematocrit on blood flow which would improve systemic O_2 transport leading to improved tissue oxygenation[120].

In unanaesthetised resting man during chronic hypoxia the limiting effect of haematocrit is not obvious[63]. During exercise, however, complications arise not only because of increasing work load on the heart from increased cardiac output but also because of a progressively decreasing arterial O_2 saturation due to limiting O_2 diffusing capacity[135] and an increase in pulmonary arterial pressure.

8.4.2 Coronary blood flow and oxygen uptake

Grover *et al.*[121] and Moret[122] found subnormal coronary blood flow in sojourners and natives acclimatised to high altitude (3100–4375 m) compared to sea level. These results contrast with the classical finding that acute hypoxia is a most effective vasodilating agent for coronary circulation. However, at high altitude, acute changes in P_{aO_2} changes blood flow just as at sea level[122]. Although there was no indication of O_2 insufficiency of the myocardium at rest, O_2 transport to and O_2 uptake by the left ventricle were lower at high altitude than at sea level. This restricted myocardial blood flow, may however, become critical during physical exercise and can decrease maximal work at high altitude or in chronic hypoxia at sea level. But high-altitude natives are known to do well in prolonged strenuous work.

8.4.3 Heart rate, stroke volume and cardiac output

The response of the heart to acute moderate hypoxia is to increase its rate and output and to decrease its stroke volume both at rest and during exercise[123]. The maximum heart rate (180–200 beats/min) and the maximal output are barely affected whereas maximum oxygen uptake diminishes according to the severity of hypoxia[124, 125]. In the course of short-term acclimatisation to moderate hypoxia (2 weeks at 4000 m), heart rate for a given oxygen uptake (including the maximum rate) is generally decreased, the decrement of maximum heart rate being greater at higher altitudes[47] (Figure 8.6). The cardiac output at rest and during mild exercise returned to the normal sea level values within 2 weeks at 4000–4300 m whereas the maximal output decreased and the stroke volume remained consistently low[124, 126]. Thus, performance of the heart in sojourners during short-term acclimatisation did not seem to improve. The maximal heart rate has been reported to increase from the subnormal value with prolonged acclimatisation[47, 67, 127] but it is not known if there was a corresponding increase in cardiac output.

Raised P_{IO_2} in the acclimatised sojourners immediately increased maximum heart rate if it was depressed previously[47, 67, 128]. According to Saltin *et al.*[124], raised P_{IO_2} at 4300 m did not improve maximal cardiac output in short-term acclimatisation, although the maximal $\dot{V}_{O_2}$ increased approaching the sea level controls.

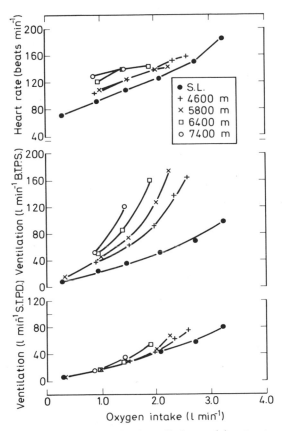

Figure 8.6. Relation of ventilation and heart rate to O_2 uptake in muscular exercise at various altitudes ranging from sea level to 7440 m (24 400 ft) (From Pugh *et al.*[47] by courtesy of the American Physiological Society and the authors)

The maximal heart rate in high-altitude natives during exercise at high altitude generally reached the maximal value observed at sea level[43, 47, 67, 129]. However, native residents of the Andes (Morococha) differed from those of the Rockies (Leadville) in several respects: the responses of natives of Morococha (4540 m) were similar to those of sea level subjects—both increased cardiac output, heart rate and $(a-v)_{O_2}$ difference similarly maintaining stroke volume practically constant[130]; native subjects at Leadville (3100 m) had decreased cardiac output and stroke volume, increased heart rate and increased $(a-v)_{O_2}$ difference for the same exercise level[129]. Leadville subjects also showed raised systemic arterial blood pressure during exercise whereas the native subjects of Morococha showed considerably lower values. What made the difference between the two groups of altitude natives is not clear.

8.5 PHYSICAL PERFORMANCE CAPACITY

During the last decade numerous investigators have studied the effect of high-altitude acclimatisation on maximal working capacity of subjects with different physiological and ethnic backgrounds. Most of the objective measurements involved cardiorespiratory parameters during short bursts of activity. The area of most agreement is that maximum O_2 uptake decreases with increasing altitude, and P_{IO_2} equivalent to sea level value promptly reversed the trend of $\dot{V}_{O_2}$ in keeping with the experience of climbers at great altitudes.

Several authors studied the time course of acclimatisation to hypoxia (3800–4300 m) for 2–8 weeks and observed little improvement of maximal $\dot{V}_{O_2}$ which contrasted with the improved sense of vigour and endurance[131, 132]. Klausen et al.[133], however, found a slow but definite increase in maximal $\dot{V}_{O_2}$ after 2 weeks of acclimatisation at 3800 m.

There is no general agreement concerning the mechanisms involved in the superior performing capacity of high altitude natives[43, 47, 134]. However, one is struck by the fact that Sherpas in the Himalayas are capable of doing a great deal more strenuous work over a longer period of time than the visiting climbers. Even those Sherpas including 'Sherpanis' (Sherpa women) who may not show great maximum oxygen uptake have been found to do sustained physical work beyond the capacity of sojourners at great altitudes. As yet, the basis for this enhanced capacity to perform has escaped measurement.

8.5.1 Limiting factors

Of the two areas of gas exchange, in the lung and tissues, transfer of O_2 across the alveolar capillary membrane appears to be by far the most important limiting factor. West et al.[135] reported progressive decreases in arterial O_2 saturation during increasing grades of exercise in the acclimatised sojourners at 5800 m in the face of a rise of alveolar O_2 pressure, observations which strongly suggest a diffusion limitation to O_2 transfer. Similar decreases in $S_{aO_2}\%$ have been found in high-altitude natives[47, 130]. It is not known if there is any significant difference in the gas diffusing properties of the lungs between the two groups but by virtue of their reported potentially available larger gas-exchange surface area, high-altitude natives show relatively large maximal diffusing capacity[95].

Taking mixed venous P_{O_2} as a measure of tissue oxygenation, West[99] discussed the roles of various limiting factors to exercise at high altitude. He found that the lung diffusing capacity was predominant whereas the effect of cardiac output and O_2 capacity on increasing P_{vO_2} was less and of the same order of magnitude. The minute output of the right heart and the restricted coronary flow in chronic hypoxia are also limiting factors. We have seen previously that the decrease in O_2-Hb affinity at high altitude may eventually have an adverse effect on P_{vO_2}. So is the effect of excessive ventilation because the gain in the rise of alveolar P_{O_2} is more than offset by the excessive O_2 cost of high levels of ventilation. Dyspnoea is a notoriously prominent feeling during exercise at high altitude. However, the maximum attainable ventilation during exercise increases as altitude increases, although the corresponding $\dot{V}_{O_2}$ decreases. At great altitude, over 6000 m, the maximum $\dot{V}_E$ decreases with the further decrease of $\dot{V}_{O_2}$ (Figure 8.6).

8.5.2 Temperature and performance capacity

It is a fortunate coincidence that ambient temperature and humidity decrease as altitude increases because raised ambient temperature and humidity can prevent elimination of body heat generated by muscular exercise. A rise in body temperature during exercise increases heart rate dramatically[136]. The heart rate increases to its limit at a low work rate in a hot and humid environment (Lahiri, unpublished WHO report), and consequently imposes extra limitation on the performing capacity. A combination of heat and hypoxia would make the cardiovascular performing capacity reach a limit at an even lower work rate.

8.6 PULMONARY CIRCULATION AND PULMONARY OEDEMA

Enormous volumes of literature have accumulated showing that acute hypoxia raises pulmonary arterial pressure, although the concomitant alkalosis minimises the effect. This active control of pulmonary circulation superimposed on the passive factors redistributes the blood in the lung[137]. The upper parts of the vertical lung in man which is relatively poorly perfused is normally expected to be better perfused under high pulmonary arterial pressure. Chronic hypoxia intensifies this pulmonary hypertension[63, 138] but the mechanism(s) of this profound change in acute and chronic hypoxia still remains elusive. In chronic mountain sickness pulmonary hypertension is most marked. Right ventricular hypertrophy and extra muscularisation of arterial branches are common structural changes in chronic hypoxia, and it is generally believed that the extra resistance to blood flow occurs in these arterial vessels. This pulmonary hypertension in the native and long-term residents is partially reversed immediately by high P_{IO_2}; it is reversed gradually almost fully at sea level. This reversal of pulmonary hypertension is in contrast with the irreversible blunted ventilatory response to hypoxia in the high-altitude natives.

As pointed out, the raised pulmonary arterial pressure in man would make the topographical distribution of blood flow more even and improve the $\dot{V}_A/\dot{Q}$ matching. However, overall gas exchange in a normal lung is not expected to improve by such a change in $\dot{V}_A/\dot{Q}$ ratio[139] even at high altitude.

Indeed pulmonary arterial pressure during exercise at high altitude is increased further but that did not prevent a decrease in S_{aO_2} %[135]. Haab et al.[140] measured $\dot{V}_A/\dot{Q}$ during altitude (2750 m) acclimatisation and concluded that transition from low to high altitude decreased the gas-exchange efficiency of the lung.

Occasionally associated with the rise of pulmonary arterial pressure in hypoxia is pulmonary oedema which has also been extensively investigated in man and animals. All investigators have emphasised the haemodynamic aspects and passive transfer of fluid from the intra-vascular to extra-vascular space in the lungs; but its mechanism of production in hypoxia is not clear.

Slow circulation of water from pulmonary vessels through lung tissue into the systemic vessels is a normal physiological phenomenon. The circulating water originates from the gas-exchanging alveolar capillaries and runs through the interstitial space into the pulmonary lymphatic capillaries (which are present in the perivascular space beyond the alveoli) to return to the systemic circulation. This flow is aided by the balance of hydrostatic and osmotic pressures between the intra- and extra-vascular compartments and gradients of subatmospheric pressures towards the lymphatic capillaries in the extra-vascular space. Any imbalance in these forces which enhances fluid input into the interstitial space from the alveolar capillary and/or impedes its removal from the extra-vascular space can lead first to interstitial and eventually to alveolar oedema. Although the lung capillary endothelium is known to be freely permeable to water, most of the vascular water is retained in the vessels because of the balance of hydrostatic and osmotic pressures.

Since pulmonary oedema of high altitude in man is associated with pulmonary hypertension, a causative role for increased hydrostatic pressure has been suspected but not established. This pulmonary hypertension is due to arteriolar constriction since there are no concomitant increases in left atrial pressure and cardiac output. If oedema formation were to be linked to this hypertension, one has to postulate functional inhomogeneities which allow some capillaries to leak but not others. The result would be the patchy oedema seen at high altitude and the mechanism would be non-homogeneous distribution of precapillary resistances. The leakage in these instances may occur through endothelial junctions which presumably open under hydrostatic pressure. This opening, if large enough, could allow passage of more plasma protein into the interstitium than the drainage system could cope with —thus potentiating pulmonary oedema. A third possibility of leakage through larger arteriolar vessels has been considered but direct passage of water through these thick-walled vessels is open to question. Fishman has presented various aspects of this unsolved problem in an elegant review[141]. A small transient increase in lung water is presumably a constant feature during the initial phase of acclimatisation to altitude[142].

8.7 TISSUE AND CELLULAR ADAPTATION

It seems that capillary density in tissues is influenced by O_2 demand and O_2 supply. In chronic hypoxia, proliferation of small blood vessels and capillaries has been repeatedly observed and recently supported by physiological evidence for O_2 diffusion[143]. The ultimate objective of all the transport processes is to help bring the molecular O_2 to the mitochondrial surface where it is reduced by electron transport from the substrate through the final common pathway of respiratory chain (cytochrome $b \rightarrow c_1 \rightarrow c \rightarrow a \rightarrow a_3 \rightarrow O_2$) to produce H_2O. This respiratory function is coupled to, and controlled by, the phosphorylating system (phosphate and phosphate acceptor). During hypoxia the rate of reaction at the level of cytochrome system may become the predominant controlling factor. If the cytochrome oxidase becomes partially reduced, electron flow will decrease. Since the P_{O_2} at which cytochrome oxidase reacts at half its maximum rate (K_m) has been found to be small—less than 1 mmHg[144] it may be assumed that normal oxidative rate is impaired only around such low P_{O_2}. If impaired, ADP/ATP ratio and DPHN will increase, in turn stimulating further lactic acid production. Thus, a lack of oxygen tends, *per se*, to prevent its use in the cells.

What adaptive change can take place in the cells to combat too low a P_{O_2} at the mitochondria is the crucial question. Although there is little room for adjustment of P_{O_2} within such low and narrow limit so that the cell can function normally, information is not adequate. It is known, however, that mitochondrial concentration and membrane surface per unit mass of tissue and cells are increased in altitude-adapted rats[145]. This finding is consistent with the observations that the enzymes of the respiratory chain[146] are increased in animals acclimatised to chronic hypoxia. But the physiological meaning of increased mitochondrial mass is not clear. To Van Liere and Stickney[147] it was not readily apparent how increased cytochrome c content could be advantageous to an organism, for increased metabolic rate which is facilitated by increased cytochromes has been observed to be inimical to hypoxic tolerance. Ou and Tenney[145] postulated that during hypoxia the fewer O_2 molecules will have a greater chance of colliding with the active site if the oxidative enzymes are increased in concentration. That is, the rate of O_2 uptake may be maintained by this mechanism. Increased mitochondria concentration may also facilitate O_2 diffusion by the stirring produced by the pumping of water and electrolyte by mitochondria as proposed by Longmuir[144] since diffusion is a limiting factor in O_2 transport in cells.[148]

Two other pigments of the same family as cytochrome are haemoglobin and myoglobin. We have seen previously how the production of haemoglobin is stimulated by hypoxia. Myoglobin, which is present in small quantities in muscle cells, has high affinity for O_2, and combines reversibly with O_2. Thus, it also stores a small amount of O_2. Myoglobin has also been thought to facilitate O_2 diffusion as does haemoglobin in red blood cells. Chronic hypoxia increases myoglobin concentration in some species[145] but how vital this response is for adaptation is not apparent.

There is another interesting line of evidence developed with respect to heart and skeletal muscle. Meerson[149] noted that acclimatisation to chronic hypoxia protects the myocardium from the damaging action of overload. Overloading the left ventricle by aortic coarctation promptly activated nucleic acid and protein synthesis in the control rats but not in those adapted to hypoxia. Meerson tentatively suggested that increased mitochondrial mass and enhanced capacity of the mechanism of energy transformation in the acclimatised rats prevented breakdown of cells and the consequent synthesis of new cells. This reaction is not, however, unique to hypoxia because physical training does the same.

8.8 GENERAL CONCLUSION

Problems of response and adaptation to oxygen want are encountered at many levels in the organism. The *responses* to low environmental P_{O_2} can be divided into two main categories: (a) The fast response, examples of which are reflex hyperventilation mediated by the peripheral chemoreceptors and the increase in total and regional blood flow, e.g. in the brain, heart and kidney. These fast responses, however, tend to subside in time as a complex function of duration and strength of the stimulus. (b) Slow and sustained responses in the form of hyperplasia and hypertrophy of tissues and cells, such as the blood and the lungs. The mitochondrial cellular contents which are directly concerned with O_2 transport and utilisation also respond, although we do not know the molecular basis of the initiation and maintenance of this cellular activity. Intuitively the role of autonomic nervous system is bound to be important in these responses to hypoxia but there is not much published material on the subject. However, there are instances[86] which suggest that in the absence of normal autonomic function some of the physiological responses to hypoxia may not be sustained.

Where the response ends and adaptation begins is difficult to define. This problem is further complicated by the fact that there are processes which are linked in series as well as others which develop in parallel. Eventual adaptation depends on the pattern of the multiphasic responses. Hypoxic adaptation not only leads to an increase in tolerance to hypoxia but increases tolerance to other stressful stimuli thereby showing the phenomenon of cross-adaptation.

Studies on the natives of high altitude has focused our attention on the fact that much of the adaptation to hypoxia not only depends on its duration (e.g. years, lifelong, or generations) but also on the period of life when the exposure to hypoxia begins. This is a promising line of investigation which is currently being pursued.

Note added in proof

An account of the work on cardiocirculatory adaptation to chronic hypoxia during a Swiss Scientific expedition to Peru and Bolivia[150] and two review articles[151,152] dealing with some aspects of adaptation to high altitude have been published recently.

It is of interest to note that Frisancho *et al.*[153] added evidence to the effect that the attainment of aerobic capacity at high altitude is influenced by adaptations acquired during the developmental period. They investigated the effect of duration of hypoxia at varying ages on maximal O_2 uptake and ventilation in man and found that the sea level subjects who were acclimatised to high altitude (3400 m) from childhood were comparable to the high altitude natives, whereas sea level subjects who were exposed to high altitude as adults attained a lower aerobic capacity and higher ventilation (see p. 10–14, 30).

Acknowledgements

I am grateful to Dr Alfred P. Fishman for his support and helpful comments during preparation of this manuscript, and to several of my colleagues for many illuminating discussions.

My thanks are due to the Library of the College of Physicians of Philadelphia for making MEDLINE assistance available to locate some of the bibliographic citations.

Supported in part by a grant from the National Heart and Lung Institute, National Institutes of Health, U.S.A., HL-08805.

References

1. Cherniack, N. S. and Longobardo, G. S. (1970). Oxygen and carbon dioxide gas stores of the body. *Physiol. Rev.*, **50**, 196
2. Lefrançois, R., Gautier, H. and Pasquis, P. (1968). Ventilatory oxygen drive in acute and chronic hypoxia. *Resp. Physiol.*, **4**, 217
3. Milledge, J. S. and Lahiri, S. (1967). Respiratory control in lowlanders and Sherpa highlanders at altitude. *Resp. Physiol.*, **2**, 310
4. Severinghaus, J. W., Bainton, C. R. and Carcelen, A. (1966). Respiratory insensitivity to hypoxia in chronically hypoxic man. *Resp. Physiol.*, **1**, 308
5. Chanutin, A. and Curnish, R. R. (1967). Effect of organic and inorganic phosphates on the oxygen equilibrium of human erythrocytes. *Arch. Biochem. Biophys.*, **121**, 96
6. Benesch, R. and Benesch, R. E. (1967). The effect of organic phosphates from the human erythrocyte on the allosteric properties of hemoglobin. *Biochem. Biophys. Res. Commun.*, **26**, 162
7. Tenney, S. M. and Remmers, J. E. (1963). Quantitative comparative morphology of mammalian lungs; diffusing areas. *Nature (London)*, **197**, 54
8. Hornbein, T. F., Griffo, Z. J. and Roos, A. (1961). Quantitation of chemoreceptor activity: interrelation of hypoxia and hypercapnia. *J. Neurophysiol.*, **24**, 561
9. Sampson, S. R. and Biscoe, T. J. (1970). Efferent control of the carotid body chemoreceptor. *Experientia*, **26**, 261
10. Åstrand, P-O. (1954). A study of chemoreceptor activity in animals exposed to prolonged hypoxia. *Acta Physiol. Scand.*, **30**, 335
11. Hornbein, T. F. and Severinghaus, J. W. (1969). Carotid chemoreceptor response to hypoxia and acidosis in cats living at high altitude. *J. Appl. Physiol.*, **27**, 837
12. Rahn, H. and Otis, A. B. (1949). Man's respiratory response during and after acclimatisation to high altitude. *Amer. J. Physiol.*, **157**, 445
13. Dejours, P. (1962). Chemoreflexes in breathing. *Physiol. Rev.*, **42**, 335
14. Cunningham, D. J. C., Spurr, D. and Lloyd, B. B. (1966). The drive to ventilation from arterial chemoreceptors in hypoxic exercise. *Proc. Wates Foundation Symp. Arterial Chemoreceptors*, 301 (R. W. Torrance editor) (Oxford, 1968: Blackwell)
15. Nielsen, M. and Smith, H. (1952). Studies on the regulation of respiration in acute hypoxia. *Acta Physiol. Scand.*, **24**, 293
16. Kellogg, R. H. (1963). Effect of altitude on respiratory regulation. *Ann. N. Y. Acad. Sci.*, **109**, 815
17. Severinghaus, J. W., Mitchell, R. A., Richardson, B. W. and Singer, M. M. (1963). Respiratory control at high altitude suggesting active transport regulation of CSF pH. *J. Appl. Physiol.*, **18**, 1155
18. Sørensen, S. C. (1970). Ventilatory acclimatisation to hypoxia in rabbits after denervation of peripheral chemoreceptors. *J. Appl. Physiol.*, **28**, 836
19. Pauli, H. G., Vorburger, C. and Reubi, F. (1962). Chronic derangements of cerebrospinal fluid acid-base components in man. *J. Appl. Physiol.*, **17**, 993
20. Mitchell, R. A. (1964). The regulation of respiration in metabolic acidosis and alkalosis. *Proc. Symp. Cerebrospinal Fluid and the Regulation of Ventilation*, 109 (Oxford, 1965: Blackwell) (McC. C. Brooks, F. F. Kao and B. B. Lloyd editors)

21. Wade, J. G., Larson, D. P. Jr, Hickey, R. F. Ehrenfeld, W. K. and Severinghaus, J. W. (1970). Effect of carotid endarterectomy on carotid chemoreceptor and baro-receptor function in man. *New Eng. J. Med.*, **282**, 823

22. Fitzgerald, M. P. (1913). The changes in the breathing and the blood at various high altitudes. *Phil. Trans. Roy. Soc. Ser. B*, **203**, 351

23. Kellogg, R. H. (1968). Altitude acclimatization, a historical introduction emphasising the regulation of breathing. *The Physiologist*, **11**, 37

24. Michel, C. C. and Milledge, J. S. (1963). Respiratory regulation in man during acclimatisation to high altitude. *J. Physiol. (London)*, **168**, 631

25. Cunningham, D. J. C., Shaw, D. G., Lahiri, S. and Lloyd, B. B. (1961). The effect of maintained ammonium chloride acidosis on the relation between pulmonary ventilation and alveolar oxygen and carbon dioxide in man. *Quart. J. Expt. Physiol.*, **46**, 323

26. Eger, E. I., Kellogg, R. H., Mines, A. H., Lima-Ostos, M., Morrill, C. G. and Kent, D. W. (1968). Influence of CO_2 on ventilatory acclimatisation to altitude. *J. Appl. Physiol.*, **24**, 607

27. Weil, J. V., Byrne-Quinn, E., Ingvar, E., Filley, G. F. and Grover, R. F. (1971). Acquired attenuation of chemoreceptor function in chronically hypoxic man at high altitude. *J. Clin. Invest.*, **50**, 186

28. Houston, C. S. and Riley, R. L. (1949). Respiratory and circulatory changes during acclimatization to high altitude. *Amer. J. Physiol.*, **149**, 565

29. Hurtado, A. and Aste-Salazar, H. (1948). Arterial blood gases and acid-base balance at sea level and at high altitudes. *J. Appl. Physiol.*, **1**, 304

30. Rennie, D., Lozano, R., Monge, C., Sime, F. and Whittenbury, J. (1971). Renal oxygenation in male Peruvian natives living permanently at high altitude. *J. Appl. Physiol.*, **30**, 450

31. Lambertsen, C. J. (1958). Regulation of brain oxygen and acid-base environment. *Man's Dependence on the Earthly Atmosphere*, 234 (K. E. Schaefer editor) (New York, 1962: Macmillan)

32. Fencl, V., Vale, J. R. and Broch, J. A. (1969). Respiration and cerebral blood flow in metabolic acidosis and alkalosis in humans. *J. Appl. Physiol.*, **27**, 67

33. Roy, S. B., Guleria, J. S., Khanna, P. K., Talwar, J. R., Manchanda, S. C., Pande, J. N., Kaushik, V. S., Subba, P. S. and Wood, J. E. (1968). Immediate circulatory response to high altitude in man. *Nature (London)*, **217**, 1177

34. Kogure, K., Scheinberg, P., Reinmuth, O. M. P., Fujishima, J. and Bustu, R. (1970). Mechanism of cerebral vasodilation in hypoxia. *J. Appl. Physiol.*, **29**, 223

35. Milledge, J. S. and Sørensen, S. C. (1972). Cerebral arteriovenous oxygen difference in man native to high altitude. *J. Appl. Physiol.*, **32**, 687

36. Lahiri, S. and Milledge, J. S. (1967). Acid-base in Sherpa altitude residents and low-landers at 4880 m. *Resp. Physiol.*, **2**, 323

37. Sørensen, S. C. and Milledge, J. S. (1971). Cerebrospinal fluid acid-base composition at high altitude. *J. Appl. Physiol.*, **31**, 28

38. Forster, H. V., Dempsey, J. A., Birnbaum, M. L., Reddan, W. G., Thoden, J., Grover, R. F. and Rankin, J. (1971). Effect of chronic exposure to hypoxia on ventilatory response to CO_2 and hypoxia. *J. Appl. Physiol.*, **31**, 586

39. Lahiri, S. (1972). Dynamic aspects of regulation of ventilation in man during acclimatisation to high altitude. *Resp. Physiol.*, **16**, 245

40. Åstrand, P–O. (1954). The respiratory activity in man exposed to prolonged hypoxia. *Acta Physiol., Scand.*, **30**, 343

41. Dejours, P., Kellogg, R. H. and Pace, N. (1963). Regulation of respiration and heart rate response in exercise during altitude acclimatisation. *J. Appl. Physiol.*, **18**, 10

42. Chiodi, H. (1957). Respiratory adaptations to chronic high altitude hypoxia. *J. Appl. Physiol.*, **10**, 81

43. Hurtado, A. (1964). Animals in high altitudes: resident man. *Adaptation to Environment, Handbook of Physiology*, Section 4, 843 (D. B. Dill editor) (Washington, D. C.: Amer. Physiol. Soc.)

44. Barcoft, J., Binger, C. A., Bock, A. V., Doggart, J. H., Forbes, H. S., Harrop, G. A., Meakins, J. C. and Redfield, A. C. (1923). Observations on the effect of high altitude on the physiological processes on the human body, carried in the Peruvian Andes. *Phil. Trans. Roy. Soc. Ser. B*, **211**, 351

45. Dill, D. B., Talbott, J. H. and Consolazio, W. V. (1937). Blood gas as a physioco-chemical system. XII. Man at high altitudes. *J. Biol. Chem.*, **118**, 649
46. Keys, A., Hall, F. G. and Guzman Barron, E. S. (1936). The position of the oxygen dissociation curve of human blood at high altitude. *Amer. J. Physiol.*, **115**, 292
47. Pugh, L. G. C. E., Gill, M. B., Lahiri, S., Milledge, J. S., Ward, M. P. and West, J. B. (1964). Muscular exercise at great altitudes. *J. Appl. Physiol.*, **19**, 431
48. Lahiri, S. and Milledge, J. S. (1965). Sherpa physiology. *Nature (London)*, **207**, 610
49. Lloyd, B. B., Jukes, M. G. M. and Cunningham, D. J. C. (1958). The relation between alveolar oxygen pressure and the respiratory responses to carbon dioxide in man. *Quart. J. Exp. Physiol.*, **43**, 214
50. Cormack, R. S., Cunningham, D. J. C. and Gee, J. B. L. (1961). The effect of carbon dioxide on the respiratory response to want of oxygen in man. *Quart. J. Exp. Physiol.*, **46**, 323
51. Lahiri, S., Kao, F. F., Velásquez, T., Martinez, C. and Pezzia, W. (1969). Irreversible blunted respiratory sensitivity to hypoxia in high altitude natives. *Resp. Physiol.*, **6**, 360
52. Sørensen, S. C. and Severinghaus, J. W. (1968). Irreversible respiratory insensitivity to acute hypoxia in man born at high altitude. *J. Appl. Physiol.*, **25**, 217
53. Husson, G. and Otis, A. B. (1957). Adaptive value of respiratory adjustments to shunt hypoxia and to altitude hypoxia. *J. Clin. Invest.*, **36**, 270
54. Lahiri, S. (1968). Alveolar gas pressures in man with life-time hypoxia. *Resp. Physiol.*, **4**, 373
55. Sørensen, S. C. and Severinghaus, J. W. (1968). Respiratory insensitivity to acute hypoxia persisting after correction of tetralogy of Fallot. *J. Appl. Physiol.*, **25**, 221
56. Edelman, N. H., Lahiri, S., Braudo, L., Cherniack, N. S. and Fishman, A. P. (1970). The blunted ventilatory response to hypoxia in cyanotic congenital heart disease. *New Eng. J. Med.*, **282**, 405
57. Velásquez, T., Martinez, C., Pezzia, W. and Gallardo, N. (1968). Ventilatory effects of oxygen in high altitude natives *Resp. Physiol.*, **5**, 211
58. Sørensen, S. C. and Severinghaus, J. W. (1968). Respiratory sensitivity to acute hypoxia in man born at sea level, living at high altitude. *J. Appl. Physiol.*, **25**, 211
59. Grover, R. F., Reeves, J. T., Grover, E. B. and Leathers, J. E. (1967). Muscular exercise in young men native to 3100 m altitude. *J. Appl. Physiol.*, **22**, 553
60. Dempsey, J. A., Forster, H. V., Birnbaum, M. L., Reddan, W. G., Thoden, J., Grover, R. F. and Rankin, J. (1972). Control of exercise hyperpnea under varying durations of exposure to moderate hypoxia. *Resp. Physiol.* (in press)
61. Byrne-Quinn, E., Sodal, I. E. and Weil, J. V. (1972). Hypoxic and hypercapnic ventilatory drives in children native to high altitude. *J. Appl. Physiol.*, **32**, 44
62. Monge, C. M. and Monge, C. C. (1966). *High Altitude Diseases*, 32 (Springfield: Thomas)
63. Penaloza, D., Sime, F. and Ruiz, L. (1971). Cor pulmonale in chronic mountain sickness: present concept of Monge's disease. *Proc. Ciba Foundation Symp. High Altitude Physiology: Cardiac and Respiratory Aspects*, 41 (R. Porter and J. Knight editors) (Edinburgh, 1971: Churchill)
64. Pare, P. and Lowenstein, L. (1956). Polycythemia associated with disturbed function of the respiratory center. *Blood*, **11**, 1077
65. Ratto, O., Briscoe, W. A., Morton, J. W. and Comroe, J. H., Jr. (1955). Anoxemia secondary to polycythemia and polycythemia secondary to anoxemia. *Amer. J. Med.*, **19**. 958
66. Lahiri, S. and Edelman, N. H. (1969). Peripheral chemoreflexes in the regulation of breathing of high altitude natives. *Resp. Physiol.*, **6**, 375
67. Lahiri, S., Milledge, J. S., Chattopadhyay, H. P., Bhattacharyya, A. K. and Sinha, A. K. (1967). Respiration and heart rate of Sherpa highlanders during exercise. *J. Appl. Physiol.*, **23**, 545
68. Lahiri, S., Kao, F. F., Velásquez, T., Martinez, C. and Pezzia, W. (1970). Respiration of man during exercise at high altitude. *Resp. Physiol.*, **8**, 361
69. Lahiri, S., Milledge, J. S. and Sørensen, S. C. (1972). Ventilation in man during exercise at high altitude. *J. Appl. Physiol.*, **32**, 766
70. Brooks, J. G. Jr. and Tenney, S. M. (1968). Ventilatory response of llama to hypoxia at sea level and high altitude. *Resp. Physiol.*, **5**, 269

71. Lahiri, S. (1972). Unattenuated ventilatory hypoxic drive in ovine and bovine species native to high altitude. *J. Appl. Physiol.*, **32**, 95

72. Mines, A. H. and Sørensen, S. C. (1970). Ventilatory responses of awake normal goats during acute and chronic hypoxia. *J. Appl. Physiol.*, **28**, 826

73. Lahiri, S., Edelman, N. H., Cherniack, N. S. and Fishman, A. P. (1971). Regulation of respiration in goat and its adaptation to chronic and life-long hypoxia. *Resp. Physiol.*, **12**, 388

74. Hornbein, T. F. and Sørensen, S. C. (1969). Ventilatory response to hypoxia and hypercapnia in cats living at high altitude. *J. Appl. Physiol.*, **27**, 833

75. Tenney, S. M., Scotto, P., Ou, L. C., Bartlett, D. Jr. and Remmers, J. E. (1971). Suprapontine influences on hypoxic ventilatory control. *Proc. Ciba Foundation Symp. High Altitude Physiology: Cardiac and Respiratory Aspects*, 89 (R. Porter and J. Knight editors) (Edinburgh, 1971: Churchill)

76. Grover, R. F., Reeves, J. T., Will, D. H. and Blount, S. G. Jr. (1963). Pulmonary vasoconstriction in steers at high altitude. *J. Appl. Physiol.*, **18**, 567

77. Bisgard, G. E., Ruiz, A. V., Will, J. A. and Filley, G. F. (1972). Ventilatory response to acute and chronic hypoxia in the calf. *Fed. Proc.*, **31**, 389 Abstr.

78. Bisgard, G. E. and Vogel, J. H. K. (1971). Hypoventilation and pulmonary hypertension in calves following carotid body excision. *J. Appl. Physiol.*, **31**, 431

79. Hall, F. G., Dill, D. B. and Guzman Barron, E. S. (1936). Comparative physiology in high altitudes. *J. Cell. Comp. Physiol.*, **8**, 301

80. DeLaney, R. G. and Lahiri, S. (1972). Neonatal hypoxia and the development of attentuated ventilatory sensitivity to hypoxia. *Fed. Proc.*, **31**, 390 Abstr.

81. Brady, J. P. and Ceruti, E. (1966). Chemoreceptor reflexes in the newborn infant: effects of varying degrees of hypoxia on heart rate and ventilation in a warm environment. *J. Physiol. (London)*, **184**, 631

82. Schwieler, G. H. (1968). Respiratory regulation during postnatal development in cats and rabbits and some of its morphological substrate. *Acta Physiol. Scand. Suppl.*, **304**, 58

83. Biscoe, T. J. (1971). Carotid body: structure and function. *Physiol. Rev.*, **51**, 437

84. Sørensen, S. C. and Cruz, J. C. (1969). Ventilatory response to a single breath of CO_2 in O_2 in normal man at sea level and high altitude. *J. Appl. Physiol.*, **27**, 186

85. Cherniack, N. S., Edelman, N. H. and Lahiri, S. (1970/71). Hypoxia and hypercapnia as respiratory stimulants and depressants. *Resp. Physiol.*, **11**, 113

86. Edelman, N. H., Cherniack, N. S., Lahiri, S. and Fishman, A. P. (1970). The effects of abnormal sympathetic nervous function upon the ventilatory response to hypoxia. *J. Clin. Invest.*, **49**, 1153

87. Edwards, C. W. (1971). The carotid body in animals at high altitude. *Proc. Ciba Foundation Symp. High Altitude Physiology: Cardiac and Respiratory Aspects*, 79 (R. Porter and J. Knight editors) (Edinburgh, 1971: Churchill)

88. Heath, D., Edwards, C. and Harris, P. (1970). Postmortem size and structure of the human carotid body. *Thorax*, **25**, 129

89. Cross, K. W. (1961). Respiration in the newborn baby. *Brit. Med. Bull.*, **17**, 160

90. Brody, S. (1945). *Bioenergetics and Growth*, 575 (New York: Reinhold Publishing Corporation)

91. Tenney, S. M. (1971). Discussion. *Proc. Ciba Foundation Symp. High Altitude Physiology: Cardiac and Respiratory Aspects*, 26 (R. Porter and J. Knight editors) (Edinburgh, 1971: Churchill)

92. Burri, P. H. and Weibel, E. R. (1971). Morphometric evaluation of changes in lung structure due to high altitude. *Proc. Ciba Foundation Symp. High Altitude Physiology: Cardiac and Respiratory Aspects*, 15 (R. Porter and J. Knight editors) (Edinburgh, 1971: Churchill)

93. Baker, P. T. (1969). Human adaptation to high altitude. *Science*, **163**, 1149

94. Frisancho, R. A. (1969). Human growth and pulmonary function of a high altitude Peruvian Quechua population. *Human Biol.*, **41**, 365

95. Velásquez, T. (1956). Maximal diffusing capacity of the lungs at high altitudes. *Report 56–108, School of Aviation Medicine, USAF, Randolph Field, Texas*, 1956

96. Guleria, G. S., Pande, J. N., Sethi, A. K. and Roy, S. B. (1971). Pulmonary diffusing capacity at high altitude. *J. Appl. Physiol.*, **31**, 536

97. Dempsey, J. A., Reddan, W. G., Birnbaum, M. L., Forster, H. V., Thoden, J. S., Grover, R. F. and Rankin, J. (1971). Effects of acute through life-long hypoxic exposure on exercise pulmonary gas exchange. *Resp. Physiol.*, **13**, 62

98. DeGraff, A. C., Jr., Grover, R. F., Johnson, R. L., Jr., Hammond, J. W. Jr., and Miller, J. M. (1970). Diffusing capacity of the lung in Caucasian native to 3100 m. *J. Appl. Physiol.*, **29**, 71

99. West, J. B. (1966). Gas diffusion in the lung at altitude. *Exercise at Altitude*, 75 (R. Margaria editor) (Amsterdam, 1967: Excerpta Medica Foundation)

100. Dunnill, M. S. (1962). Postnatal growth of the lung. *Thorax*, **17**, 329

101. Reynafarje, C. (1966). Humoral control of erythropoiesis at altitude. *Proc. Symp. Exercise at Altitude*, 165 (R. Margaria editor) (Amsterdam, 1967: Excerpta Medica Foundation)

102. Pugh, L. G. C. E. (1964). Blood volume and hemoglobin concentration at altitudes above 18 000 ft. (5500 m). *J. Physiol. (London)*, **170**, 344

103. Sánchez, C., Merino, C. and Figallo, M. (1970). Simultaneous measurement of plasma volume and cell mass in polycythemia of high altitude. *J. Appl. Physiol.*, **28**, 775

104. Vérel, D. (1961). Blood volume changes in cyanotic congenital heart disease and polycythemia rubra vera. *Circulation*, **23**, 1961

105. Sobrevilla, L. A., Cassinelli, M. T., Carcelen, A. and Malaga, J. (1971). Tension de oxigeno y equilibrio acido-base de nadre y feto durante el parto en la altura. *Estudios Sobre la Gestacion y el Recien Nacido en la Altura. Separata de Ginecologia y Obstetricia*, **17**, 45

106. Bartels, H. (1970). Prenatal respiration. *Frontiers of Biology*, Vol. 17, 92, 104 (A. Neuberger and E. L. Tatum editors) (Amsterdam: North-Holland Publishing Co.)

107. Lenfant, C., Torrance, J., English, E., Finch, C. A., Reynafarje, C., Ramos, J. and Faura, J. (1968). Effect of altitude on oxygen binding by hemoglobin and on organic phosphate levels. *J. Clin. Invest.*, **47**, 2652

108. Mulhausen, R. O., Astrup, P. A. and Mellemgaard, K. (1968). Oxygen affinity and acid-base status of human blood during exposure to hypoxia and carbon monoxide. *Scand. J. Clin. Lab. Invest. Suppl.*, **103**, 9

109. Torrance, J. D., Lenfant, C., Cruz, J. and Marticorena, E. (1970/71). Oxygen transport mechanisms in residents at high altitude. *Resp. Physiol.*, **11**, 1

110. Baumann, R., Bauer, C. and Bartels, H. (1971). Influence of chronic and acute hypoxia on oxygen affinity and red cell 2,3 diphosphoglycerate of rats and guinea pigs. *Resp. Physiol.*, **11**, 135

111. Lenfant, C., Torrance, J. D. and Reynafarje, C. (1971). Shift of the O_2-Hb dissociation curve at altitude: mechanism and effect. *J. Appl. Physiol.*, **30**, 625

112. Duhm, J. and Gerlach, E. (1971). On the mechanism of the hypoxia-induced increase of 2,3 diphosphoglycerate in erythrocytes. *Pflügers Arch.*, **326**, 254

113. Chiodi, H. (1970/71). Comparative study of the blood gas transport in high altitude and sea level camelidae and goats. *Resp. Physiol.*, **11**, 84

114. Reynafarje, C., Faura, J., Paredes, A. and Villavicencio, D. (1968). Erythrokinetics in high-altitude adapted animals (llama, alpaca, and vicuña). *J. Appl. Physiol.*, **24**, 93

115. Bartels, H., Hilpert, P., Barbey, K., Betke, K., Riegel, K., Lang, E. M. and Metcalf, J. (1963). Respiratory functions of blood of the yak, llama, camel, Dybowsik deer, and African elephant. *Amer. J. Physiol.*, **205**, 331

116. Schmidt-Neilsen and Larimer, J. L. (1958). Oxygen dissociation curves of mammalian blood in relation to body size. *Amer. J. Physiol.*, **195**, 424

117. Riggs, A. (1960). The nature and significance of the Bohr effect in mammalian hemoglobins. *J. Gen. Physiol.*, **43**, 737

118. Hilpert, P., Fleischman, R. G., Kempe, D. and Bartels, H. (1963). The Bohr effect related to blood and erythrocyte pH. *Amer. J. Physiol.*, **205**, 337

119. Rossi-Bernardi, L. and Roughton, F.J.W. (1967). The specific influence of carbon dioxide and carbamate compounds on the buffer power and Bohr effects in human hemoglobin solutions. *J. Physiol. (London)*, **189**, 1

120. Throling, E. B. and Erslev, A. J. (1968). The "tissue" tension of oxygen and its relation to hematocrit and erythropoiesis. *Blood*, **31**, 332

121. Grover, R. F., Lufschanowski, R. and Alexander, J. A. (1969). Decreased coronary blood flow in man following ascent to high altitude. *Proc. Symp. Hypoxia, High Altitude and Heart*, 72 (J. Vogel editor) (Basel, 1970: S. Karger)

122. Moret, P. R. (1971). Coronary blood flow and myocardial metabolism in man at high altitude. *Proc. Symp. High Altitude Physiology: Cardiac and Respiratory Aspects*, 131 (R. Porter and J. Knight editors) (Edinburgh, 1971: Churchill)

123. Asmussen, E. and Nielsen, M. (1955). The cardiac output in rest and work at low and high oxygen pressure. *Acta Physiol. Scand.*, **35**, 73

124. Saltin, B., Grover, R. F., Blomquist, C. G., Hartley, L. H. and Johnson, R. L. Jr. (1968). Maximal oxygen uptake and cardiac output after two weeks at 4300 m. *J. Physiol.*, **25**, 400

125. Stenberg, J., Ekblom, B. and Messin. R. (1966). Hemodynamic response to work at simulated altitude, 4000 m. *J. Appl. Physiol.*, **21**, 1589

126. Pugh, L. G. C. E. (1964). Cardiac output in muscular exercise at 5800 m (19 000 ft.). *J. Appl. Physiol.*, **19**, 441

127. Mazes, R. B. (1968). Cardiorespiratory characteristics and adaptation to high altitudes. *J. Phys. Anthrop., Appl.* **32**, 267

128. Åstrand, P–O. and Åstrand, I. (1958). Heart rate during muscular work in man exposed to prolonged hypoxia. *J. Appl. Physiol.*, **13**, 75

129. Hartley, L. H., Alexander, J. K., Modelski, M. and Grover, R. F. (1967). Subnormal cardiac output at rest and during exercise in residents at 3100 m altitude. *J. Appl. Physiol.*, **23**, 839

130. Banchero, N., Sime, F., Penaloza, D., Cruz, J., Gamboa, R. and Marticorena, E. (1966). Pulmonary pressure, cardiac output, and arterial oxygen saturation during exercise at high altitude and at sea level. *Circulation*, **33**, 249

131. Hansen, J. E., Vogel, J. A., Stelter, G. P. and Consolazio, C. F. (1967). Oxygen uptake in man during exhaustive work at sea level and high altitude. *J. Appl. Physiol.*, **23**, 511

132. Buskirk, E. R., Kollias, J., Akers, R. F., Prokop, E. K. and Reategui, E. P. (1967). Maximal performance at altitude and on return from altitude in conditioned runners. *J. Appl. Physiol.*, **23**, 259

133. Klausen, K., Robinson, S., Micahel, E. D. and Myhre, L. G. (1966). Effect of high altitude on maximal working capacity. *J. Appl. Physiol.*, **21**, 1191

134. Balke, B. (1962). Work capacity and its limiting factors at high altitude. *Proc. Symp. The Physiological Effects of High Altitude*, 233 (W. H. Weihe editor) (New York, 1964: Pergamon)

135. West, J. B., Lahiri, S., Gill, M. B., Milledge, J. S., Pugh, L. G. C. E. and Ward, M. P. (1962). Arterial oxygen saturation during exercise at high altitude, *J. Appl. Physiol.*, **17**, 617

136. Wyndham, C. H., Strydom, N. B., Munro, A., MacPherson, R. K., Metz, B., Schaff, G. and Schieber, J. (1964). Heat reactions of Caucasians in temperate, in hot, dry and in hot, humid climates. *J. Appl. Physiol.*, **19**, 607

137. Fishman, A. P. (1963). Dynamics of pulmonary circulation. *Circulation, II, Handbook of Physiology*, Section 2, 1667 (W. F. Hamilton editor) (Washington, D. C.; Amer. Physiol. Soc.)

138. Gorver, R. F., Vogel, J. H. K., Voigt, G. C. and Blount, G. S. Jr. (1966). Reversal of high altitude pulmonary hypertension. *Amer. J. Cardio.* **18**, 928

139. West, J. B. (1965). *Ventilation/Blood Flow and Gas Exchange*, 110 (Oxford: Blackwell)

140. Haab, P., Held, D. R., Ernst, H. and Farhi, L. E. (1969). Ventilation perfusion relationship during high altitude adaptation. *J. Appl. Physiol.*, **26**, 77

141. Fishman, A. P. (1972). Pulmonary edema: the water exchanging function of the lung. *Circulation*, **46**, 390

142. Reeves, J. T., Halpin, J., Cohn, J. E. and Daoud, F. (1969). Increased alveolar-arterial oxygen difference during simulated high altitude exposure. *J. Appl. Physiol.*, **27**, 658

143. Tenney, S. M. and Ou, L. C. (1970). Physiological evidence for increased tissue capillarity in rats acclimatized to high altitude. *Resp. Physiol.*, **8**, 137

144. Longmuir, I. S. (1966). Tissue respiration. *Advances in Respiratory Physiology*, 297 (C. G. Caro editor) (London: Arnold)

145. Ou, L. C. and Tenney, S. M. (1970). Properties of mitochondria from hearts of cattle acclimatized to high altitude. *Resp. Physiol.*, **8**, 151

146. Reynafarje, B. (1962). Myoglobin content and enzymatic activity of muscle in altitude adaptation. *J. Appl. Physiol.*, **17**, 301

147. Van Liere, E. J. and Stickney, J. C. (1963). *Hypoxia*, 190 (Chicago: The University of Chicago Press)
148. Forster, R. E. (1965). Diffusion as a limiting factor in oxygen transport in cells. *Proc. Int. Symp. Cardiovascular and Respiratory Effects of Hypoxia*, 16 (J. D. Hatcher and D. B. Jennings editors) (Basel, 1966: S. Karger)
149. Meerson, F. Z. (1971). Mechanisms of hypertrophy of the heart and experimental prevention of acute cardiac insufficiency. *Brit. Heart J.*, **33**, 100
150. Moret, P., Covarrubias, E., Coudert, J. and Duchosal, F. (1972). Cardiocirculatory adaptation to chronic hypoxia. *Acta Cardiologica*, **27**, 283
151. Lenfant, C. and Sullivan, K. (1971). Adaptation to high altitude. *New Eng. J. Med.*, **284**, 1298
152. Severinghaus, J. W. (1972). Hypoxic respiratory drive and its loss during chronic hypoxia. *Clin. Physiol. (Japan)*, **2**, 57
153. Frisancho, R. A., Martinez, C., Velasquez, T., Sanchez, J. and Montoye, H. (1973). Influence of developmental adaptation on aerobic capacity at high altitude. *J. Appl. Physiol.*, **34**, 176

Index

313